Interactive Homework Workbook

Grade 3

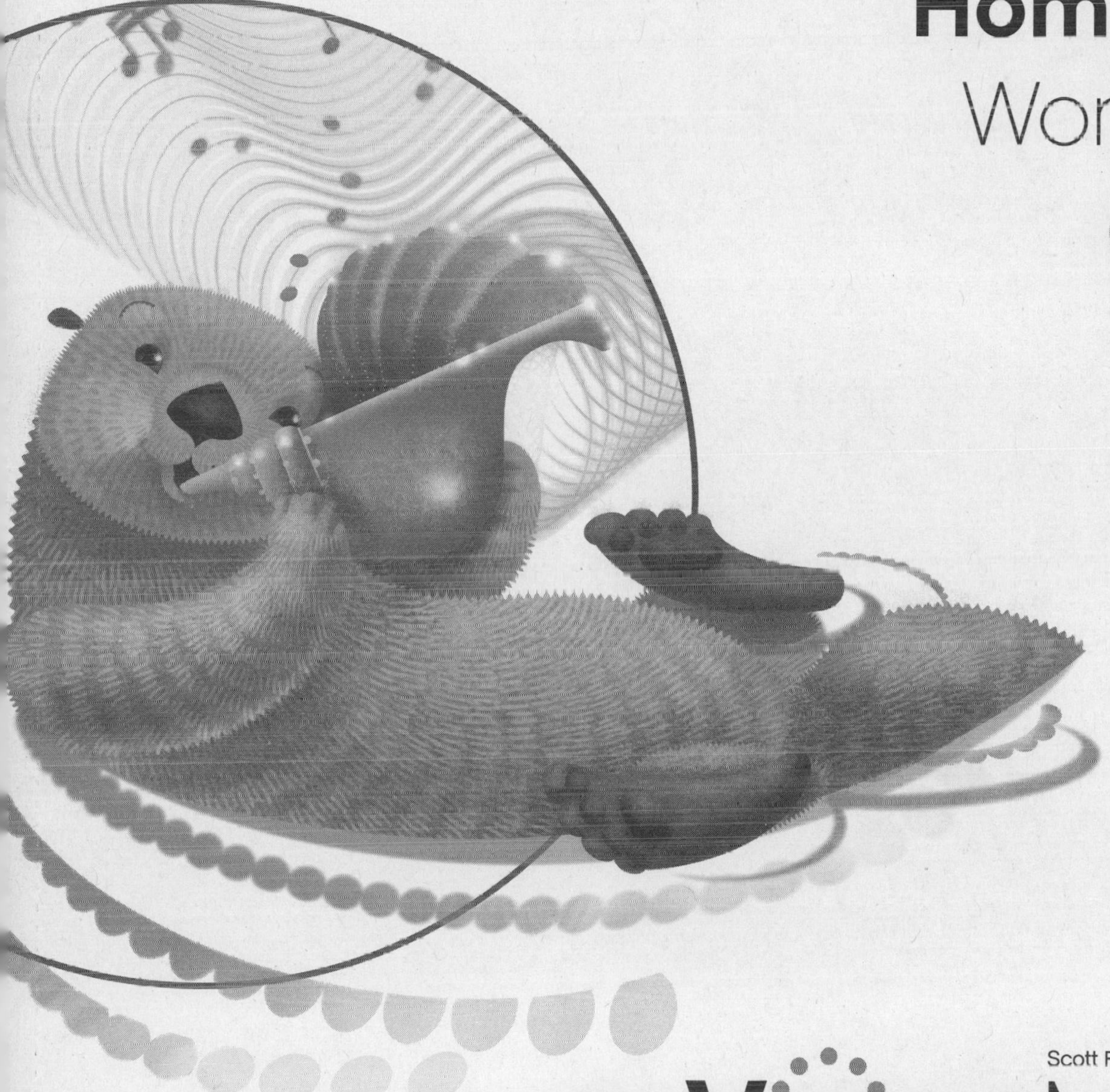

Scott Foresman·Addison Wesley

enVisionMATH™ California

Scott Foresman is an imprint of PEARSON

Glenview, Illinois • Boston, Massachusetts • Mesa, Arizona • Shoreview, Minnesota, • Upper Saddle River, New Jersey

pearsonschool.com

ISBN – 13: 978-0-328-38443-3

ISBN – 10: 0-328-38443-7

1 2 3 4 5 6 7 8 9 10 V004 12 11 10 09 08 07

Contents

Name ______________________________

Hundreds

Here are different ways to show 612.

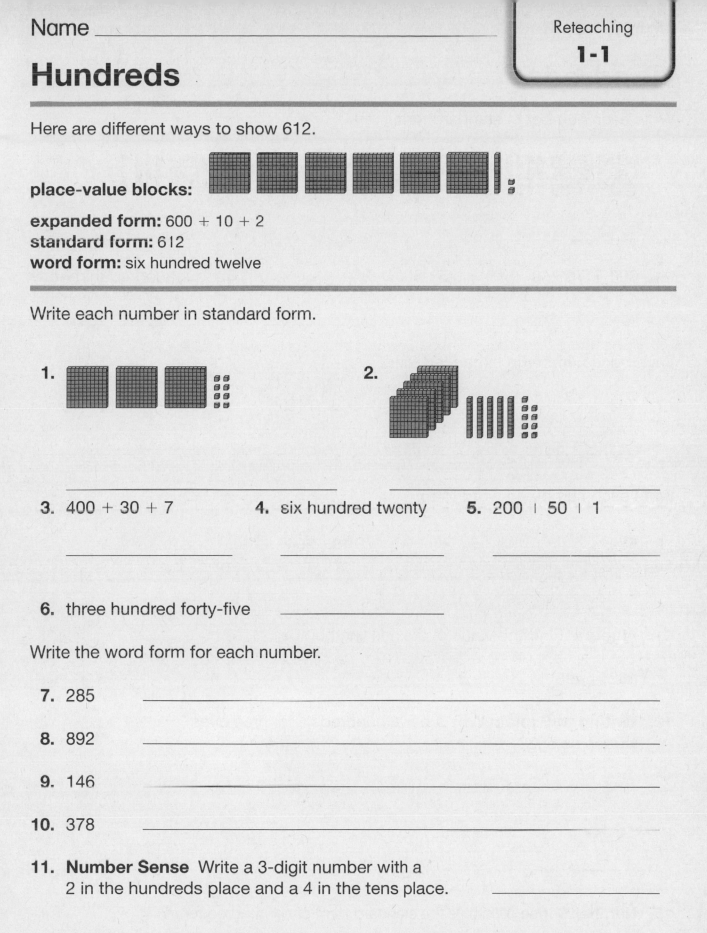

place-value blocks: 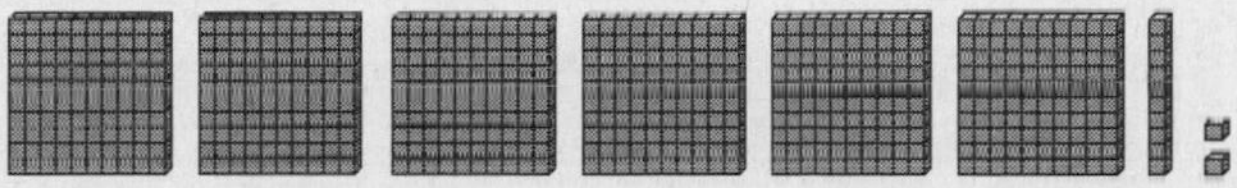

expanded form: 600 + 10 + 2
standard form: 612
word form: six hundred twelve

Write each number in standard form.

1. 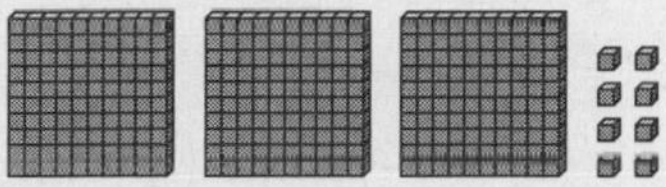

____

2. 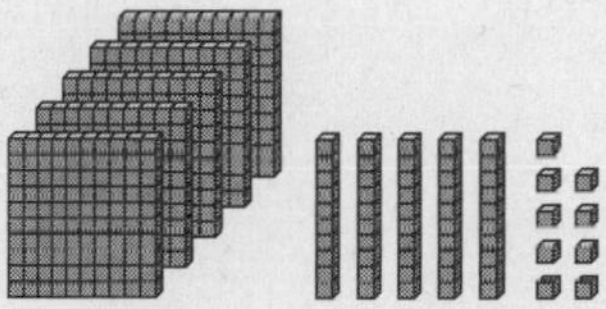

____

3. 400 + 30 + 7 ____________

4. six hundred twenty ____________

5. 200 + 50 + 1 ____________

6. three hundred forty-five ____________

Write the word form for each number.

7. 285 ______________________________

8. 892 ______________________________

9. 146 ______________________________

10. 378 ______________________________

11. **Number Sense** Write a 3-digit number with a 2 in the hundreds place and a 4 in the tens place. ____________

Name ______________________

Practice 1-1

Hundreds

Write each number in standard form.

1. 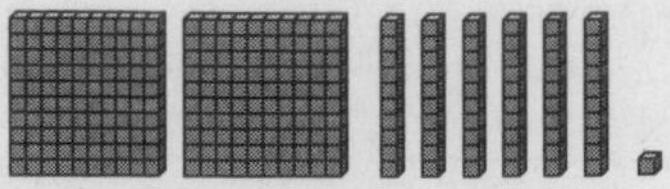 ______

2. 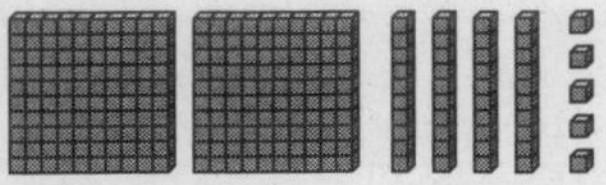 ______

3. 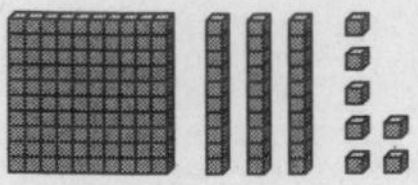 ______

4. 600 + 70 + 9 ______

5. 800 + 3 ______

6. four hundred thirty-one ______

Write each number in expanded form.

7. 392 ______

8. 710 ______

Write each number in word form.

9. 539 ______

10. 904 ______

11. **Algebra** Find the value of the missing number.

    462 = 400 + ☐ + 2

12. **Writing to Explain** Why are five hundreds and three ones written as 503?

    ______
    ______
    ______

13. **Number Sense** Which is the standard form of six hundred forty?

    ○ 64 ○ 604 ○ 614 ○ 640

Name ______________________________

Reteaching
1-2

Thousands

Here are different ways to show 2,263.

place-value blocks:

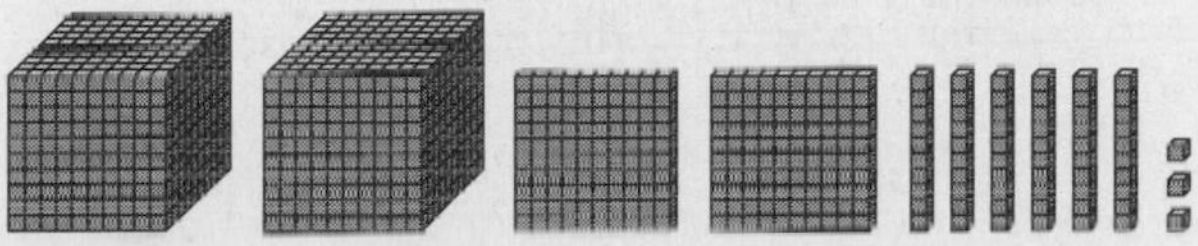

expanded form: 2,000 + 200 + 60 + 3

standard form: 2,263

word form: two thousand, two hundred sixty-three

Write each number in standard form.

1. 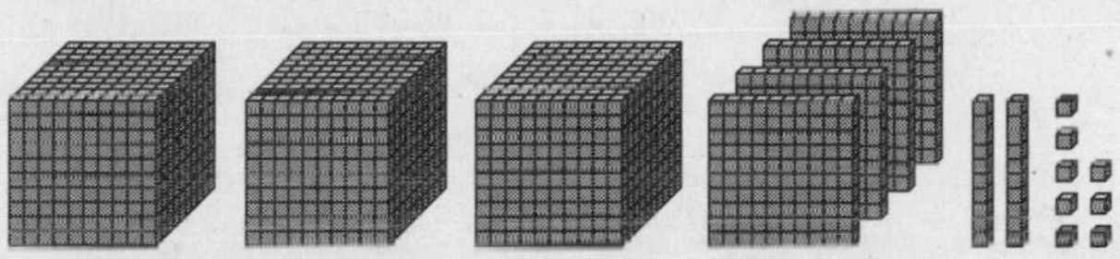 ____________

2. 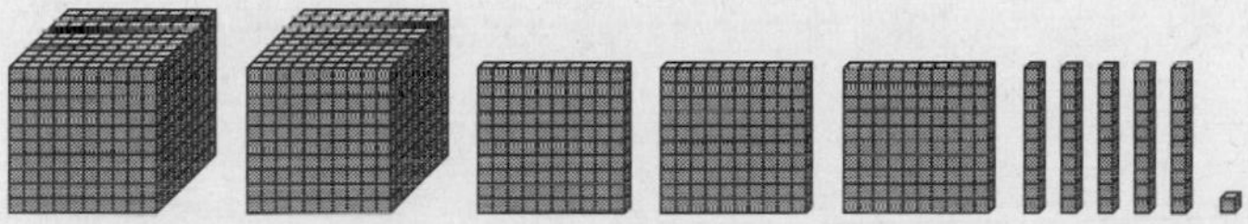 ____________

3. 7,000 + 400 + 40 + 8 ____________

4. five thousand, seven hundred fifty-five ____________

Write each number in expanded form.

5. 1,240 ______________________________

6. 6,381 ______________________________

7. **Number Sense** Write a 4-digit number with a 7 in the thousands place and a 6 in the ones place. ____________

8. **Reasoning** Jason will build a number with the digits 4, 7, 2, and 6. In what order should he put the digits if he wants to make the greatest number possible? ____________

Name ______________________

Practice
1-2

Thousands

Write each number in standard form.

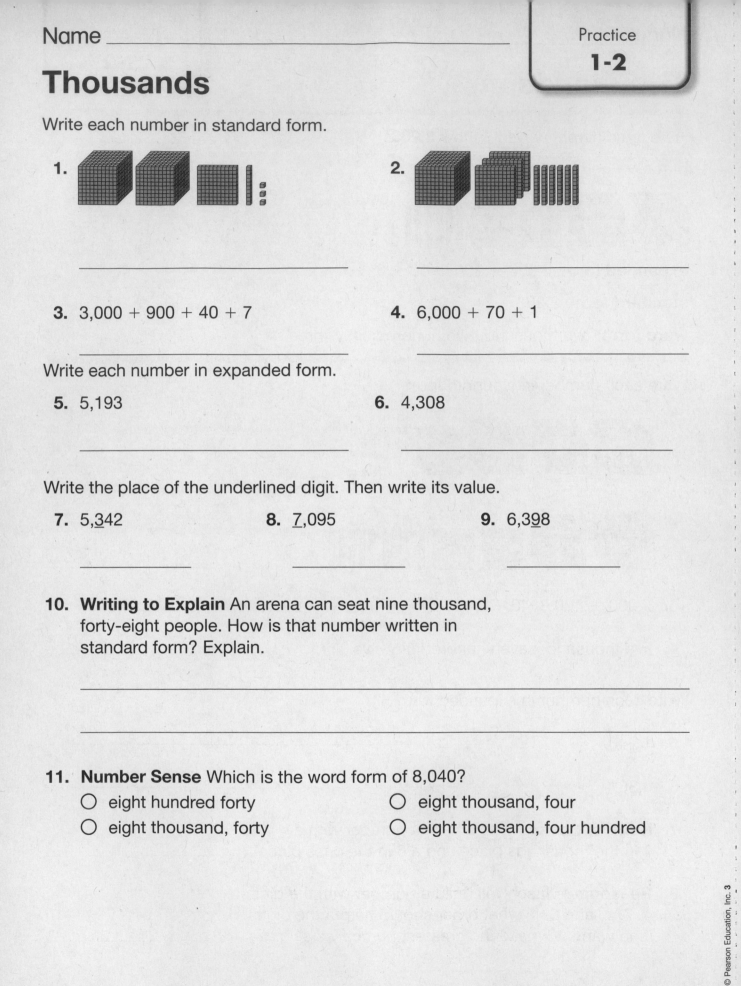

1. 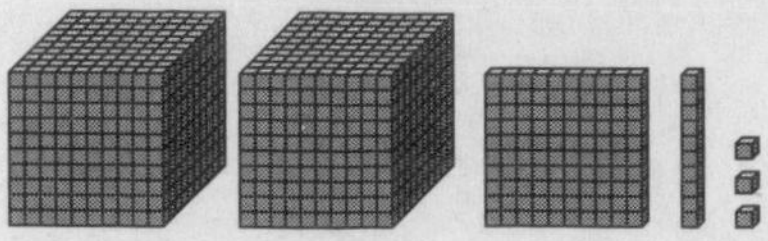

____

2. 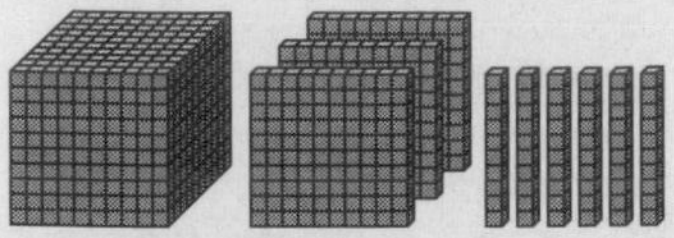

____

3. 3,000 + 900 + 40 + 7

____

4. 6,000 + 70 + 1

____

Write each number in expanded form.

5. 5,193

____

6. 4,308

____

Write the place of the underlined digit. Then write its value.

7. 5,342 ____________

8. 7,095 ____________

9. 6,398 ____________

10. Writing to Explain An arena can seat nine thousand, forty-eight people. How is that number written in standard form? Explain.

____

____

11. Number Sense Which is the word form of 8,040?

- ○ eight hundred forty
- ○ eight thousand, four
- ○ eight thousand, forty
- ○ eight thousand, four hundred

Name ______________________

Greater Numbers

A period is a group of three digits in a number, starting from the right. A comma is used to separate two periods.

Thousands Period			Ones Period		
hundred thousands	ten thousands	thousands	hundreds	tens	ones
2	4	7,	0	6	2

Here are different ways to show 247,062.

expanded form: 200,000 + 40,000 + 7,000 + 60 + 2

standard form: 247,062

word form: two hundred forty-seven thousand, sixty-two

Write each number in standard form.

1. 60,000 + 8,000 + 200 + 50 + 1 ______

2. 30,000 + 600 + 30 + 2 ______

3. four hundred one thousand, four hundred fifty-four ______

4. five hundred twenty-nine thousand, three hundred seventy-eight ______

5. Write 522,438 in expanded form.

______

6. Write 349,281 in expanded form.

______

7. **Number Sense** What is the value of the 7 in 86,752? ______

8. The area of Lake Ontario is 18,960 square kilometers. Write the area of Lake Ontario in expanded form.

______

Name ____________________

Practice 1-3

Greater Numbers

Write each number in standard form.

1. seventy-five thousand, three hundred twelve ________
2. one hundred fourteen thousand, seven ________
3. 100,000 + 40,000 + 2,000 + 500 + 30 + 2 ________
4. 600,000 + 70,000 + 8,000 + 30 + 9 ________

Write each number in expanded form.

5. 73,581 ____________________
6. 390,062 ____________________

Write the place of the underlined digit. Then write its value.

7. 6<u>3</u>,219 ________
8. 3<u>8</u>2,407 ________
9. <u>9</u>72,362 ________

10. **Algebra** Find the missing number.

    57,026 = 50,000 + ■ + 20 + 6 ________

11. **Writing to Explain** Which is greater, the greatest whole number with 5 digits or the least whole number with 6 digits?

    ____

    ____

    ____

12. **Number Sense** Which is the word form for 280,309?
    - ○ two hundred eight thousand, three hundred ninety
    - ○ two hundred eighty thousand, thirty-nine
    - ○ two hundred eighty thousand, three hundred nine
    - ○ two hundred eighty thousand, three hundred ninety

Name ______________________________

Comparing Numbers

Use these symbols to compare numbers.

< is less than **> is greater than** **= is equal to**

Compare 375 and 353.

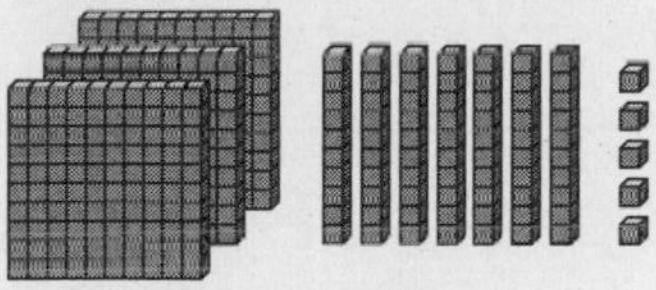

375

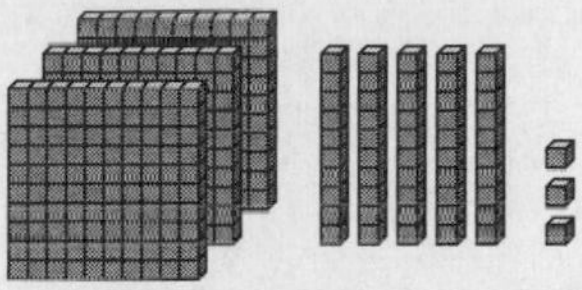

353

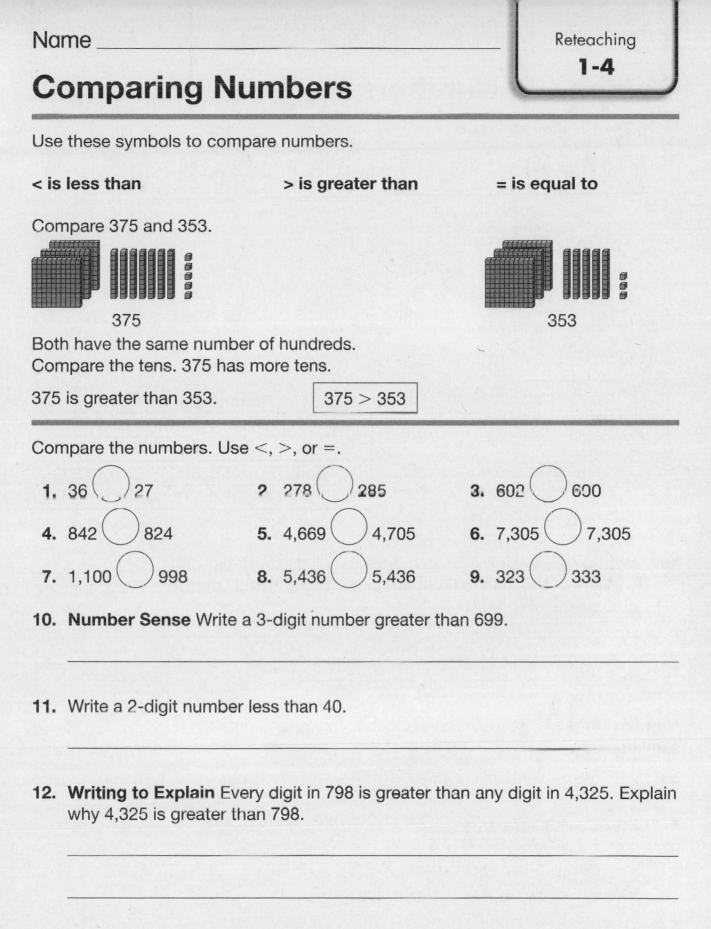

Both have the same number of hundreds.
Compare the tens. 375 has more tens.

375 is greater than 353. $375 > 353$

Compare the numbers. Use $<$, $>$, or $=$.

1. 36 ◯ 27 **2.** 278 ◯ 285 **3.** 602 ◯ 600

4. 842 ◯ 824 **5.** 4,669 ◯ 4,705 **6.** 7,305 ◯ 7,305

7. 1,100 ◯ 998 **8.** 5,436 ◯ 5,436 **9.** 323 ◯ 333

10. **Number Sense** Write a 3-digit number greater than 699.

____

11. Write a 2-digit number less than 40.

____

12. **Writing to Explain** Every digit in 798 is greater than any digit in 4,325. Explain why 4,325 is greater than 798.

____

____

____

Name ______________________________

Comparing Numbers

Compare the numbers. Use <, >, or =.

1. 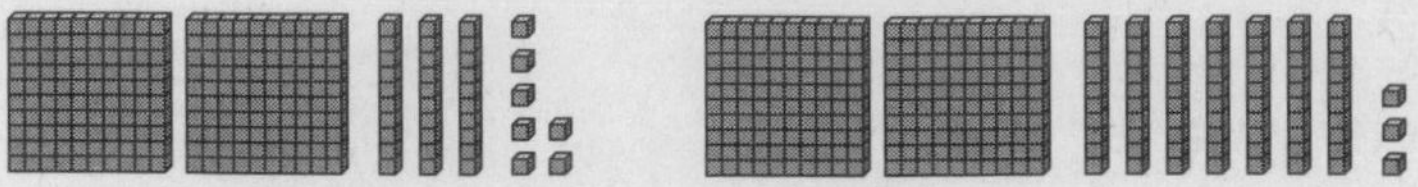

237 _____ 273

2. 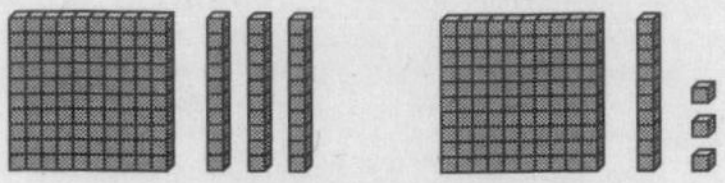

130 _____ 113

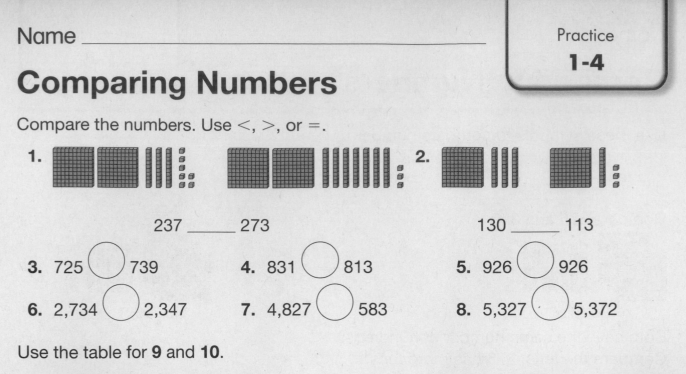

3. 725 ◯ 739 4. 831 ◯ 813 5. 926 ◯ 926

6. 2,734 ◯ 2,347 7. 4,827 ◯ 583 8. 5,327 ◯ 5,372

Use the table for **9** and **10**.

9. Between which pair of cities is the distance the greatest? See table.

____

____

Distance in Miles

New York, NY to Rapid City, SD	1,701
Rapid City, SD to Miami, FL	2,167
Miami, FL to Seattle, WA	3,334
Portland, OR to Little Rock, AR	2,217

10. **Writing to Explain** Which has a greater distance, Rapid City to Miami or Portland to Little Rock? Which digits did you use to compare? See table.

____

____

Number Sense Write the missing digits to make each number sentence true.

11. 7☐7 < 713 12. 8☐5 > 889 13. 3,☐64 = 3,2☐4

14. Which sentence is true?

◯ 4,375 > 4,722 ◯ 5,106 = 5,160
◯ 6,372 > 6,327 ◯ 7,095 < 795

15. Which number is greater than 8,264?

◯ 8,246 ◯ 8,275 ◯ 6,842 ◯ 8,195

Name ____________________

Ordering Numbers

You can use place value to order numbers.
Order these from least to greatest.

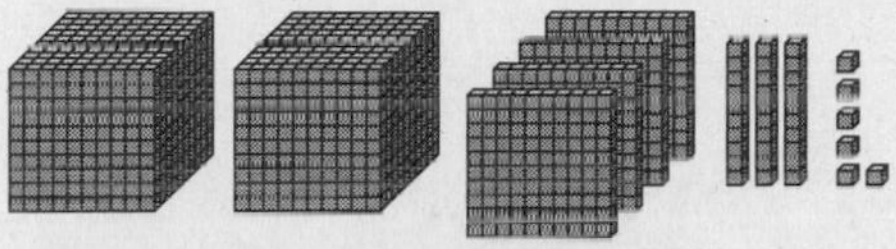

2,436

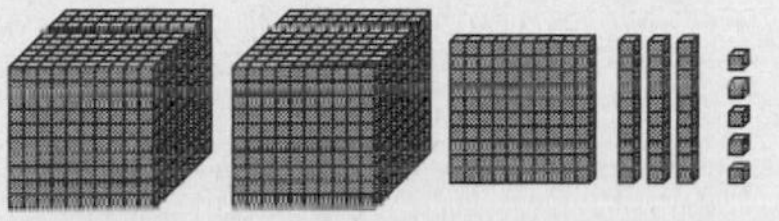

2,135

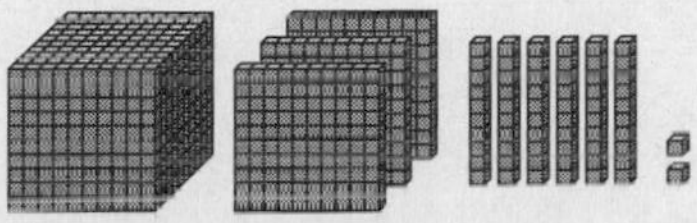

1,362

Compare the thousands.
1 thousand < 2 thousands, so 1,362 is the least number.

Compare the hundreds in the remaining two numbers.
4 hundreds > 1 hundred, so 2,436 is the greatest number.

From least to greatest, the order is: **1,362** (least) **2,135** **2,436** (greatest)

Order the numbers from least to greatest.

1. 560 583 552 ____________

2. 583 575 590 ____________

3. 576 580 557 ____________

Order the numbers from greatest to least.

4. 973 1,007 996 ____________

5. 5,626 5,636 5,716 ____________

6. Number Sense Use the table. Put the roller coasters in order from shortest to longest.

____

____

____

Roller Coaster	Length
Boss Eureka, Missouri	5,051 feet
Chang Louisville, Kentucky	4,155 feet
Titan Arlington, Texas	5,312 feet

Name ______________________

Practice
1-5

Ordering Numbers

Order the numbers from least to greatest.

1. 216 208 222

____

2. 3,795 3,659 3,747

____

Order the numbers from greatest to least.

3. 633 336 363

____

4. 5,017 5,352 5,193

____

Use the table for **5–6**.

5. Number Sense New Hampshire has a land area of 8,968 square miles. Which states have a greater land area than New Hampshire?

____

____

Land Areas (in square miles)

State	Land Area
Maryland	9,774
Massachusetts	7,840
New Jersey	7,417
Vermont	9,250

6. Order the states in the table from greatest to least land area.

____

7. Writing to Explain The Amazon River is 4,000 miles long. The Yangtze River is 3,964 miles long and the Nile River is 4,145 miles long. Write the steps you would use to order the lengths of the rivers from greatest to least.

____

____

8. Which number is between 6,532 and 6,600?

○ 6,570 ○ 6,523 ○ 6,325 ○ 5,623

9. Which number makes this sentence true?
4,735 < _____ < 4,820

○ 4,396 ○ 4,758 ○ 4,832 ○ 4,915

Name ______________________

Problem Solving: Make an Organized List

Todd has given Maclan these clues to guess the identities of one or more 3-digit numbers.

- The ones digit is odd.
- The tens digit is greater than 8.
- The hundreds digit is less than 2.

Use the clues for each digit to make an organized list.

The ones digit is odd. The odd numbers are 1, 3, 5, 7, and 9.	The tens digit is greater than 8. The only digit greater than 8 is 9. The tens digit is 9.	The hundreds digit is less than 2. The digit in the greatest place of a whole number cannot be 0. The hundreds digit is 1.

So, the list would have 191, 193, 195, 197, or 199.

Make an organized list to solve.

1. Barbara, Lisa, and Maria are having their picture taken for the yearbook. List the ways that they can line up in a straight line for the picture. You can use their initials.

____

____

2. List all the 3-digit numbers that fit these clues.

- The hundreds digit is greater than 7.
- The tens digit is less than 2.
- The ones digit is the same as the hundreds digit.

____

____

3. Reasoning In how many ways can you make 10 cents using dimes, nickels, and pennies? List them.

____

____

Name ______________________

Practice
1-6

Problem Solving: Make an Organized List

Make an organized list to solve.

1. List all the 3-digit numbers that fit these clues.

- The hundreds digit is less than 3.
- The tens digit is less than 2.
- The ones digit is greater than 7.

____

____

2. List all the 4-digit numbers that fit these clues.

- The thousands digit is greater than 8.
- The hundreds digit is less than 4.
- The tens and ones digits are the same as the thousands digit.

____

____

3. Jim and Sarah are running for class president. Cayla and Daniel are running for vice president. What combinations of president and vice president could there be?

____

____

____

4. List the ways that can you arrange the letters A, B, and C.

____

____

5. **Reasoning** What is this 3-digit number?

- The hundreds digit is 4 greater than 3.
- The tens digit is 1 more than the hundreds digit.
- The ones digit is 3 less than the tens digit.

____

6. In how many ways can you make 30 cents using quarters, dimes, or nickels.

○ 4 ○ 5

○ 6 ○ 8

Name ____________________

Reteaching
2-1

Finding the Halfway Number

A halfway number is a number that is the same distance away from two other numbers. One number will be less than the halfway number. The other number will be greater than the halfway number.

What number is halfway between 0 and 10?

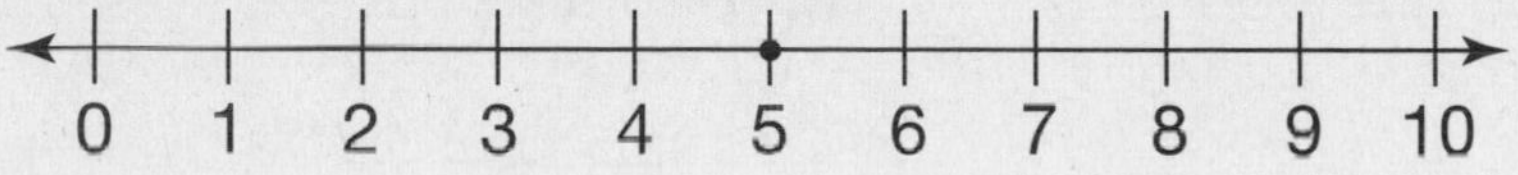

Try 5.

There are 5 numbers before 5: 0, 1, 2, 3, 4.
There are 5 numbers after 5: 6, 7, 8, 9, 10.

So, 5 is the halfway number between 0 and 10.

Find the number halfway between each pair of numbers.

1.

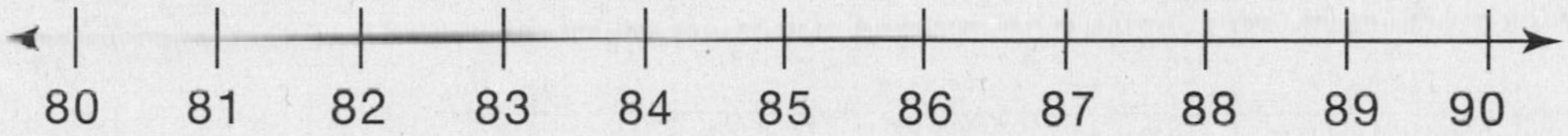

____

2.

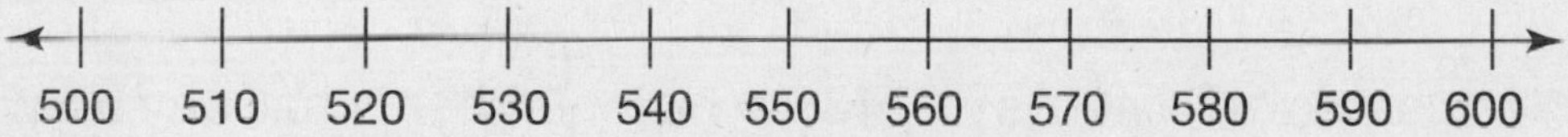

____

3.

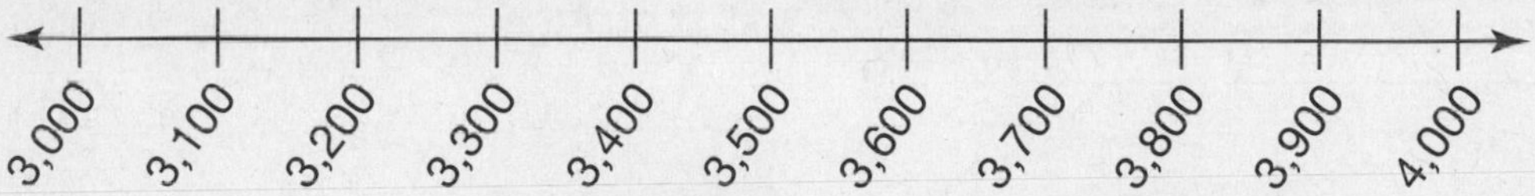

____

4. **Draw It** Draw a number line from 70 to 80 by ones. Place a dot at the halfway number.

Name ____________________

Practice
2-1

Finding the Halfway Number

Find the number halfway between each pair of numbers.
You may draw number lines to help.

1. 30 and 40 ________

2. 60 and 70 ________

3. 80 and 90 ________

4. 200 and 300 ________

5. 400 and 500 ________

6. 600 and 700 ________

7. 3,000 and 4,000 ________

8. 6,000 and 7,000 ________

9. 7,000 and 8,000 ________

Find the halfway number for each number line.

10.
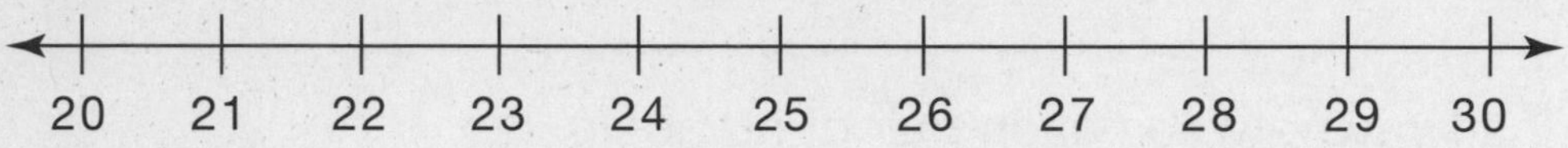

____

11.
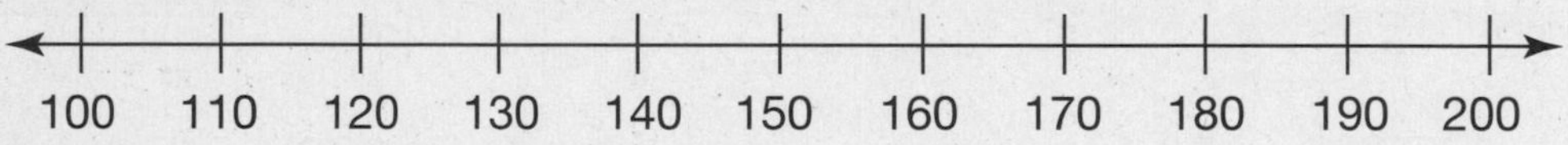

____

12. Reasoning Tony says that 4,400 is halfway between 4,000 and 5,000. Is he correct? Why or why not?

____

____

____

____

13. Which number is halfway between 2,000 and 3,000?

- ○ 2,050
- ○ 2,500
- ○ 2,550
- ○ 2,750

Name ______________________

Reteaching
2-2

Rounding 2- and 3-Digit Numbers

You can use place value to round to the nearest ten or hundred.

Find the rounding place. If the digit in the ones or the tens place is 5, 6, 7, 8, or 9, then round to the next greater number. If the digit is less than 5, do not change the digit in the rounding place.

Round 17 to the nearest ten: __________

Explain. ______________________

Round 153 to the nearest ten. __________

Explain. ______________________

____

Round 575 to the nearest hundred. __________

Explain. ______________________

____

1. Round 63 to the nearest ten: __________

Explain. ______________________

Round each number to the nearest ten.

2. 58 __________ **3.** 71 __________ **4.** 927 __________ **5.** 3,121 __________

Round each number to the nearest hundred.

6. 577 __________ **7.** 820 __________ **8.** 2,345 __________ **9.** 8,750 __________

10. Reasoning If you live 71 mi from a river, does it make sense to say you live about 80 mi from the river? Explain.

____

Name ____________________

Practice
2-2

Rounding 2- and 3-Digit Numbers

Round to the nearest ten.

1. 37 ______ **2.** 93 ______ **3.** 78 ______ **4.** 82 ______ **5.** 24 ______

6. 426 ______ **7.** 329 ______ **8.** 815 ______ **9.** 163 ______ **10.** 896 ______

Round to the nearest hundred.

11. 395 ______ **12.** 638 ______ **13.** 782 ______ **14.** 246 ______ **15.** 453 ______

16. 529 ______ **17.** 877 ______ **18.** 634 ______ **19.** 329 ______ **20.** 587 ______

21. **Number Sense** Tyrell says 753 rounds to 800. Sara says 753 rounds to 750. Who is correct? Explain.

____

____

22. **Writing to Explain** How would you use a number line to round 148 to the nearest ten.

____

____

23. There are 254 counties in Texas. What is that number rounded to the nearest ten? What is that number rounded to the nearest hundred?

____

24. Which number does not round to 400?

○ 347 ○ 369 ○ 413 ○ 448

Name ____________________

Reteaching **2-3**

Rounding 4-Digit Numbers

As for rounding 2- and 3-digit numbers, you can use place value to round 4-digit numbers.

How do you round 4,623 to the nearest hundred? nearest thousand?

To round a 4-digit number to the nearest hundred, look at the digit in the *tens* place. If the tens digit is 5 or greater, round up. If the tens digit is less than 5 round down.

4,6**2**3

$2 < 5$, so 4,623 rounds to 4,600

To round a 4-digit number to the nearest thousand, look at the digit in the *hundreds* place. If the hundreds digit is 5 or greater, round up. If the hundreds digit is less than 5 round down.

4,**6**23

$6 > 5$, so 4,623 rounds to 5,000

Whether you round up or down, the digits in the place or places less than the rounding place change to 0.

Round to the nearest hundred.

1. 3,376 ________ **2.** 5,629 ________ **3.** 6,742 ________ **4.** 7,095 ________ **5.** 9,976 ________

Round to the nearest thousand.

6. 2,752 ________ **7.** 3,421 ________ **8.** 5,714 ________ **9.** 8,326 ________ **10.** 9,287 ________

11. Explain It How do you round 6,318 to the nearest hundred? Give the rounded number.

____

____

____

Name ______________________

Practice **2-3**

Rounding 4-Digit Numbers

Round to the nearest hundred.

1. 2,382 ______ **2.** 3,726 ______ **3.** 5,067 ______ **4.** 6,348 ______ **5.** 7,957 ______

6. 1,738 ______ **7.** 7,451 ______ **8.** 9,682 ______ **9.** 8,046 ______ **10.** 9,974 ______

Round to the nearest thousand.

11. 3,295 ______ **12.** 6,724 ______ **13.** 2,439 ______ **14.** 7,805 ______ **15.** 5,525 ______

16. 9,359 ______ **17.** 4,610 ______ **18.** 7,500 ______ **19.** 3,715 ______ **20.** 9,641 ______

Use the digits 3, 7, 1, 5 to write a number that rounds to each of the following.

21. 2,000 ______ **22.** 3,500 ______ **23.** 6,000 ______ **24.** 7,400 ______

25. Reasoning Alice said that 3,642 rounds to 3,600. Ned said it rounds to 4,000. Who is correct?

____

____

____

____

____

26. Which number rounds to 3,800 when you round it to the nearest hundred?

- ○ 3,736
- ○ 3,748
- ○ 3,829
- ○ 3,853

Name ______________________________

Problem Solving: Try, Check, and Revise

Bryce, Julie, and Katie saved a total of $50 to buy a birthday present for their mother. Julie and Katie saved the same amount of money. Bryce saved $5 more. How much money did Bryce save?

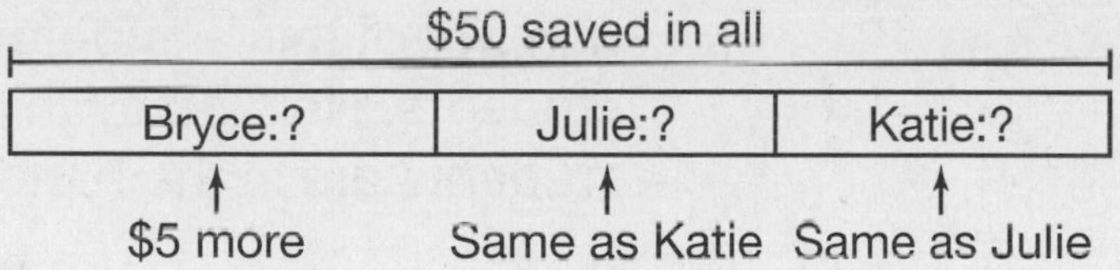

Try three numbers that add to 50. Julie and Katie saved the same amount, so their numbers are equal. Bryce's amount is $5 more.

Try #1

Try: $15 + $10 + $10 = $35

Check: $35 is too low.

You need $15 more.

Bryce saved $20 for the present.

Try #2

Revise by adding $5 more for each person.

Try: $20 + $15 + $15 = $50

Check: This is correct.

1. Ben and Cole have 36 airplane models all together. Ben has 8 more than Cole. How many airplane models does Ben have?

   ____

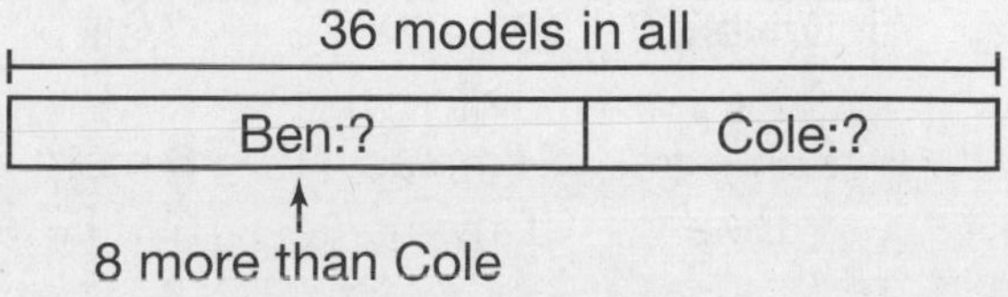

2. Jan, Mya, and Sara ran a total of 64 miles last week. Jan and Mya ran the same number of miles. Sara ran 8 less miles than Jan and Mya. How many miles did Sara run?

   ____

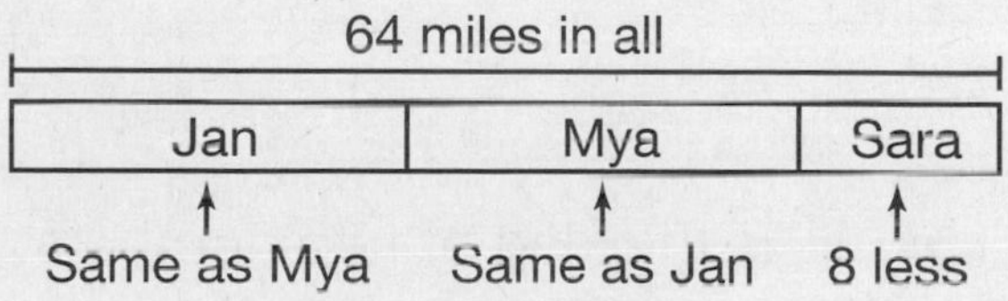

Name ______________________________

Practice
2-4

Problem Solving: Try, Check, and Revise

1. Carly and Rob combined their DVD collections. Now they have 42 DVDs in all. Carly had 4 more DVDs than Rob. How many DVDs did Carly have?

____

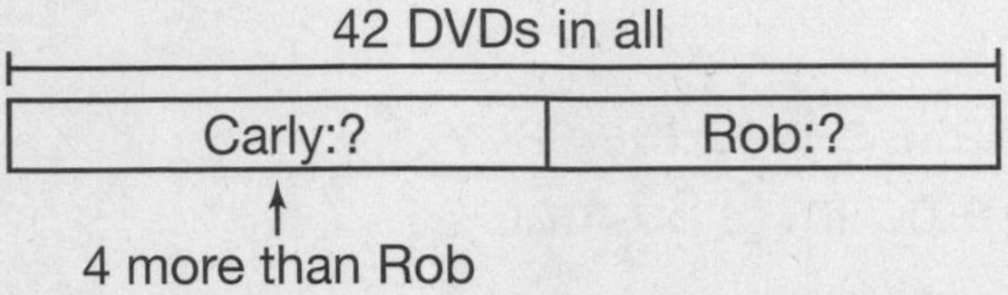

2. There are 33 students in the band. There are 6 more fifth-grade students than third-grade students. There are an equal number of third- and fourth-grade students. How many third-grade students are in the band?

____

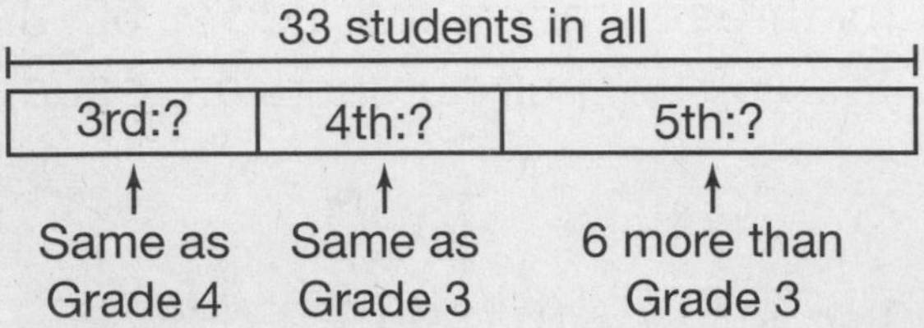

3. Dave delivered 52 newspapers in all. Saturday and Sunday. He delivered 8 more newspapers on Sunday than on Saturday. How many newspapers did Dave deliver on Sunday?

____

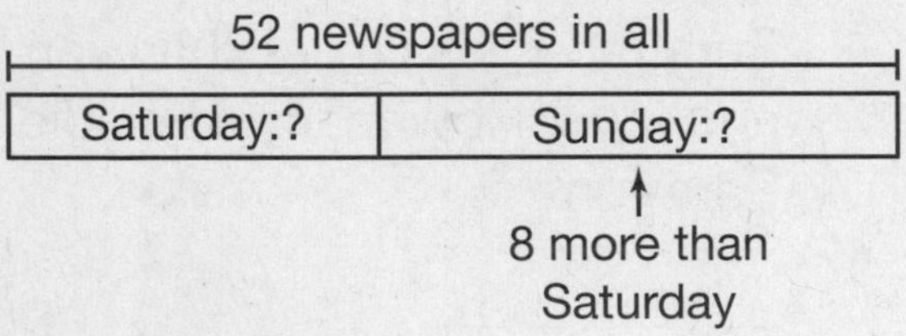

4. There are 24 students in Ms. Messing's class. Six more students walk to school than ride their bikes. The same number of students ride their bikes as students that are driven to school. How many students walk to school?

____

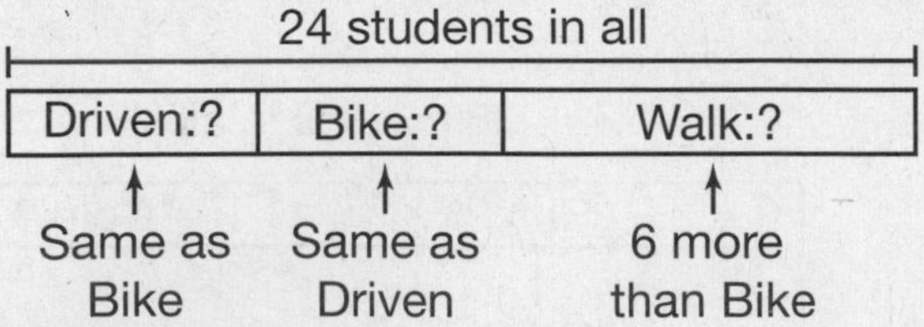

5. Jill is thinking of two numbers. They have a sum of 16 and a difference of 6. What are the two numbers?

○ 16 and 6 ○ 13 and 3 ○ 12 and 4 ○ 11 and 5

Name ____________________

Reteaching **3-1**

Addition Meaning and Properties

The Commutative (Order) Property

You can add numbers in any order, and the sum will be the same.

6 + 2 = 8

2 + 6 = 8

The Associative (Grouping) Property

You can group addends in any way, and the sum will be the same.

(3 + 4) + 1 = 8

3 + (4 + 1) = 8

The Identity (Zero) Property

The sum of any number and zero equals that same number.

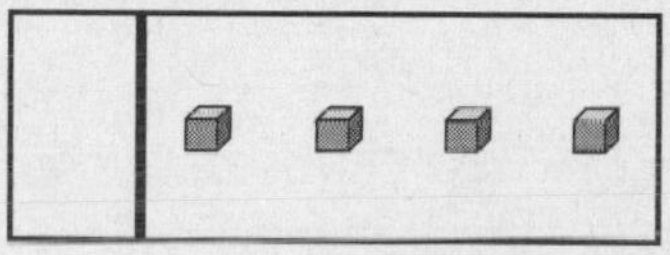

0 + 4 = 4

Find each sum.

1. 3 + (2 + 4) = ______

2. (0 + 5) + 2 = ______

3. (8 + 3) + 4 = ______

4. 9 + 2 + 6 = ______

Write each missing number.

5. 3 + 4 = 4 + ______

6. ______ + 7 = 7

7. (2 + 3) + 4 = ______ + (2 + 4)

8. 9 + (2 + 7) = (9 + 2) + ______

9. **Reasoning** Does (4 + 5) + 2 = 9 + 2? Explain.

____

____

Name ____________________

Practice
3-1

Addition Meaning and Properties

Write each missing number.

1. 7 + 2 = 2 + ■ ______
2. 3 + ■ = 3 ______
3. (2 + 4) + 5 = 2 + (■ + 5) ______
4. 3 + ■ = 5 + 3 ______
5. ■ + 0 = 6 ______
6. (5 + 3) + 9 = 8 + ■ ______

7. **Reasoning** What property of addition is shown in the following number sentence? Explain.

   7 + (3 + 5) = (7 + 3) + 5

8. **Number Sense** Minnie has 6 country CDs and 5 rock CDs. Amanda has 5 rock CDs and 6 country CDs. Who has more CDs? Explain.

9. Show how the Commutative Property of Addition works using the numbers 2, 3, and 5.

10. **Writing to Explain** Jake says that adding 0 does not change a sum. Is he correct? Explain.

11. Which property of addition is shown by 5 + 2 = 2 + 5?

   ○ Associative Property
   ○ Commutative Property
   ○ Distributive Property
   ○ Identity Property

Name ______________________

Reteaching
3-2

Adding on a Hundred Chart

You can use a hundred chart to add.
To add 37 + 26, follow these steps:

- Start at 37.
- Go down 2 rows to add 20.
- Go right 3 spaces to add 3 more.
- Go down to the next row and go right 3 more.
- You end at 63.

So, 37 + 26 = 63.

1	2	3	4	5	6	7	8	9	10
11	12	13	14	15	16	17	18	19	20
21	22	23	24	25	26	27	28	29	30
31	32	33	34	35	36	37	38	39	40
41	42	43	44	45	46	47	48	49	50
51	52	53	54	55	56	57	58	59	60
61	62	63	64	65	66	67	68	69	70
71	72	73	74	75	76	77	78	79	80
81	82	83	84	85	86	87	88	89	90
91	92	93	94	95	96	97	98	99	100

You could also do it this way.

- Start at 37.
- Go down 3 rows to add 30.
- Go left 4 spaces to subtract 4.
- You end at 63.

So, 37 + 26 = 63

1	2	3	4	5	6	7	8	9	10
11	12	13	14	15	16	17	18	19	20
21	22	23	24	25	26	27	28	29	30
31	32	33	34	35	36	37	38	39	40
41	42	43	44	45	46	47	48	49	50
51	52	53	54	55	56	57	58	59	60
61	62	63	64	65	66	67	68	69	70
71	72	73	74	75	76	77	78	79	80
81	82	83	84	85	86	87	88	89	90
91	92	93	94	95	96	97	98	99	100

Use a hundred chart to add.

1. 30 + 45 ______

2. 52 + 40 ______

3. 26 + 43 ______

4. 37 + 23 ______

5. 28 + 45 ______

6. 47 + 18 ______

7. 39 + 35 ______

8. 26 + 54 ______

9. **Reasoning** To find 38 + 45, you could first find 38 + 50 = 88. Then what should you do?

____

Name ______________________

Practice
3-2

Adding on a Hundred Chart

Use a hundred chart to add.

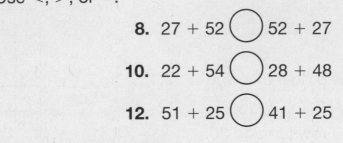

1	2	3	4	5	6	7	8	9	10
11	12	13	14	15	16	17	18	19	20
21	22	23	24	25	26	27	28	29	30
31	32	33	34	35	36	37	38	39	40
41	42	43	44	45	46	47	48	49	50
51	52	53	54	55	56	57	58	59	60
61	62	63	64	65	66	67	68	69	70
71	72	73	74	75	76	77	78	79	80
81	82	83	84	85	86	87	88	89	90
91	92	93	94	95	96	97	98	99	100

1. 45 + 30 ______

2. 36 + 33 ______

3. 52 + 46 ______

4. 27 + 23 ______

5. 36 + 45 ______

6. 49 + 24 ______

Number Sense Compare. Use <, >, or =.

7. 32 + 40 ◯ 42 + 38

8. 27 + 52 ◯ 52 + 27

9. 46 + 34 ◯ 33 + 45

10. 22 + 54 ◯ 28 + 48

11. 37 + 44 ◯ 32 + 50

12. 51 + 25 ◯ 41 + 25

13. **Number Sense** Mickey lives 35 miles away from his grandparents' home. His Aunt Roz lives 24 miles farther than his grandparents. How far does Mickey live from his Aunt Roz?

____

14. Kirsten spent 45 minutes doing her math homework and 35 minutes studying for science class. How much time did Kirsten spend studying all together? ______________

15. Which addition problem has a sum of 65?

◯ 37 + 28 ◯ 46 + 29 ◯ 34 + 32 ◯ 27 + 39

Name ____________________

Reteaching **3-3**

Using Mental Math to Add

You can break apart numbers to make them easier to add mentally.

Add 31 + 45 by breaking apart numbers.

Break the numbers into tens and ones.

	tens		ones
31 =	30	+	1
45 =	40	+	5

Add the tens: 30 + 40 = 70.

Add the ones: 1 + 5 = 6.

Add the sums: 70 + 6 = 76.

So, 31 + 45 = 76.

Add 26 + 17 by breaking apart numbers to make a ten.

Use a number that adds with the 6 in 26 to make a 10. Since 6 + 4 = 10, use 4.

Think: 17 = 4 + 13.

Add 26 + 4 = 30.

Add 30 + 13 = 43.

So, 26 + 17 = 43.

Find each sum using mental math.

1. 24 + 71 = ________ **2.** 36 + 43 = ________ **3.** 54 + 23 = ________

4. 25 + 49 = ________ **5.** 37 + 56 = ________ **6.** 77 + 13 = ________

7. Number Sense To add 32 + 56, Juanita first added 30 + 50. What two steps does she still need to do to find the sum? What is Juanita's sum?

____

____

8. Reasoning How can Steve add 48 + 34 by making a ten? What is the sum?

____

____

____

Name ______________________

Practice
3-3

Using Mental Math to Add

Use breaking apart to add mentally.

1. 53 + 34

34 = 30 + ☐

53 + ☐ = 83

83 + ☐ = 87

So, 53 + 34 = ☐

2. 42 + 29

29 = 20 + ☐

42 + ☐ = 62

☐ + 9 = 71

So, 42 + 29 = ☐

3. 47 + 41

41 = ☐ + 1

47 + ☐ = 87

☐ + 1 = 88

So, 47 + 41 = ☐

Make a ten to add mentally.

4. 27 + 24

24 = 3 + ☐

27 + ☐ = 30

☐ + 21 = 51

So, 27 + 24 = ☐

5. 54 + 19

19 = ☐ + 6

☐ + 6 = 60

60 + ☐ = 73

So, 54 + 19 = ☐

6. 38 + 27

27 = ☐ + 25

38 + ☐ = 40

40 + ☐ = 65

So, 38 + 27 = ☐

Find each sum using mental math.

7. 52 + 26 ______

8. 47 + 8 ______

9. 32 + 17 ______

10. 28 + 31 ______

11. 43 + 38 ______

12. 72 + 7 ______

13. 42 + 33 ______

14. 36 + 14 ______

15. **Number Sense** Ashton broke apart a number into 30 + 7. What number did he start with? ______

16. What is the sum of 27 + 42 using mental math?

○ 68 ○ 69 ○ 78 ○ 79

Name ________________________

Reteaching
3-4

Estimating Sums

Suppose your class has a goal of saving 275 cereal box tops.

136

152

Does your class have enough box tops to reach the goal?

Since you only need to know if you have enough, you can estimate.

You can estimate by rounding. You can round each addend to the nearest ten or hundred. Then add the rounded numbers.

Round to the nearest ten.

136	→	140
+ 152	→	150
		290

Since 290 > 275, you have enough.

Round to the nearest hundred.

136	→	100
+ 152	→	200
		300

Since 300 > 275, you have enough.

Round to the nearest ten to estimate each sum.

1. 42 + 98 = ________ **2.** 36 + 59 = ________ **3.** 288 + 475 = ________

Round to the nearest hundred to estimate each sum.

4. 378 + 136 = ________ **5.** 436 + 309 = ________ **6.** 76 + 487 = ________

7. Reasonableness Sun-Yi estimated 270 + 146 and got 300. Is her estimate reasonable? Explain.

____

____

Name ______________________

Practice
3-4

Estimating Sums

Round to the nearest ten to estimate.

1. 58 + 43 ______

2. 87 + 69 ______

3. 37 + 141 ______

4. 422 + 296 ______

Round to the nearest hundred to estimate.

5. 536 + 393 ______

6. 242 + 359 ______

7. 713 + 82 ______

8. 313 + 405 ______

Use compatible numbers to estimate. Sample answers are given. Accept reasonable answers.

9. 83 + 34 ______

10. 329 + 64 ______

11. 212 + 347 ______

12. 537 + 244 ______

13. Reasonableness Miguel has 325 baseball cards and 272 football cards. He said that he has 597 cards in all. Is his answer reasonable? Explain using estimation.

____

____

____

14. Write a Problem Natalie has 138 DVDs and 419 CDs. If you were to estimate the sum of the DVDs and CDs, what sentence could you write? Then find your estimated sum.

____

15. Which of the following shows estimating 287 + 491 by using compatible numbers?

○ 100 + 500 ○ 300 + 400 ○ 280 + 400 ○ 280 + 500

Name ______________________________

Reteaching **3-5**

Adding 2-Digit Numbers

To find 27 + 57, first estimate by rounding. Since 7 > 5, round 27 to 30 and 57 to 60. Then add: 30 + 60 = 90.

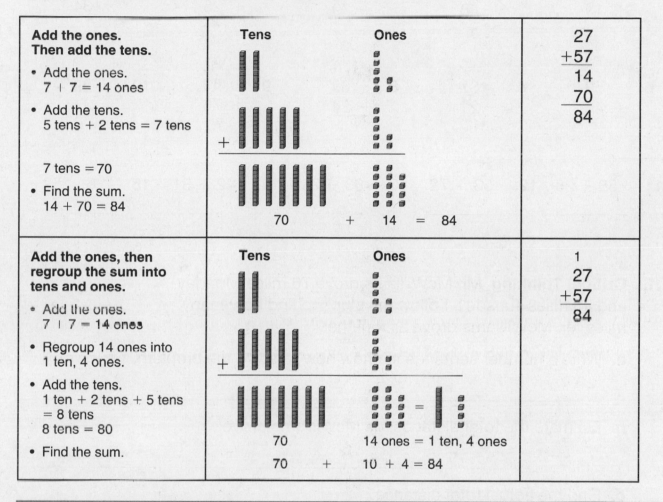

Add the ones. Then add the tens. • Add the ones. 7 + 7 = 14 ones • Add the tens. 5 tens + 2 tens = 7 tens 7 tens = 70 • Find the sum. 14 + 70 = 84	**Tens** **Ones** 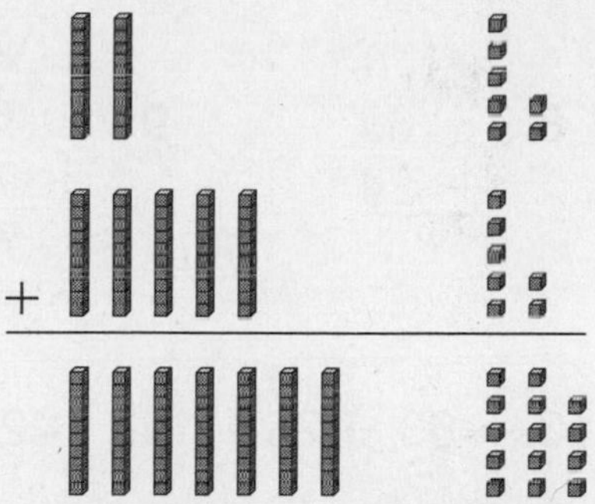 70 + 14 = 84	27 +57 14 70 84
Add the ones, then regroup the sum into tens and ones. • Add the ones. 7 + 7 = 14 ones • Regroup 14 ones into 1 ten, 4 ones. • Add the tens. 1 ten + 2 tens + 5 tens = 8 tens 8 tens = 80 • Find the sum.	**Tens** **Ones** 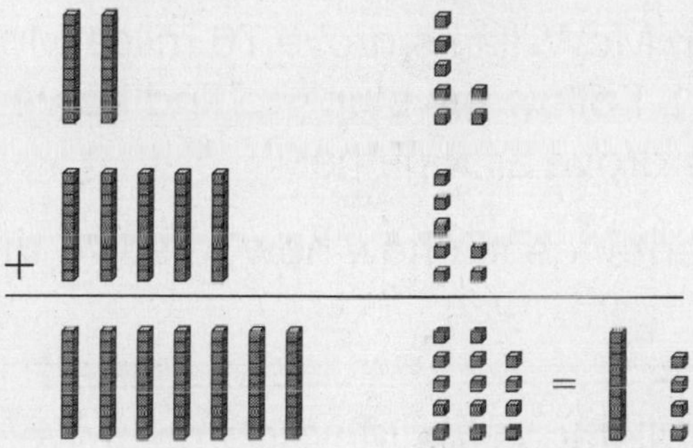 70 14 ones = 1 ten, 4 ones 70 + 10 + 4 = 84	1 27 +57 84

Estimate. Then find each sum.

1. 28 + 34

2. 56 + 22

3. 84 + 17

4. 49 + 72

5. 26 + 19

6. 65 + 23

7. 22 + 79

8. 38 + 85

9. **Reasonableness** Hannah added 65 and 26 and got 81. Is this answer reasonable? Explain.

____

Name ____________________

Practice
3-5

Adding 2-Digit Numbers

Estimate. Then find each sum.

1. $73 + 19$ **2.** $16 + 48$ **3.** $52 + 79$ **4.** $28 + 25$ **5.** $47 + 34$

6. $53 + 45$ **7.** $37 + 21$ **8.** $63 + 24$ **9.** $59 + 76$ **10.** $29 + 44$

11. 58 + 28 **12.** 53 + 72 **13.** 66 + 23 **14.** 42 + 31 **15.** 36 + 52

16. Critical Thinking Mr. McWilliams drove 76 miles Monday and 43 miles Tuesday. Follow the steps to find how many miles Mr. McWilliams drove all together.

a. Write a number sentence to show how to solve the problem.

____

b. Estimate the total distance Mr. McWilliams drove.

____

c. Find the actual total distance.

____

17. Reasoning Using four different digits, what is the least sum you can get when you add two 2-digit numbers? Write your problem.

____

18. There are 72 people on a train when 25 more people enter. How many people are on the train now?

○ 79 ○ 87 ○ 97 ○ 98

Name ______________________________

Reteaching
3-6

Adding 3- and 4-Digit Numbers

Add 3,725 + 4,369.

Estimate: 4,000 + 4,000 = 8,000, so the answer should be about 8,000.

Align the digits on the ones place. Then add from right to left.

Step 1

Add the ones:

5 + 9 = 14.

Write the 4 and regroup the 1 ten.

$$\begin{array}{r} ^{1}\quad \\ 3{,}725 \\ +\ 4{,}369 \\ \hline 4 \end{array}$$

Step 2

Add the tens:

1 + 2 + 6 = 9.

Write the 9.

$$\begin{array}{r} ^{1}\quad \\ 3{,}725 \\ +\ 4{,}369 \\ \hline 94 \end{array}$$

Step 3

Add the hundreds:

7 + 3 = 10. Write the 0 and regroup the 1 thousand.

$$\begin{array}{r} ^{1\ 1}\quad\ \ \\ 3{,}725 \\ +\ 4{,}369 \\ \hline 094 \end{array}$$

Step 4

Add the thousands:

1 + 3 + 4 = 8.

Write the 8.

$$\begin{array}{r} ^{1\ 1}\quad\ \ \\ 3{,}725 \\ +\ 4{,}369 \\ \hline 8{,}094 \end{array}$$

So, 3,725 + 4,369 = 8,094.

Estimate. Then find each sum.

1. 229 + 521
2. 379 + 413
3. 267 + 495
4. 137 + 358
5. 572 + 387
6. 1,938 + 3,625
7. 8,319 + 785
8. 2,654 + 3,795
9. 4,205 + 3,167
10. 7,656 + 495

11. **Reasonableness** Jayson said that 3,533 + 3,925 is 6,458. Is Jayson's answer reasonable? Explain why or why not.

____

____

____

Name ______________________

Practice 3-6

Adding 3- and 4-Digit Numbers

Estimate. Then find each sum.

1. 329 + 468

2. 148 + 231

3. 555 + 222

4. 472 + 515

5. 396 + 428

6. 4,328 + 3,692

7. 2,915 + 639

8. 5,873 + 3,965

9. 3,627 + 2,759

10. 7,342 + 395

Find each sum.

11. 645 + 79 ______

12. 536 + 399 ______

13. 268 + 422 ______

14. 633 + 210 ______

15. 3,295 + 4,127 ______

16. 6,057 + 868 ______

17. 2,439 + 3,358 ______

18. 8,576 + 735 ______

19. **Number Sense** Did the two boys score more points all together than the two girls? Explain.

____

____

____

____

____

____

Computer Game Scores

Player	Score
Jill	3,352
Nick	2,746
Sasha	2,836
Tyler	3,218

20. How many points did Jill and Sasha score in all?

○ 5,188 ○ 6,188
○ 6,198 ○ 6,288

Name ____________________

Reteaching
3-7

Adding 3 or More Numbers

Find 137 + 201 + 109.

To add three numbers, you can add two numbers first. Then add the sum of the first two numbers and the third number.

Step 1	**Step 2**
Add 137 + 201.	Add 338 + 109.
$\begin{array}{r} 137 \\ +\ 201 \\ \hline 338 \end{array}$	$\begin{array}{r} {}^{1} \\ 338 \\ +\ 109 \\ \hline 447 \end{array}$

So, 137 + 201 + 109 = 447.

Find each sum.

1. $\begin{array}{r} 32 \\ 64 \\ +\ 71 \\ \hline \end{array}$

2. $\begin{array}{r} 127 \\ 39 \\ +\ \ 87 \\ \hline \end{array}$

3. $\begin{array}{r} 293 \\ 312 \\ +\ \ 78 \\ \hline \end{array}$

4. $\begin{array}{r} 358 \\ 427 \\ +\ 127 \\ \hline \end{array}$

5. 382 + 45 + 181 = ____________

6. 52 + 238 + 76 = ____________

7. Number Sense Ranier has 37 baseball cards, 65 football cards, and 151 hockey cards. How many sports cards does he have in all? Explain how you found your answer.

____

____

Name ____________________

Adding 3 or More Numbers

Find each sum.

1. 75 + 36 + 58

2. 142 + 297 + 116

3. 524 + 97 + 176

4. 273 + 187 + 64 + 249

5. 319 + 48 + 136 + 347

6. 237 + 75 + 49 ________

7. 49 + 7 + 63 + 8 ________

8. 143 + 47 + 219 + 136 ________

9. **Estimation** Estimate the sum of 327 + 419 + 173.

____

10. **Number Sense** Justine has 162 red buttons, 98 blue buttons, and 284 green buttons. She says she knows she has more than 500 buttons without adding. Do you agree? Explain.

____

____

11. Carlos ate or drank everything that is listed in the table. How many calories did Carlos consume?

____

Food	Amount	Calories
Bran flakes	1 ounce	90
Banana	1	105
Orange juice	1 cup	110
Milk	1 cup	150

12. In winning the 1884 U.S. presidential election, Grover Cleveland received 219 electoral votes. He received 168 electoral votes in 1888, and lost. Then he received 277 electoral votes and won in 1892. How many electoral votes did Cleveland receive in all?

____

13. Kyle has 378 pennies, 192 nickels, and 117 dimes. How many coins does he have all together?

○ 495 ○ 570 ○ 677 ○ 687

Name ____________________

Problem Solving: Reasonableness

The island of Elba has an area of 86 square miles. The island of St. Helena has an area of 47 square miles. How many square miles larger is Elba than St. Helena?

You can subtract to find how many square miles larger Elba is than St. Helena.

$$\begin{array}{r} 86 \\ -\ 47 \\ \hline 39 \end{array}$$

Make sure you answered the correct question.

The question asked how many square miles larger Elba is than St. Helena. The correct question was answered.

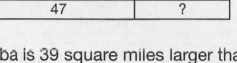

86 square miles in all

47	?

Elba is 39 square miles larger than St. Helena.

Make sure that your answer is reasonable.

Since $47 + 39 = 86$, the answer is reasonable.

1. The JP Morgan Chase Tower in Houston has 75 stories. The Renaissance Tower in Dallas has 56 stories. How many more stories does the JP Morgan Chase Tower have than the Renaissance Tower?

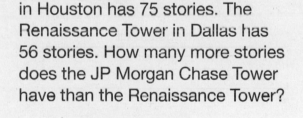

75 stories in all

56	

2. The Bulldogs scored 49 points in last week's game. This week, they scored 62 points. How many points did the Bulldogs score in all in the two games?

________ points in all

49	62

3. Write a Problem Write a problem about something you did that can be solved using addition or subtraction. Then solve the problem and check that your answer is reasonable.

____

____

____

Name ______________________________

Practice **3-8**

Problem Solving: Reasonableness

Solve. Then check that your answer is reasonable.

1. The Aggies scored 59 points in the first half and 56 points in the second half. How many points did the Aggies score altogether?

_________ points in all

59	56

2. Ms. Rice is driving 92 miles to a meeting. After driving 54 miles, she stops to buy gasoline. How many more miles does she have left?

92 miles in all

54	

3. There are 45 students going on a field trip. Of those students 27 are from Mrs. Unser's class. The rest are from Mr. King's class. How many students are from Mr. King's class?

45 students in all

27	

4. **Estimation** In the 2004 Summer Olympics, the United States won 35 gold, 39 silver, and 29 bronze medals. About how many medals did the United States win?

_________ medals in all

40	40	30

5. Christine is reading a short story that is 76 pages long. She just finished reading page 47. How many more pages does she have left to read?

76 pages in all

47	

6. Wyoming has 23 counties. Wisconsin has 49 more counties than Wyoming. How many counties does Wisconsin have?

○ 26 ○ 62 ○ 72 ○ 82

Name ______________________________

Reteaching
4-1

Subtraction Meanings

Dawn received a total of 12 stars on Monday and Tuesday. She received 7 of the stars on Monday. How many stars did she receive on Tuesday?

You can draw a picture to find how many stars Dawn received on Tuesday.

First, draw 12 stars.

Next, put a line through the 7 stars that Dawn received Monday.

Count the number of stars that are not crossed off.
There are 5.
So, 12 − 7 = 5.

You can add to check subtraction: 7 + 5 = 12, so 12 − 7 = 5.

Dawn received 5 stars on Tuesday.

Find each difference. Make a drawing to help you.

1. 13 − 4 = ________ **2.** 16 − 9 = ________ **3.** 15 − 7 = ________

4. 11 − 6 = ________ **5.** 12 − 8 = ________ **6.** 14 − 5 = ________

7. There are 15 players on the Titans baseball team. Only 9 players can play at any one time. How many players are not playing? ________

8. **Geometry** An octagon has 8 sides. A pentagon has 5 sides. How many more sides does an octagon have than a pentagon? ________

Name ______________________________

Subtraction Meanings

Write a number sentence for each situation. Solve.

1. Terrance has 14 CDs. Robyn has 9 CDs. How many more CDs does Terrance have than Robyn?

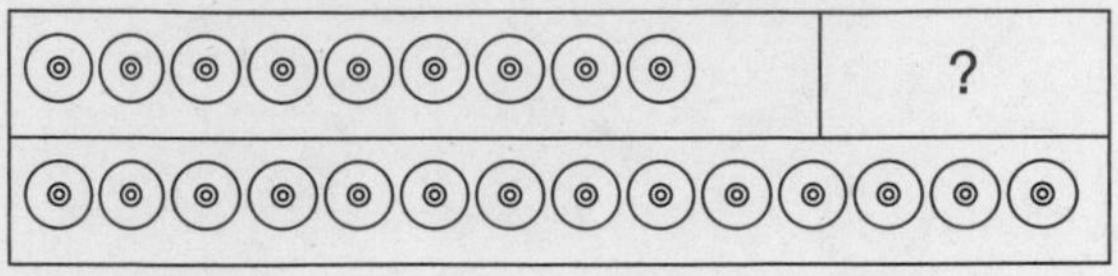

____

2. How many more black stars are there than white stars?

____

3. Arizona has 15 counties. Connecticut has 8 counties. How many more counties does Arizona have than Connecticut?

____

4. A baseball hat costs $12. Nancy has a coupon for $4 off. How much money will Nancy spend on the baseball hat?

____

5. **Draw a Picture** Carrie invited 13 girls to a party. Five of the girls have already arrived. How many girls have yet to arrive? Draw a picture to show the problem.

____

6. **Number Sense** Write the fact family for 3, 9, and 12.

____

____

____

____

7. LaToya has 12 postcards and 4 photographs on a bulletin board. How many more postcards does LaToya have than photographs?

○ 7 ○ 8 ○ 9 ○ 16

Name ______________________

Reteaching **4-2**

Subtracting on a Hundred Chart

You can use a hundred chart to subtract.
To subtract 72 − 37, follow these steps:

- Start at 72.
- Go up 3 rows to subtract 30.
- Go left 1 space to subtract 1.
- Move up to the row above and go left 6.
- End at 35.

So, 72 − 37 = 35.

1	2	3	4	5	6	7	8	9	10
11	12	13	14	15	16	17	18	19	20
21	22	23	24	25	26	27	28	29	30
31	32	33	34	35	36	37	38	39	40
41	42	43	44	45	46	47	48	49	50
51	52	53	54	55	56	57	58	59	60
61	62	63	64	65	66	67	68	69	70
71	72	73	74	75	76	77	78	79	80
81	82	83	84	85	86	87	88	89	90
91	92	93	94	95	96	97	98	99	100

You could also do it this way.

- Start at 72.
- Go up 4 rows to subtract 40.
- Go right 3 spaces to add 3.
- You end up at 35.

So, 72 − 37 = 35

1	2	3	4	5	6	7	8	9	10
11	12	13	14	15	16	17	18	19	20
21	22	23	24	25	26	27	28	29	30
31	32	33	34	35	36	37	38	39	40
41	42	43	44	45	46	47	48	49	50
51	52	53	54	55	56	57	58	59	60
61	62	63	64	65	66	67	68	69	70
71	72	73	74	75	76	77	78	79	80
81	82	83	84	85	86	87	88	89	90
91	92	93	94	95	96	97	98	99	100

Use a hundred chart to subtract.

1. 57 − 30 ______ **2.** 63 − 20 ______ **3.** 77 − 52 ______ **4.** 54 − 33 ______

5. 51 − 18 ______ **6.** 74 − 27 ______ **7.** 93 − 36 ______ **8.** 84 − 25 ______

9. **Reasoning** To find 62 − 24, you could first find 64 24 = 40.
Then what should you do? Explain.

____

____

____

Name ________________________________

Practice
4-2

Subtracting on a Hundred Chart

Use a hundred chart to subtract.

1	2	3	4	5	6	7	8	9	10
11	12	13	14	15	16	17	18	19	20
21	22	23	24	25	26	27	28	29	30
31	32	33	34	35	36	37	38	39	40
41	42	43	44	45	46	47	48	49	50
51	52	53	54	55	56	57	58	59	60
61	62	63	64	65	66	67	68	69	70
71	72	73	74	75	76	77	78	79	80
81	82	83	84	85	86	87	88	89	90
91	92	93	94	95	96	97	98	99	100

1. 53 − 20 ______

2. 76 − 40 ______

3. 73 − 30 ______

4. 67 − 50 ______

5. 94 − 26 ______

6. 34 − 18 ______

7. 56 − 24 ______

8. 84 − 39 ______

9. 63 − 49 ______

10. 77 − 40 ______

11. 93 − 55 ______

12. 64 − 36 ______

13. At full speed, a lion can run 50 miles per hour.
A grizzly bear can run 30 miles per hour.
How much faster can a lion run than a grizzly bear? ______ miles per hour

14. **Reasonableness** Bobby subtracted 75 − 45 and said the difference is 30.
Is his answer reasonable? Why or why not?

____

____

15. By how many points did the Terriers win?

______

16. Which subtraction sentence has a difference of 34?

○ 57 − 33 = ■ ○ 72 − 37 = ■
○ 61 − 17 = ■ ○ 63 − 29 = ■

Name ______________________________

Using Mental Math to Subtract

You can change numbers to make subtraction problems easier.

There are two ways to subtract 42 − 28.

One way is to add 2 to 28.

$$\begin{array}{rcr} 42 & \rightarrow & 42 \\ -\ 28 + 2 & \rightarrow & 30 \\ \hline & & 12 \end{array}$$

Because you added 2 to 28, add 2 to the difference.

12 + 2 = 14

So, 42 − 28 = 14.

Another way is to add 2 to both 42 and 28.

$$\begin{array}{rcr} 42 + 2 & \rightarrow & 44 \\ -\ 28 + 2 & \rightarrow & 30 \\ \hline & & 14 \end{array}$$

What you do to the bottom number, also do to the top number.

So, 42 − 28 = 14.

Find each difference using mental math.

1. 32 − 17 = ______ **2.** 51 − 46 = ______ **3.** 42 − 18 = ______

4. 36 − 19 = ______ **5.** 63 − 56 = ______ **6.** 78 − 16 = ______

7. 94 − 18 = ______ **8.** 55 − 33 = ______ **9.** 81 − 13 = ______

10. Number Sense Rob had $60 when he went to the mall. He bought a DVD for $15. How much money does he have left? Write the number sentence you used to solve the problem.

____

Name ______________________

Practice
4-3

Using Mental Math to Subtract

Find each difference using mental math.

1. 38 − 14 ______

2. 42 − 13 ______

3. 55 − 12 ______

4. 62 − 17 ______

5. 72 − 19 ______

6. 94 − 11 ______

7. 32 − 15 ______

8. 85 − 18 ______

9. 43 − 16 ______

10. 66 − 15 ______

11. 53 − 19 ______

12. 72 − 16 ______

13. **Number Sense** Gillian started solving 88 − 29. This is what she did.

88 − 29 = ?
88 − 30 = 58

What should Gillian do next? ______________________

14. **Writing to Explain** Tell how to find 81 − 16 using mental math.

____

____

____

15. Tiffany needs 63 tiles for her art project. She only needs 17 more tiles. Use mental math to find how many tiles she has already.

____

16. To solve 35 − 19, Jack used 35 − 20 and then

○ added 1.
○ subtracted 1.
○ subtracted 9.
○ added 9.

Name ______________________

Estimating Differences

Members of the Biology Club caught 288 butterflies and 136 grasshoppers in their nets. About how many more butterflies than grasshoppers did the club catch?

You can estimate by rounding. To round to a certain place, look at the digit to the right of that place. If the digit is 5 or greater, round up. If the digit is less than 5, round down.

Round to the nearest hundred.
Look at the digits in the tens place.

$$\begin{array}{rcr} 288 & \rightarrow & 300 \\ -\ 136 & \rightarrow & 100 \\ \hline & & 200 \end{array}$$

There were about 200 more butterflies than grasshoppers caught.

Round to the nearest ten.
Look at the digits in the ones place.

$$\begin{array}{rcr} 288 & \rightarrow & 290 \\ -\ 136 & \rightarrow & 140 \\ \hline & & 150 \end{array}$$

There were about 150 more butterflies than grasshoppers caught.

Estimate by rounding to the nearest hundred.

1. $\begin{array}{r} 442 \\ -\ 112 \\ \hline \end{array}$

2. $\begin{array}{r} 725 \\ -\ 278 \\ \hline \end{array}$

3. $\begin{array}{r} 363 \\ -\ 187 \\ \hline \end{array}$

Estimate by rounding to the nearest ten.

4. 68 − 42 = ______

5. 88 − 17 = ______

6. 231 − 109 = ______

7. Writing to Explain Charlie estimated 293 − 44 and got a difference of about 250. Is this a reasonable estimate? Explain.

____

____

____

Name ______________________

Practice
4-4

Estimating Differences

Round to the nearest hundred to estimate each difference.

1. 478 − 267 ______

2. 236 − 119 ______

3. 588 − 321 ______

Round to the nearest ten to estimate each difference.

4. 677 − 421 ______

5. 296 − 97 ______

6. 312 − 157 ______

Use compatible numbers to estimate each difference.

7. 84 − 36 ______

8. 427 − 163 ______

9. 609 − 243 ______

10. **Number Sense** Fern rounded to the nearest ten to estimate 548 − 132. She subtracted 540 − 130 = 410. Is Fern's estimate correct? Explain.

____

____

11. Waco, TX, has an elevation of 405 feet. Dallas, TX, has an elevation of 463 feet. About how many feet greater is Dallas's elevation than Waco's elevation? ______

12. On Friday, 537 people attended a play. For Saturday's matinee, there were 812 people. About how many more people attended the play on Saturday than on Friday? ______

13. A football team scored 529 points one season and then 376 points the next. About how many points less did the team score in the second season? Round to the nearest ten. ______

14. George got a 94 on his spelling test and a 68 on his math test. Which number sentence best shows about how many more points George got on his spelling test than his math test?

- ○ 90 − 60 = 30
- ○ 100 + 60 = 160
- ○ 90 + 70 = 160
- ○ 90 − 70 = 20

Name ______________________________

Subtracting 2-Digit Numbers

Find 62 − 26.
Estimate: 60 − 30 = 30, so the answer should be about 30.

Step 1	Step 2	Step 3
There are not enough ones to subtract.	Subtract the ones.	Subtract the tens.
6 tens 2 ones = 5 tens 12 ones	12 − 6 = 6	5 − 2 = 3
$\begin{array}{r} {}^{5\,12} \\ \not{6}\not{2} \\ -\ 26 \\ \hline \end{array}$	$\begin{array}{r} {}^{5\,12} \\ \not{6}\not{2} \\ -\ 26 \\ \hline 6 \end{array}$	$\begin{array}{r} {}^{5\,12} \\ \not{6}\not{2} \\ -\ 26 \\ \hline 36 \end{array}$

Since 36 is close to 30, the answer is reasonable. Check your answer by adding: 36 + 26 = 62.

Subtract.

1. $\begin{array}{r} 25 \\ -\ 9 \\ \hline \end{array}$ **2.** $\begin{array}{r} 42 \\ -\ 24 \\ \hline \end{array}$ **3.** $\begin{array}{r} 74 \\ -\ 17 \\ \hline \end{array}$ **4.** $\begin{array}{r} 53 \\ -\ 22 \\ \hline \end{array}$ **5.** $\begin{array}{r} 65 \\ -\ 38 \\ \hline \end{array}$

6. 71 − 48 = ________ **7.** 92 − 56 = ________ **8.** 83 − 57 = ________

9. A total of 76 boys and 94 girls signed up to play soccer. How many more girls signed up for soccer than boys?

____

10. Reasonableness Melanie subtracted 76 − 35 and got 31. Is her answer reasonable? Explain.

____

____

____

Name ______________________

Practice
4-5

Subtracting 2-Digit Numbers

Subtract.

1. $\begin{array}{r} 34 \\ -\ 16 \\ \hline \end{array}$ **2.** $\begin{array}{r} 43 \\ -\ 27 \\ \hline \end{array}$ **3.** $\begin{array}{r} 76 \\ -\ 28 \\ \hline \end{array}$ **4.** $\begin{array}{r} 65 \\ -\ 38 \\ \hline \end{array}$ **5.** $\begin{array}{r} 82 \\ -\ 47 \\ \hline \end{array}$

6. 82 − 67 = ______ **7.** 63 − 35 = ______ **8.** 86 − 42 = ______

9. **Reasonableness** Rebecca subtracted 47 − 28 and got 19. Is her answer reasonable? Explain.

____

____

____

10. **Writing to Explain** Do you need to regroup to find 73 − 35? Explain your answer.

____

____

____

11. **Write a Problem** Bethany has 43 apples. Write a subtraction story about the apples that would require regrouping. Then write the answer in a complete sentence.

____

____

____

12. The tree farm had 65 shade trees for sale. It sold 39 of the trees. How many trees did the farm have left?

○ 26 ○ 36 ○ 94 ○ 104

Name ______________________________

Reteaching
4-6

Models for Subtracting 3-Digit Numbers

You can use place-value blocks to subtract.

Find 234 − 192.

Estimate: 230 − 190 = 40, so the answer should be about 40.

	What You Show	What You Write
Step 1 Show 234 with place-value blocks.	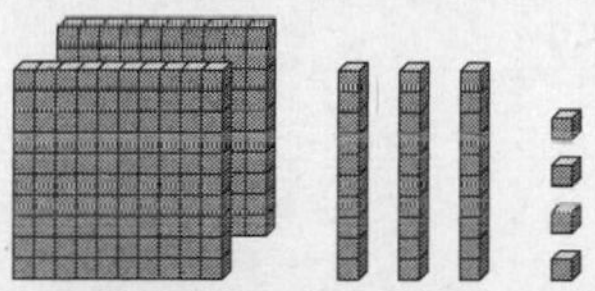	234 −192
Step 2 Subtract the ones. 4 > 2. No regrouping is needed.	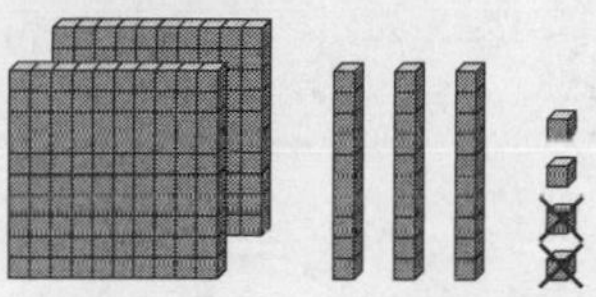 4 ones − 2 ones = 2 ones	234 −192 2
Step 3 Subtract the tens. 3 tens < 9 tens, so regroup 1 hundred for 10 tens.	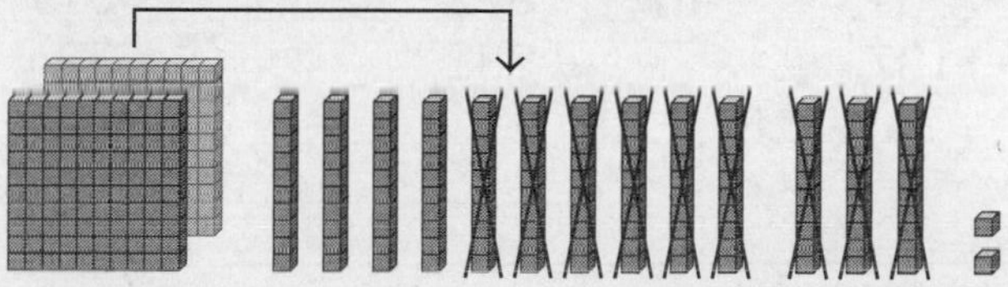 13 tens − 9 tens = 4 tens	1 13 234 −192 42
Step 4 Subtract the hundreds.	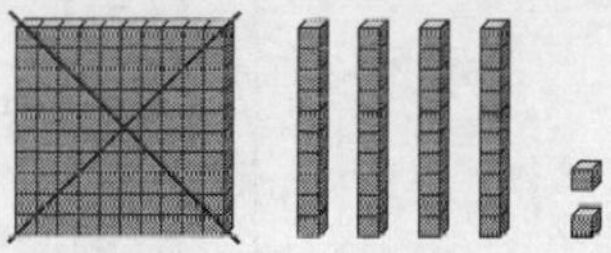 1 hundred − 1 hundred = 0 hundreds	1 13 234 −192 42

Find the value of the remaining blocks:

4 tens + 2 ones = 40 + 2 = 42

So, 234 − 192 = 42.

Use place-value blocks or draw pictures to subtract.

1. 156 − 28

2. 261 − 122

3. 321 − 76

4. 446 − 257

Name ______________________

Practice 4-6

Models for Subtracting 3-Digit Numbers

Use the place-value blocks to subtract.

1.

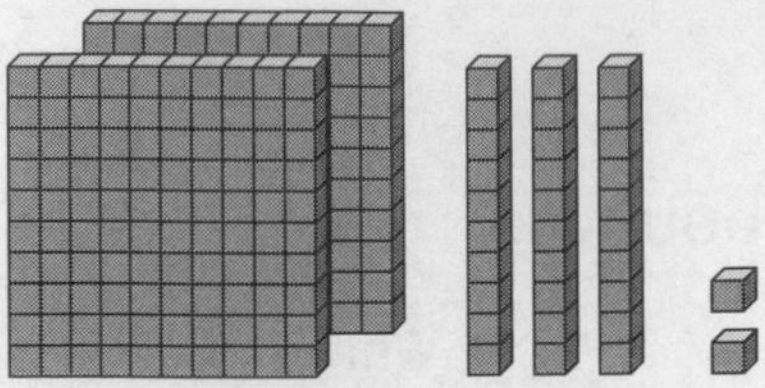

$$\begin{array}{r} 232 \\ -\ 147 \\ \hline \end{array}$$

2.

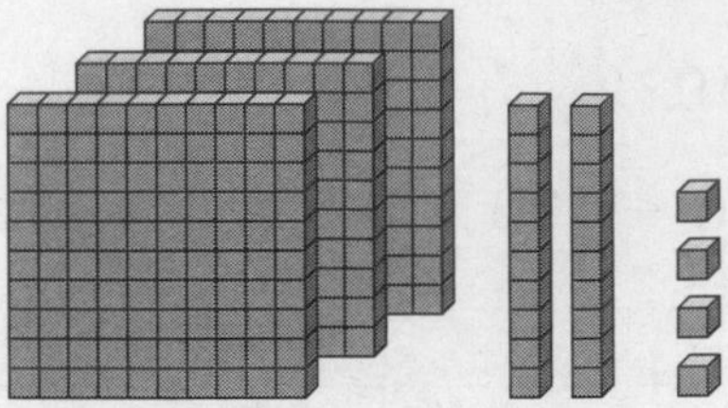

$$\begin{array}{r} 324 \\ -\ 156 \\ \hline \end{array}$$

Use place-value blocks or draw pictures to subtract.

3. $\begin{array}{r} 321 \\ -\ 176 \\ \hline \end{array}$ **4.** $\begin{array}{r} 242 \\ -\ 86 \\ \hline \end{array}$ **5.** $\begin{array}{r} 332 \\ -\ 117 \\ \hline \end{array}$ **6.** $\begin{array}{r} 267 \\ -\ 149 \\ \hline \end{array}$ **7.** $\begin{array}{r} 413 \\ -\ 237 \\ \hline \end{array}$

8. $\begin{array}{r} 165 \\ -\ 137 \\ \hline \end{array}$ **9.** $\begin{array}{r} 251 \\ -\ 137 \\ \hline \end{array}$ **10.** $\begin{array}{r} 372 \\ -\ 283 \\ \hline \end{array}$ **11.** $\begin{array}{r} 511 \\ -\ 324 \\ \hline \end{array}$ **12.** $\begin{array}{r} 346 \\ -\ 138 \\ \hline \end{array}$

For **13** and **14**, use the table at the right.

Pages Read

Name	Pages Read
Lance	322
Annie	263
Brad	415

13. What is the difference between the greatest and least number of pages read? __________

14. How many more pages did Lance read than Annie? __________

15. **Number Sense** Edie wanted to subtract 273 − 188. She began by finding 2 − 1. What did Edie do wrong?

____

____

16. Alice defeated Ralph 313 to 188 in a board game. By how many points did Alice win?

○ 115 ○ 125 ○ 215 ○ 225

Name ______________________

Subtracting 3-Digit Numbers

Find 726 − 238.

Estimate: 700 − 200 = 500, so the answer should be about 500.

Step 1

First subtract the ones.
Regroup 1 ten into 10 ones.

```
   1 16
  726
 −238
    8
```

Step 2

Subtract the tens.
Regroup 1 hundred into 10 tens.

```
   11
  6 1 16
  726
 −238
   88
```

Step 3

Subtract the hundreds.

```
   11
  6 1 16
  726
 −238
  488
```

Is your answer correct?
Check by adding:
488 + 238 = 726.
It checks.

Find each difference. Estimate and check answers for reasonableness.

1. 318 − 123 = ____ **2.** 441 − 187 = ____ **3.** 334 − 275 = ____ **4.** 512 − 299 = ____

5. 423 − 156 = ______ **6.** 327 − 159 = ______

7. The town library had 634 CDs for rent. During one week, 288 of them were rented. How many CDs were left? ______

8. Number Sense If you had to subtract 426 from 913, how many times would you need to regroup? How can you tell?

____

____

____

____

Name ______________________

Subtracting 3-Digit Numbers

Find each difference. Estimate and check answers for reasonableness.

1. 732 − 328

2. 621 − 153

3. 369 − 185

4. 267 − 78

5. 527 − 279

6. 917 − 436

7. 555 − 189

8. 422 − 244

9. 853 − 456

10. 451 − 363

11. 527 − 242 = ______ **12.** 746 − 437 = ______ **13.** 941 − 267 = ______

All Roads Lead to Omaha

Start	Finish	Miles
Dallas	Omaha	644
Chicago	Omaha	459
Tulsa	Omaha	387

14. Tulsa is how many miles closer to Omaha than Dallas? ______

15. Tulsa is how many miles closer to Omaha than Chicago? ______

16. **Strategy Practice** Jill is going on a trip from Chicago to Omaha to Tulsa. Bill will travel from Dallas to Omaha. How much farther will Jill travel than Bill?

a. What do you need to do first?

____

____

b. What is the next step?

____

c. Solve the problem.

______ miles

17. Texas has 254 counties. California has 58 counties and Florida has 67 counties. How many more counties does Texas have than California and Florida combined?

○ 125 ○ 129 ○ 139 ○ 196

Name ______________________

Subtracting Greater Numbers

Subtract 4,287 − 2,629.
Estimate: 4,000 − 3,000 = 1,000, so the answer should be about 1,000.

Align the digits on the ones place. Then subtract from right to left.

Step 1	**Step 2**	**Step 3**	**Step 4**
Subtract the ones. Regroup 1 ten into 10 ones.	Subtract the regrouped tens.	Subtract the hundreds. Regroup 1 thousand into 10 hundreds.	Subtract the regrouped thousands.
7 17 4,287 − 2,629 8	7 17 4,287 − 2,629 58	3 12 7 17 4,287 − 2,629 658	3 12 7 17 4,287 − 2,629 1,658

Check your difference by adding: 1,658 + 2,629 = 4,287.
So, 4,287 − 2,629 = 1,658.

Estimate. Then subtract.

1. 3,653 − 2,119
2. 7,538 − 474
3. 8,368 − 4,285
4. 9,635 − 3,527
5. 5,337 − 1,689
6. 6,192 − 3,715
7. 8,724 − 5,562
8. 5,145 − 857
9. 8,038 − 1,546
10. 5,337 − 1,689

11. **Reasoning** Why is estimating before you subtract a good idea?

____

____

____

Name ______________________

Practice 4-8

Subtracting Greater Numbers

Estimate. Then subtract.

1. 3,625 − 1,793
2. 6,673 − 3,258
3. 8,478 − 2,739
4. 4,315 − 692
5. 7,832 − 5,188

6. 8,162 − 6,983
7. 5,576 − 998
8. 9,736 − 4,387
9. 6,282 − 1,825
10. 5,742 − 5,163

11. 5,283 − 2,692
12. 7,391 − 3,945
13. 4,427 − 363
14. 8,753 − 1,839

Use the table at the right for **15–18**.

Population of California Towns

Town	Population
Atherton	7,127
Exeter	9,842
Huron	6,997
Needles	5,346

15. How many more people live in Huron than in Needles?

16. How many more people live in Exeter than in Huron?

17. **Estimation** To estimate how many more people live in Atherton than Needles, which is closer to the exact answer: rounding to hundreds or thousands? Explain.

18. Waterford has a population of 8,119 people. How many more people live in Waterford than in Atherton?

○ 992
○ 1,008
○ 1,002
○ 1,092

Name ______________________________

Reteaching **4-9**

Subtracting Across Zero

To subtract from a number with 0 in the tens place, you need to regroup one hundred into 10 tens.

Find 207 − 98.

Step 1	Step 2	Step 3
Subtract the ones. Since there are 0 tens, you must first regroup the hundreds.	Regroup the hundreds. 2 hundreds and 0 tens = 1 hundred and 10 tens.	Regroup the tens. 10 tens and 7 ones = 9 tens and 17 ones. Subtract.
207 − 98	1 10 ~~2~~~~0~~7 − 98	9 1 ~~10~~ 17 ~~2~~~~0~~~~7~~ − 98 109

Is your answer correct? Check by adding: 109 + 98 = 207.

Find each difference.

1. 301 − 72

2. 205 − 36

3. 400 − 228

4. 502 − 225

5. 603 − 215

6. 307 − 149 = ______ **7.** 702 − 259 = ______ **8.** 504 − 397 = ______

9. **Number Sense** Waco has an elevation of 405 feet above sea level. Texarkana has an elevation of 324 feet above sea level. How many feet greater is Waco's elevation than Texarkana's? Show your work.

______ feet

Name ______________________

Practice 4-9

Subtracting Across Zero

Find each difference.

1. $\begin{array}{r} 406 \\ -\ 28 \\ \hline \end{array}$

2. $\begin{array}{r} 300 \\ -\ 211 \\ \hline \end{array}$

3. $\begin{array}{r} 501 \\ -\ 268 \\ \hline \end{array}$

4. $\begin{array}{r} 705 \\ -\ 347 \\ \hline \end{array}$

5. $\begin{array}{r} 605 \\ -\ 219 \\ \hline \end{array}$

6. $\begin{array}{r} 800 \\ -\ 579 \\ \hline \end{array}$

7. $\begin{array}{r} 907 \\ -\ 728 \\ \hline \end{array}$

8. $\begin{array}{r} 603 \\ -\ 347 \\ \hline \end{array}$

9. $\begin{array}{r} 507 \\ -\ 388 \\ \hline \end{array}$

10. $\begin{array}{r} 706 \\ -\ 497 \\ \hline \end{array}$

11. 404 − 305 = ________ 12. 501 − 223 = ________ 13. 302 − 166 = ________

14. There were 600 ears of corn for sale at the produce market. At the end of the day, there were 212 ears left. How many ears of corn were sold? ________

15. Darrin has 702 CDs in his collection. Dana has 357 CDs in her collection. How many more CDs does Darrin have than Dana? ________

16. **Strategy Practice** Party Palace has an order for 505 party favors. It packaged 218 favors Saturday and 180 favors Sunday. How many more party favors does it still need to package? ________

17. **Write a Problem** Write a subtraction problem involving regrouping that has Ted reading 304 pages. Answer your question.

____

____

____

18. The Williams Tower in Houston, TX, is 901 feet tall. The Tower of the Americas in San Antonio, TX, is 622 feet tall. How much taller is the Williams Tower than the Tower of the Americas?

○ 279 feet ○ 289 feet ○ 379 feet ○ 389 feet

Name ____________________

Reteaching **4-10**

Problem Solving: Draw a Picture and Write a Number Sentence

The distance from Cleveland, OH, to Pittsburgh, PA, is 129 miles. Detroit, MI, is 170 miles away from Cleveland. How much closer is Pittsburgh to Cleveland than Detroit?

You can subtract to find how many miles closer Pittsburgh is to Cleveland than Detroit.

170 miles

129	?

Pittsburgh is 41 miles closer to Cleveland than Detroit.

$$\begin{array}{r} \scriptstyle 6\,10 \\ 17\not{0} \\ -\ 129 \\ \hline 41 \end{array}$$

You can estimate 170 − 130 = 40 to show that the answer is reasonable.

Solve.

1. Honolulu, HI, has an area of 86 square miles. Corpus Christi, TX, has an area that is 69 square miles greater than Honolulu. How many square miles is Corpus Christi?

________ square miles

86	69

2. Bakersfield, CA, has an area of 113 square miles. Its area is 64 square miles greater than the area of Anaheim, CA. What is the area, in square miles, of Anaheim?

113 square miles

64	________

3. Writing to Explain How did you know which operation to use to solve Problem 2?

____

____

____

Name ____________________

Practice
4-10

Problem Solving: Draw a Picture and Write a Number Sentence

The table below shows the areas of some of the smallest countries in the world. Use the table for **1–3**.

Area of Countries

Country	Area (in sq mi)
San Marino	24
Liechtenstein	62
Maldives	116
Palau	177

1. How many square miles greater is Maldives than San Marino?

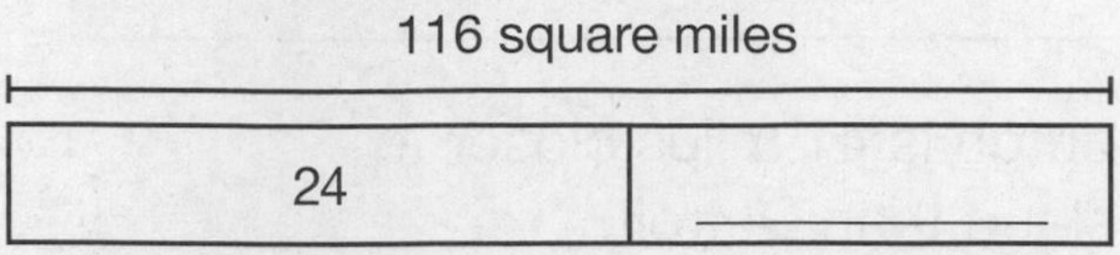

2. **Draw a Picture** Draw a diagram to show how to find the difference between the areas of Liechtenstein and San Marino. Use your diagram to solve the problem.

3. Grenada is 15 square miles greater than Maldives. What is the area of Grenada?

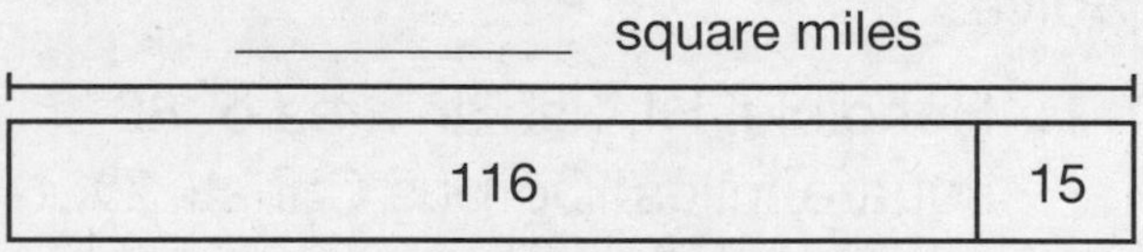

4. There are 237 students at Johnson Elementary School. There are 188 students at Hoover Elementary School. How many more students are at Johnson than at Hoover?

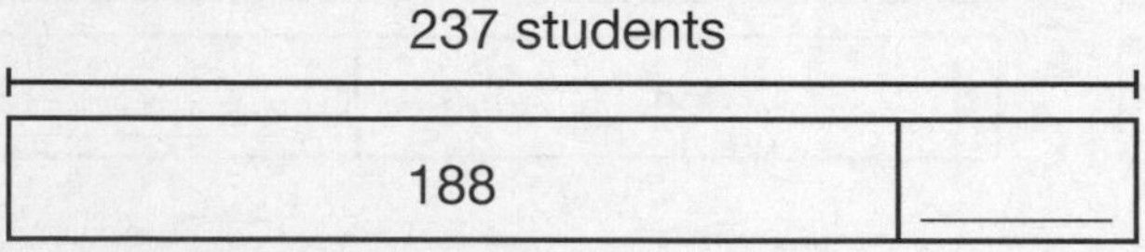

5. **Write a Problem** Write a real-world problem that you can solve by adding or subtracting. Then give your problem to a classmate to solve.

____

____

____

Name ________________________________

Solid Figures

Three-dimensional objects are called solid figures. Solid figures are found in the world in many shapes and sizes.

The battery is an example of a cylinder. A **solid figure** is named according to its features.

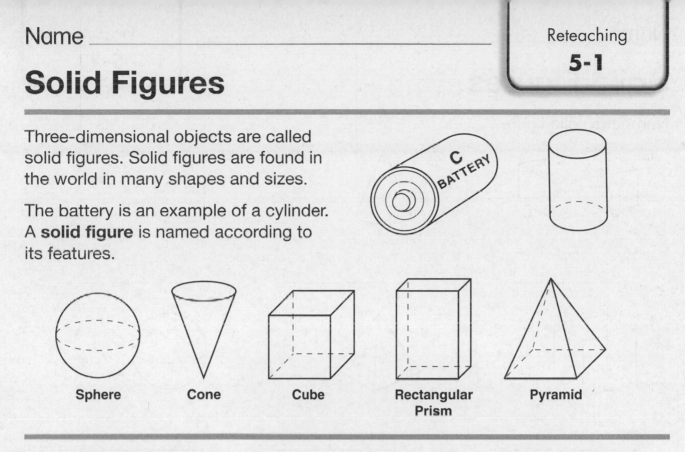

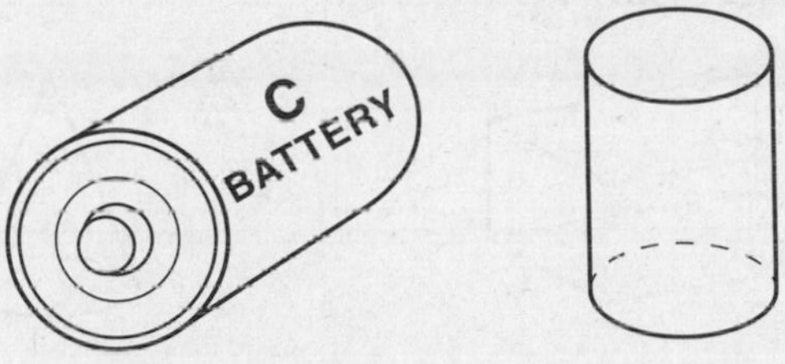

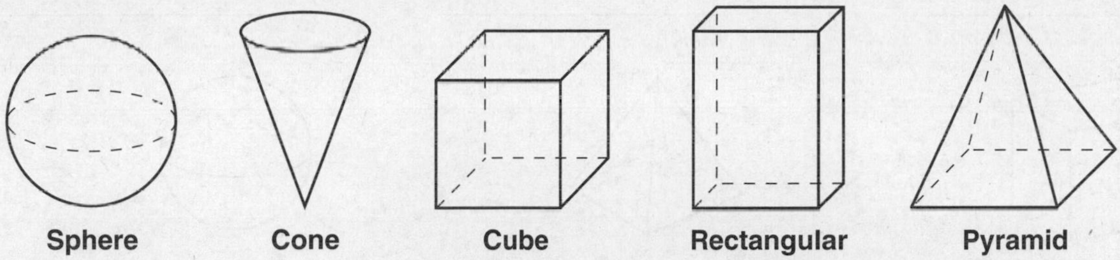

Name the solid figure that each object looks like.

1. 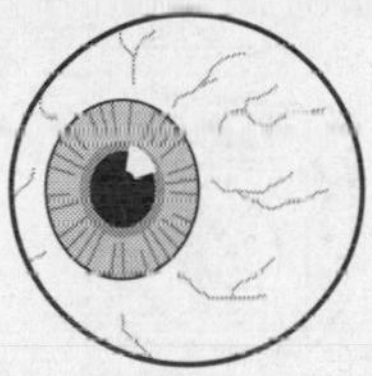

   ____

2. 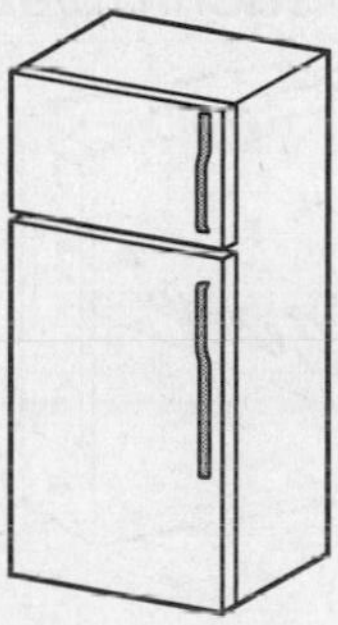

   ____

3. 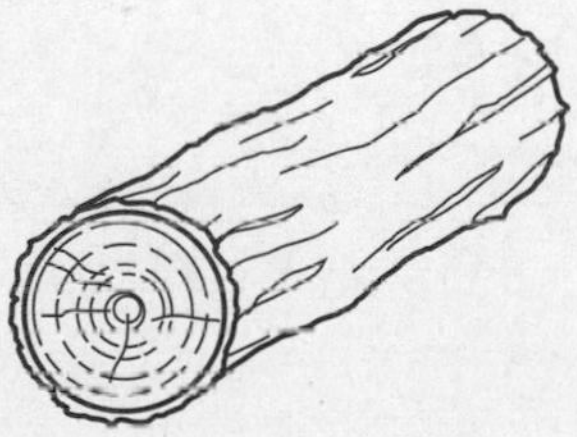

   ____

4. 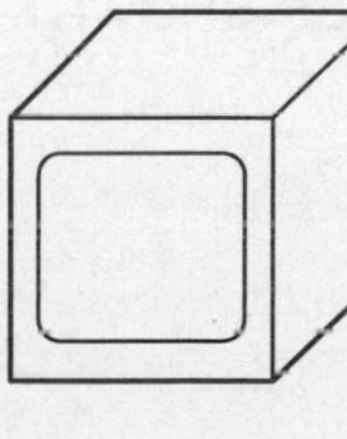

   ____

5. Mike put a pyramid and a sphere on a table. Which is most likely going to fall off the table if pushed? Explain.

____

Name ____________________

Solid Figures

Name the solid figure.

1. 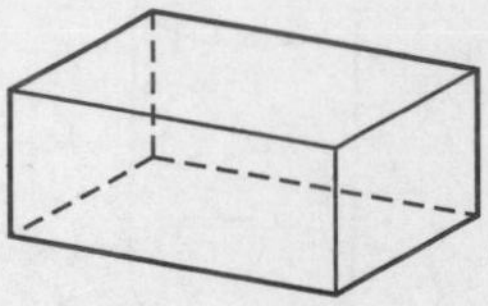
____

2. 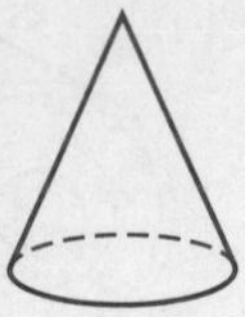
____

3. 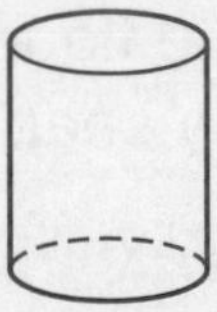
____

4. 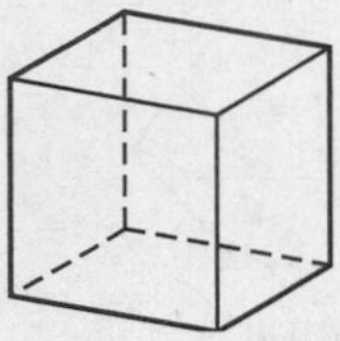
____

5. 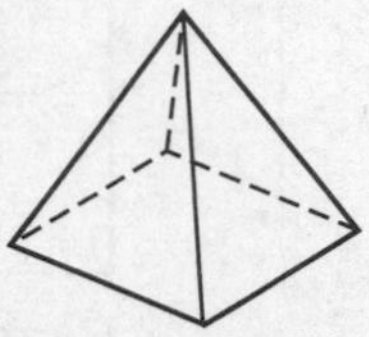
____

6. 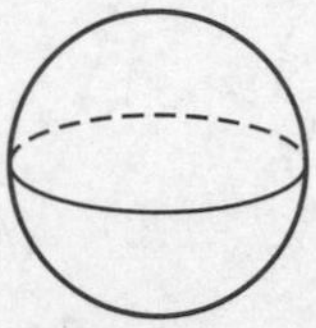
____

Name the solid figure that each object looks like.

7. 
____

8. 

____

9. 

____

10. 

____

11. **Reasoning** What solid figures would you get if you cut a cube as shown?

12. What solid figure does this figure most resemble?

○ Cylinder ○ Cone ○ Pyramid ○ Sphere

Name ______________________________

Relating Solids and Shapes

Some solid figures have faces, edges, and vertices. Below is an example of the faces, edges, and vertices of a cube.

A face is a flat surface on a solid figure.
There are 6 faces on a cube.

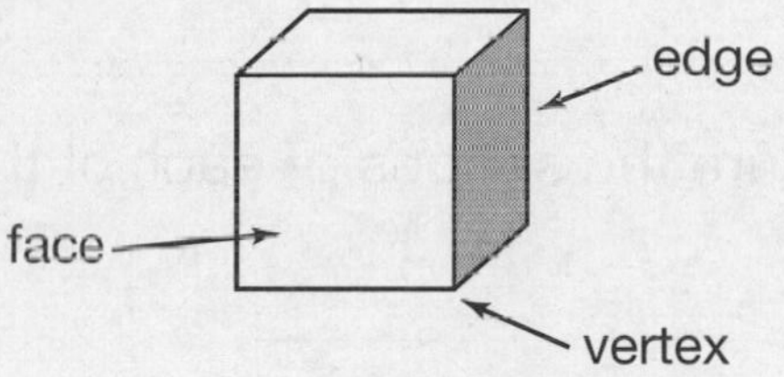

An edge is where two faces meet.
There are 12 edges on a cube.

A vertex is where 3 or more edges meet.
There are 8 vertices on a cube.

Some figures do not have edges or vertices.

Look at the solid figures below.

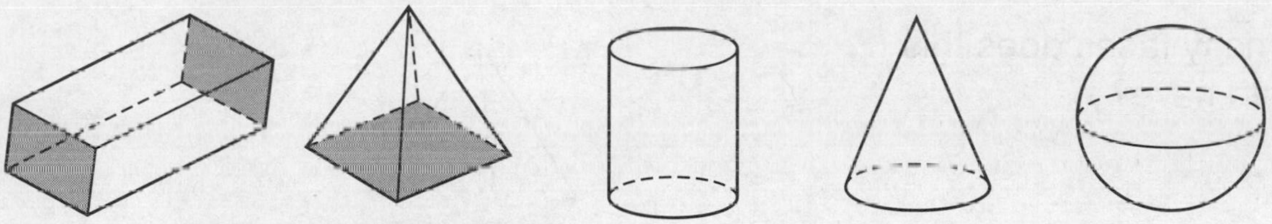

1. Which solid figure has the same number of faces, edges, and vertices as a cube?

____

2. Which solid figure has 4 triangular faces?

____

3. Which solid figure has only 2 flat surfaces?

____

4. Which solid figure does not have any faces, edges, or vertices?

____

5. **Reasoning** How are a cube and a rectangular prism alike? How are they different?

____

____

____

____

Name ______________________________

Relating Solids and Shapes

For **1–4**, use the rectangular prism pictured at the right.

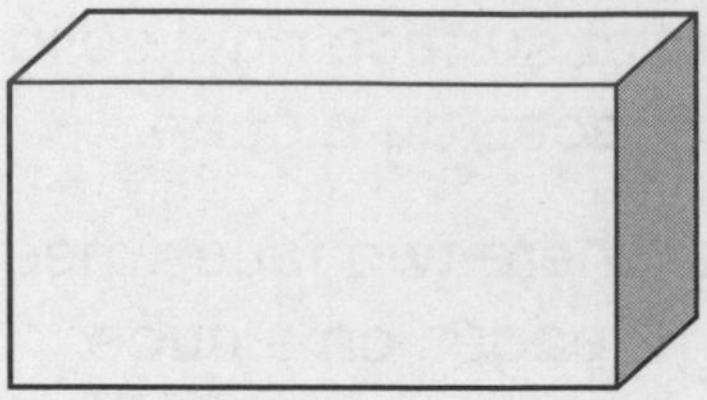

1. How many faces does this rectangular prism have?

______

2. What are the shapes of each of the faces?

____

3. How many edges does this rectangular prism have?

______

4. How many vertices does this rectangular prism have?

______

For **5–8**, use the pyramid pictured at the right.

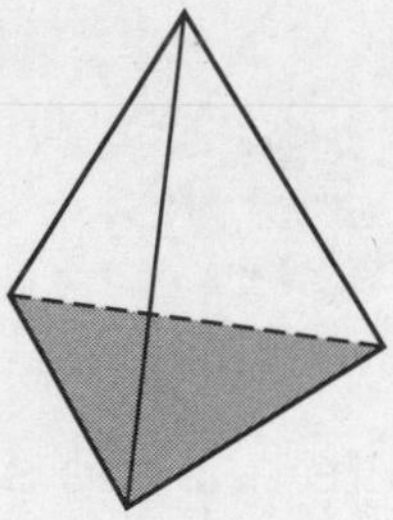

5. How many faces does this pyramid have?

______

6. What are the shapes of each of the faces?

____

7. How many edges does this pyramid have?

______

8. How many vertices does this pyramid have?

______

9. **Writing to Explain** How could you describe a cylinder to someone who has never seen one?

____

____

____

10. Which two figures have the same number of faces, edges, and vertices?

- ○ Cylinder and pyramid
- ○ Rectangular prism and sphere
- ○ Pyramid and cube
- ○ Rectangular prism and cube

Name ______________________________

Breaking Apart Solids

A solid figure can be broken apart in different ways.

Sometimes, the solid will be cut to form two smaller same type solids.

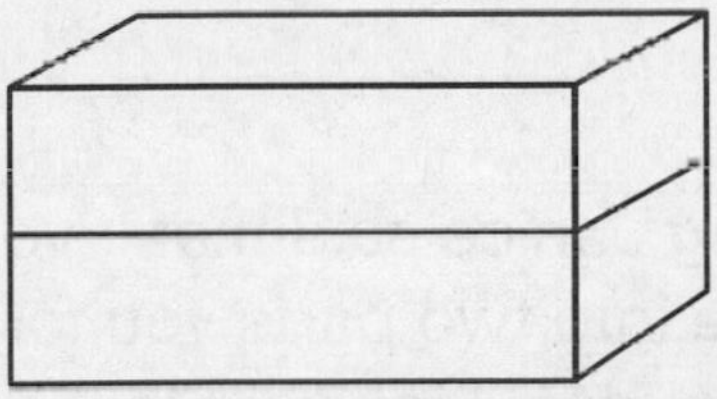

Two smaller rectangular prisms are formed.

Sometimes, the solid will be cut to form two solids that are classified as other solids.

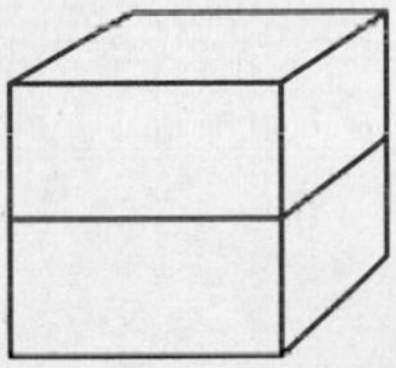

Two rectangular prisms are formed.

Sometimes, the solid will be cut to form 1 smaller same type solid and one solid that cannot be classified.

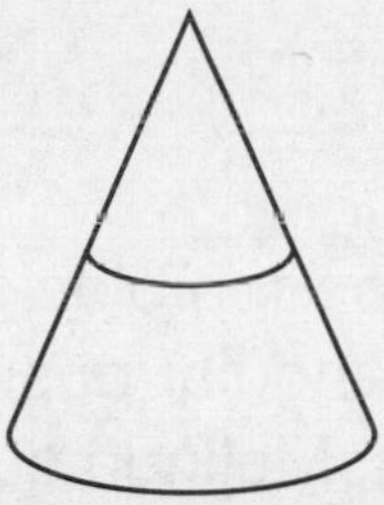

One cone and one other solid are formed.

Name the solid figures you would get if you cut the solid figure as shown.

1.

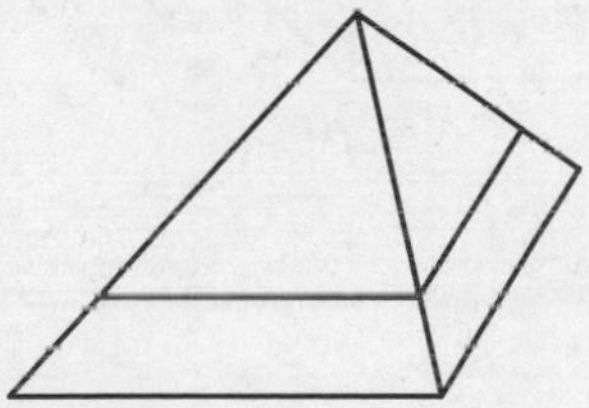

____

2.

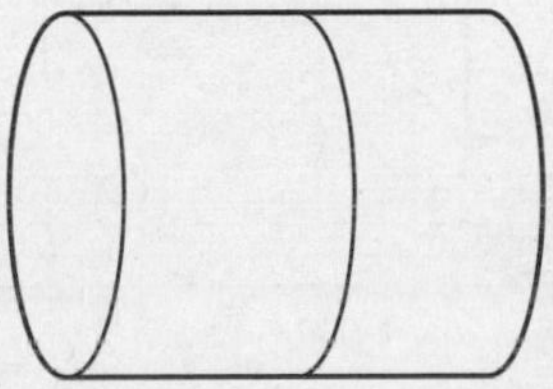

____

3.

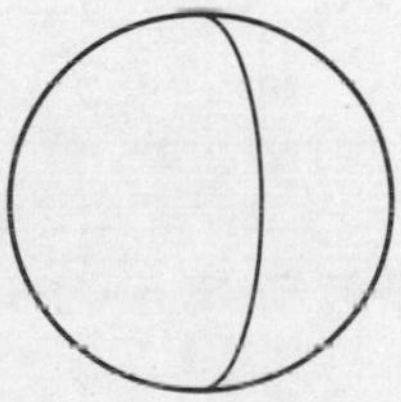

____

Name ______________________

Breaking Apart Solids

Name the solid figures you would get if you cut the solid figure as shown.

1. 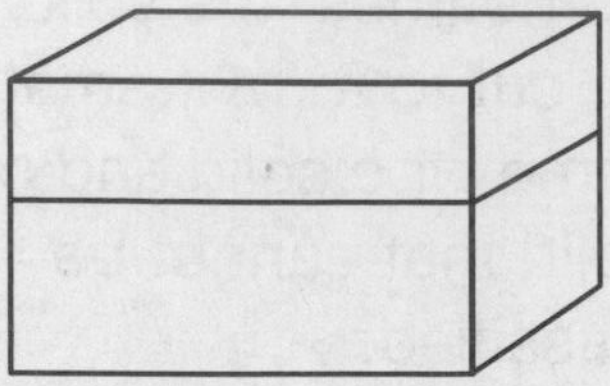

____

2. 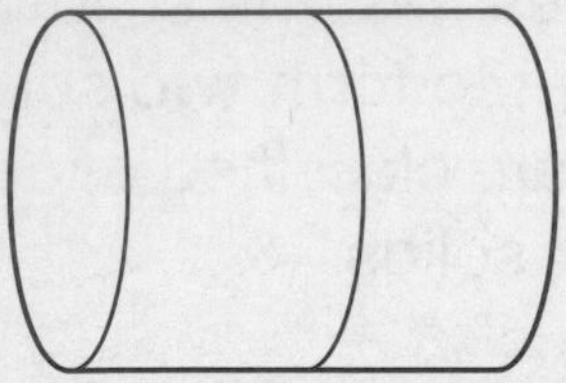

____

3. 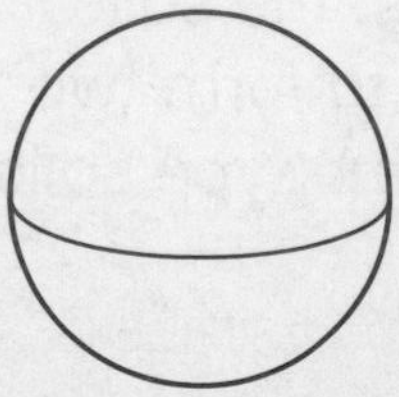

____

4. A wooden block that is a rectangular prism is 12 inches long. Melinda cuts the wooden block along its length into 4 cubes. How long is each side of the cube?

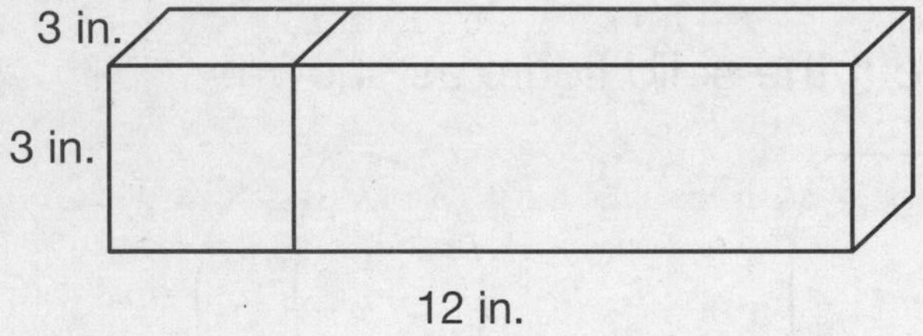

____

5. **Reasoning** Janice said that if you cut a cube into two parts you form 2 smaller cubes. Ling said that 2 rectangular prisms are formed. Who is correct? Explain.

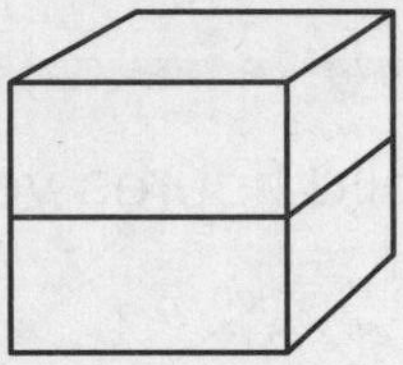

____

____

____

____

6. Which shape will have the same classification if you cut it in half?

○ 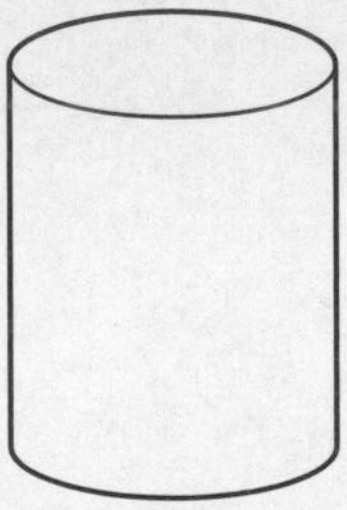
○ 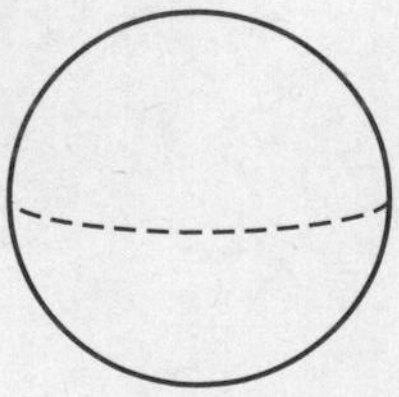
○ 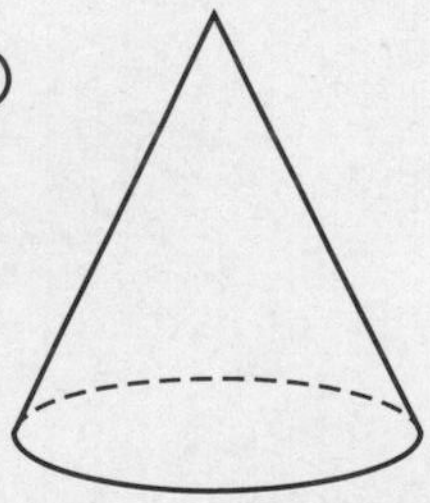
○ 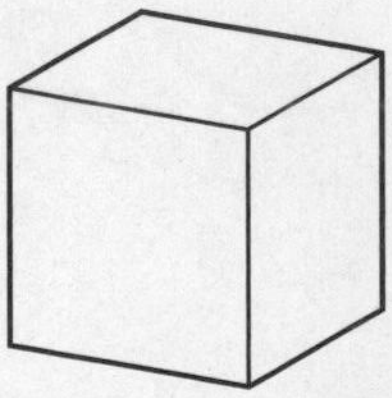

Name ______________________

Lines, Segments, and Angles

You can find lines and parts of lines in shapes and objects.

A point is an exact location in space.

A line is a set of points that goes forever in both directions.

A line segment is part of a line with two endpoints.

Parallel lines never meet or cross and remain the same distance apart.

Intersecting lines meet or cross.

Angles are formed by two rays that share a vertex. Three types of angles are right angles, acute angles, and obtuse angles.

A ray is part of a line that has one endpoint and goes forever in one direction.

A right angle forms a square corner.

An acute angle is less than a right angle.

An obtuse angle is greater than a right angle.

Write the name for each.

1.  ______________

2. 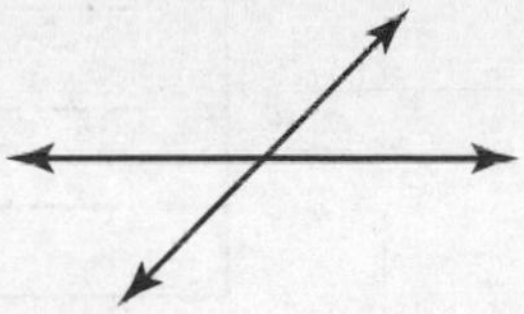 ______________

3.  ______________

4.  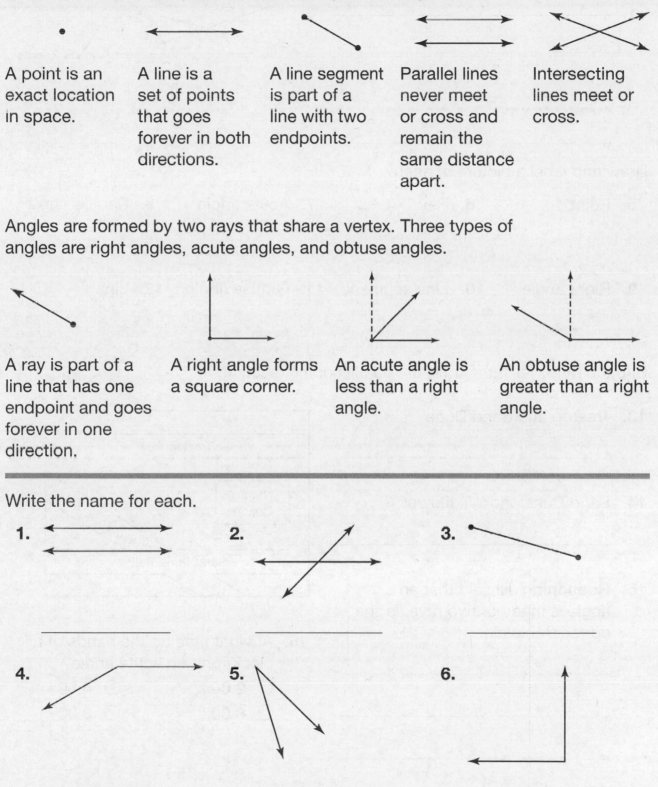 ______________

5. 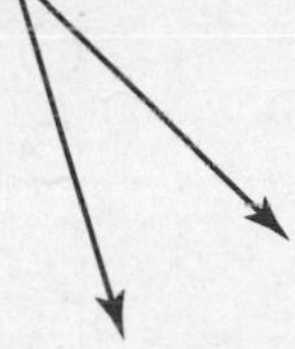 ______________

6. 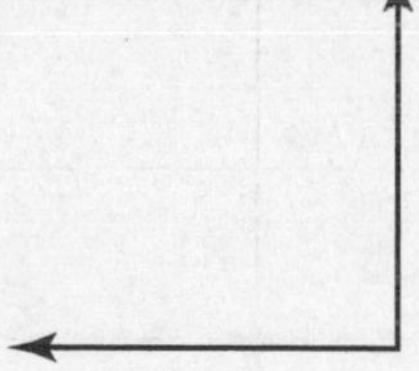 ______________

Name ______________________

Lines, Segments, and Angles

Write the name for each.

1.

2. 

3. 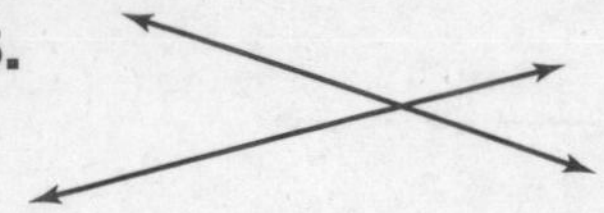

4. 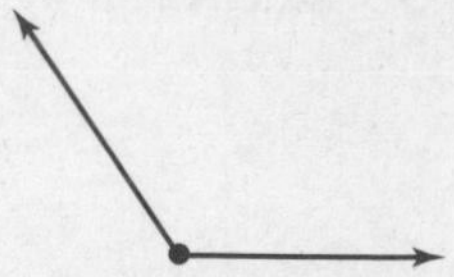

Draw and label a picture of each.

5. Point

6. Ray

7. Acute angle

8. Parallel lines

9. Right angle

10. Line segment

11. Obtuse angle

12. Line

Use the map. Tell if the trails are parallel or intersecting.

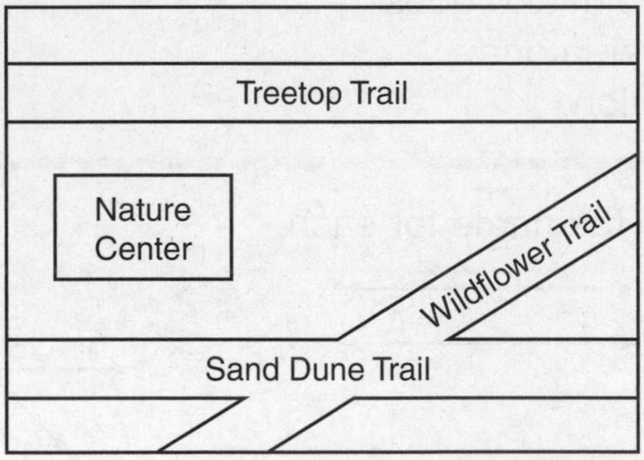

13. Treetop and Sand Dune

14. Sand Dune and Wildflower

15. **Reasoning** Jill said that an angle is made of two rays. Is she correct? Explain.

16. At what time do the hands of a clock form an acute angle?

- ○ 2:00
- ○ 4:00
- ○ 6:00
- ○ 8:00

Name ________________________

Reteaching
5-5

Polygons

Polygons are closed figures that are made up of straight line segments.

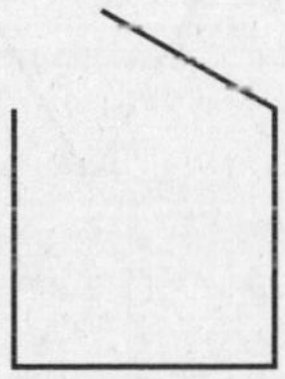

Not a polygon
Not a closed figure

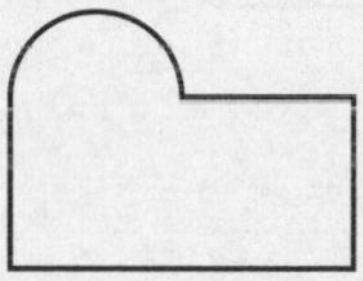

Not a polygon
Not all straight lines

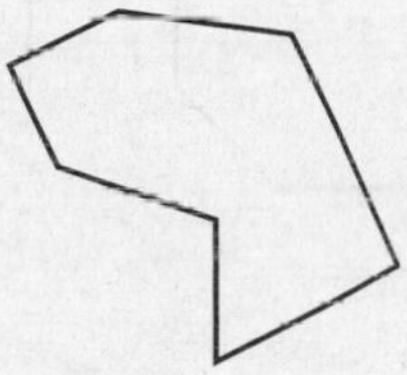

Polygon
Closed figure
All straight lines

The number of sides in a polygon gives the polygon its name.

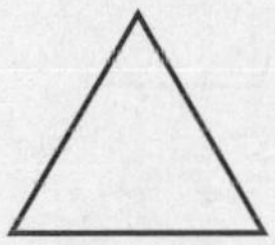

Triangle
3 sides

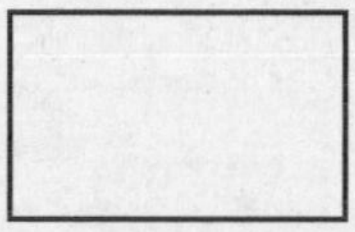

Quadrilateral
4 sides

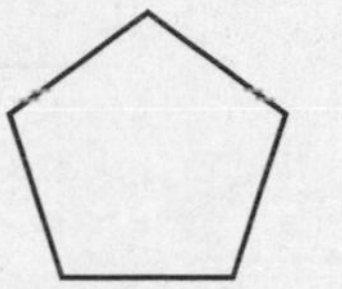

Pentagon
5 sides

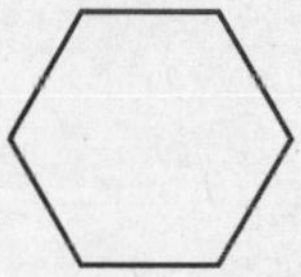

Hexagon
6 sides

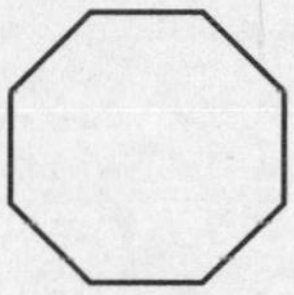

Octagon
8 sides

Is each figure a polygon? If it is a polygon, give its name. If not, explain why.

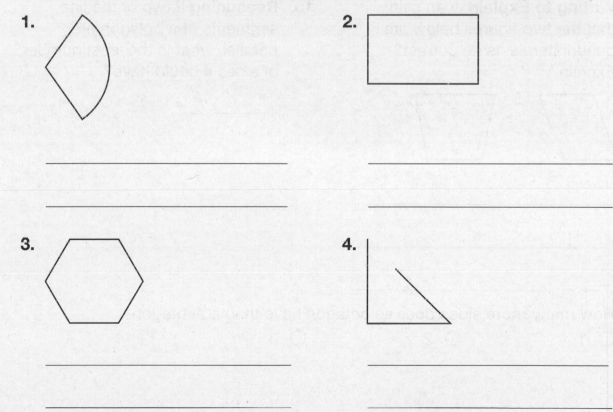

1. 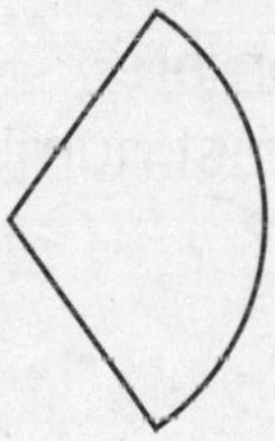

____

____

2. 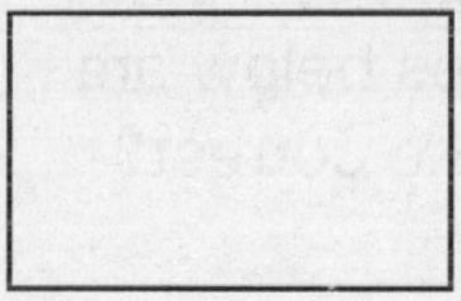

____

____

3. 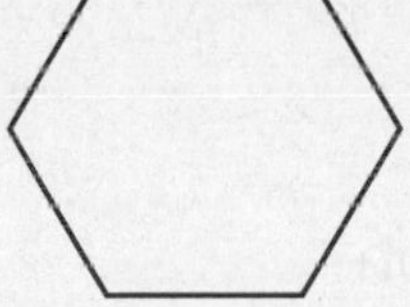

____

____

4. 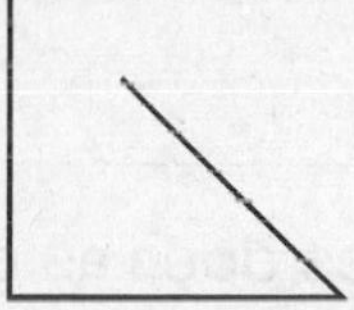

____

____

Name ____________________

Polygons

Name the polygon.

1. 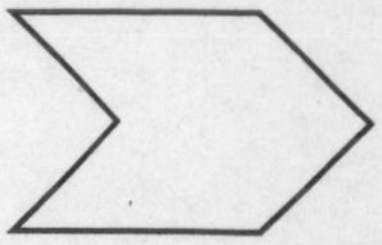

______

2. 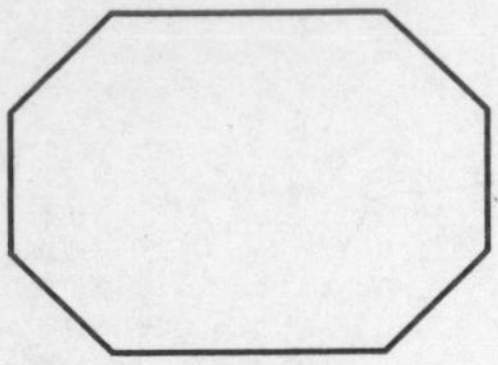

______

3. 

______

4. 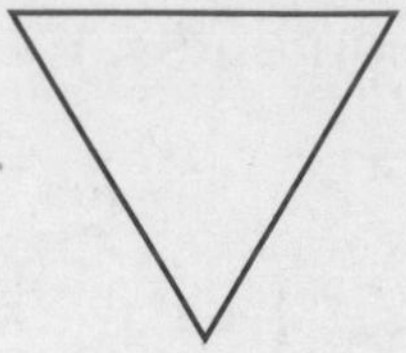

______

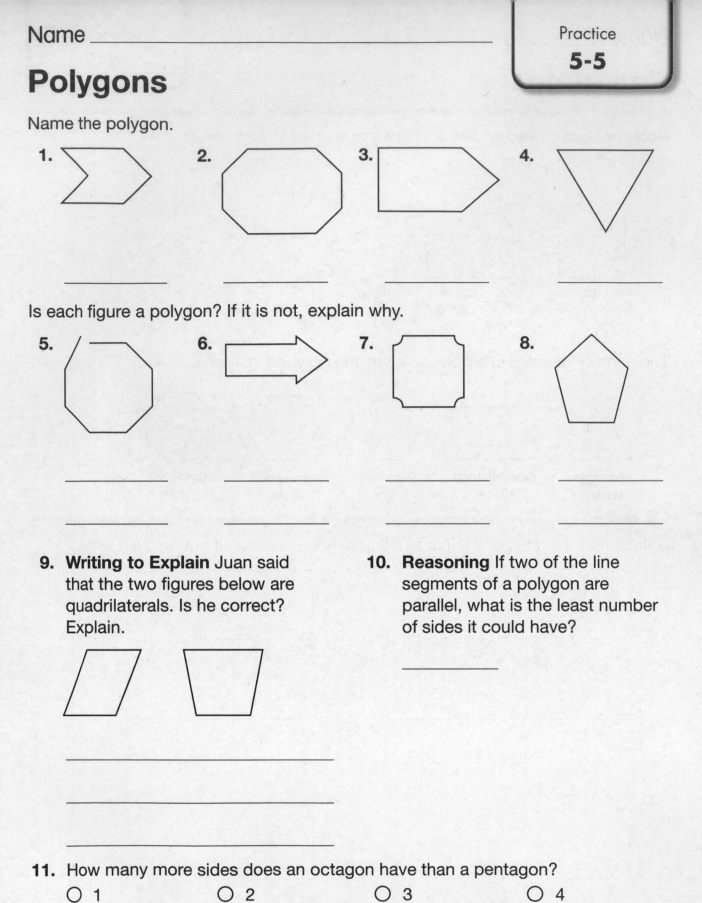

Is each figure a polygon? If it is not, explain why.

5. 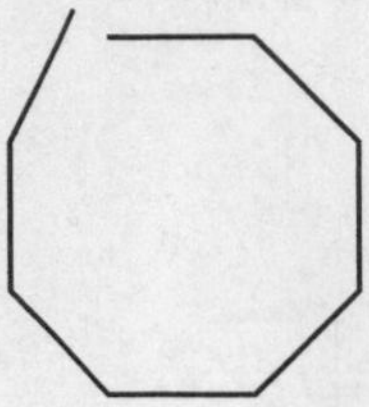

______

6. 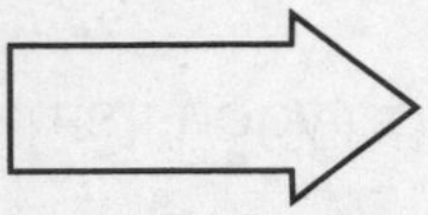

______

7. 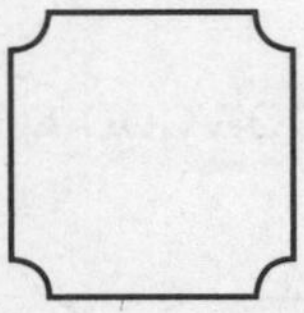

______

8. 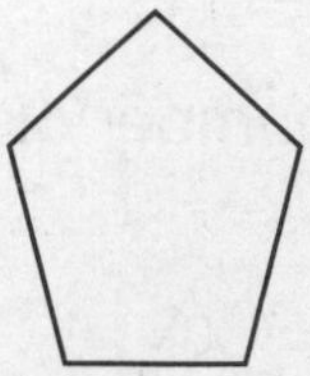

______

9. **Writing to Explain** Juan said that the two figures below are quadrilaterals. Is he correct? Explain.

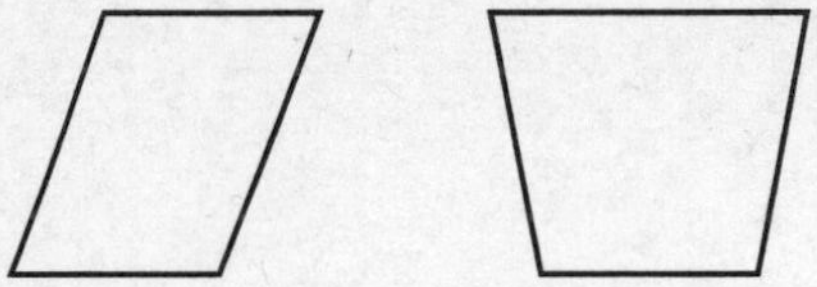

______

10. **Reasoning** If two of the line segments of a polygon are parallel, what is the least number of sides it could have?

______

11. How many more sides does an octagon have than a pentagon?

○ 1 ○ 2 ○ 3 ○ 4

Name ______________________

Reteaching
5-6

Triangles

Triangles are polygons with three sides.

Triangles can be named by the lengths of their sides.

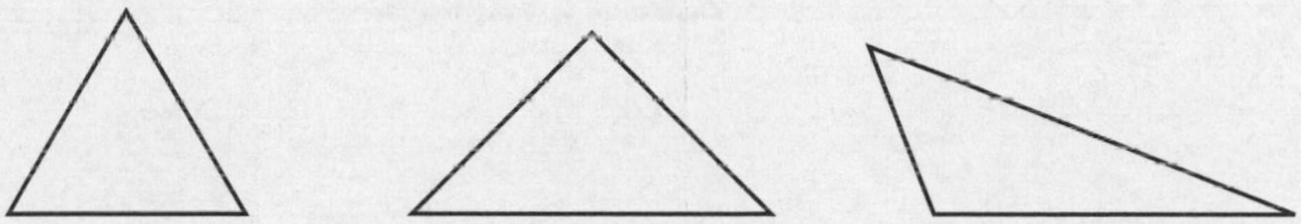

Equilateral Triangle
All sides are the same length.

Isosceles Triangle
At least two sides are the same length.

Scalene Triangle
No sides are the same length.

Triangles can also be described by their angles.

Right Triangle
One angle is a right angle.

Acute Triangle
All three angles are acute angles.

Obtuse Triangle
One angle is an obtuse angle.

Tell if the triangle is equilateral, isosceles, or scalene.

1. 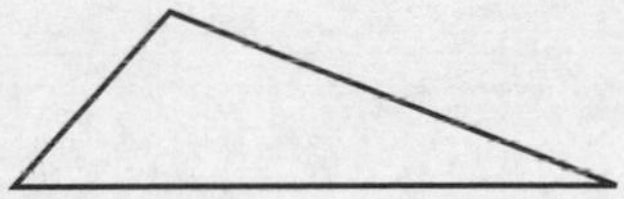 ______________

2. 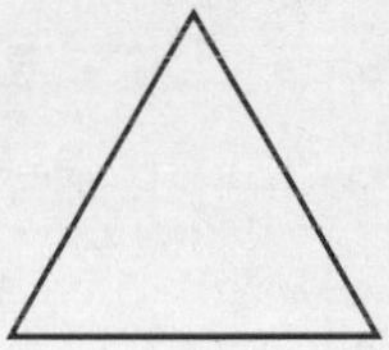 ______________

3. 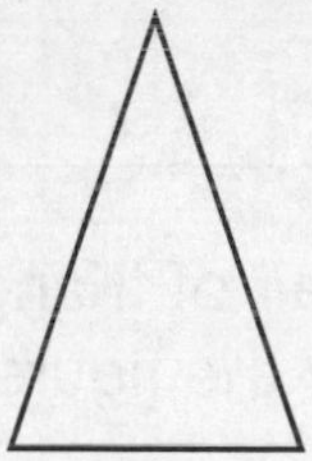 ______________

Tell if the triangle is right, acute, or obtuse.

4. 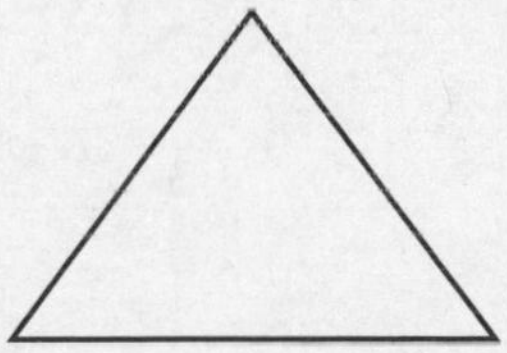 ______________

5. 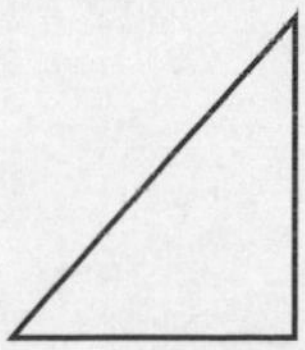 ______________

6. 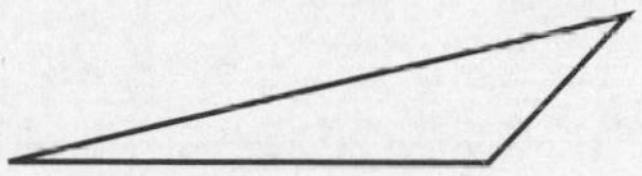 ______________

Name ______________________

Practice
5-6

Triangles

Tell if each triangle is equilateral, isosceles, or scalene.

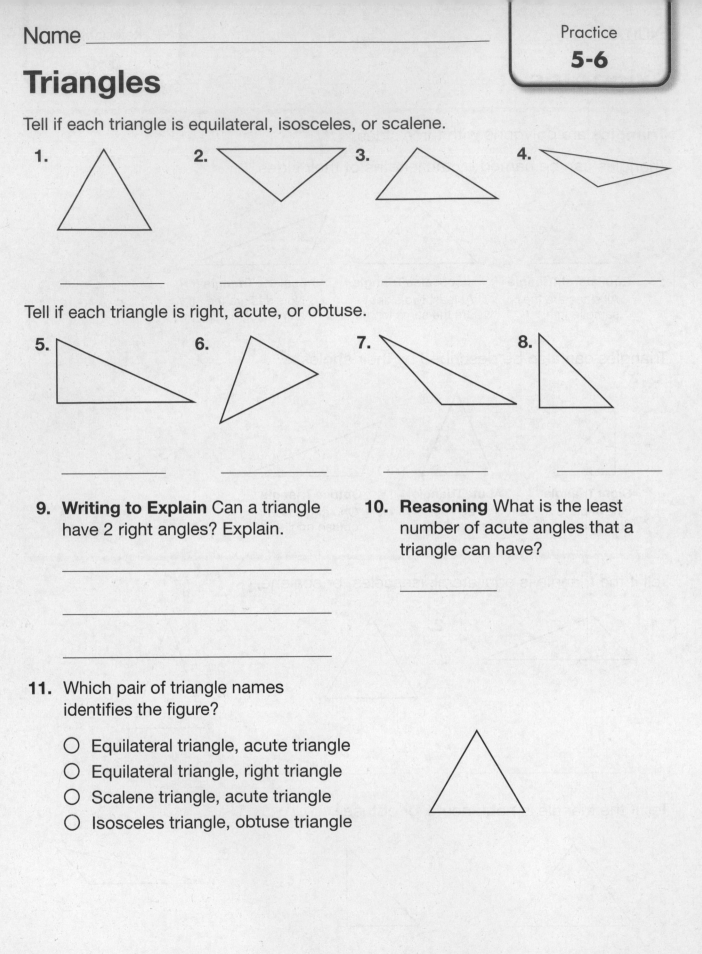

1. 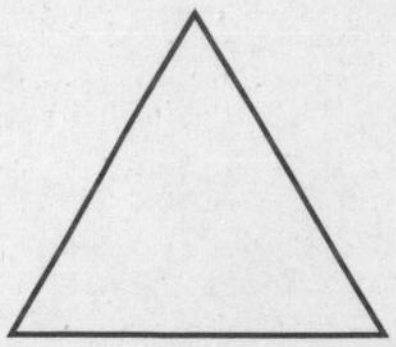

______

2. 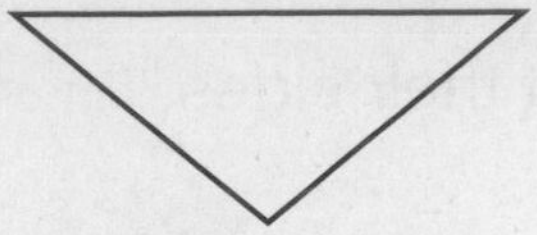

______

3. 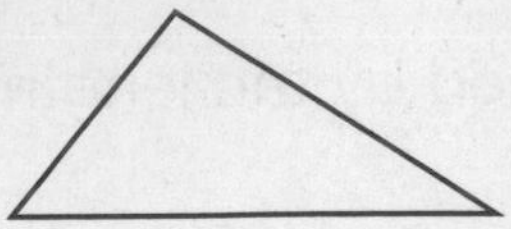

______

4. 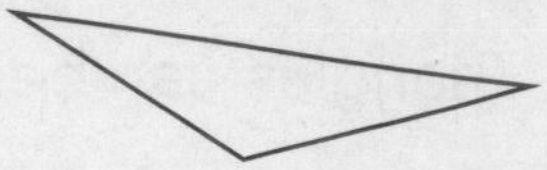

______

Tell if each triangle is right, acute, or obtuse.

5. 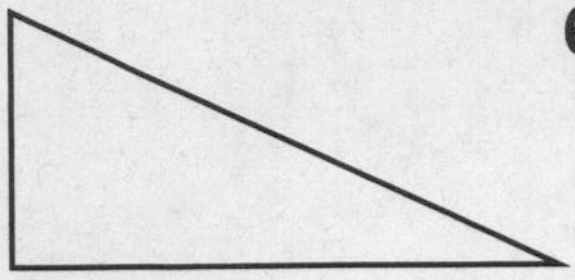

______

6. 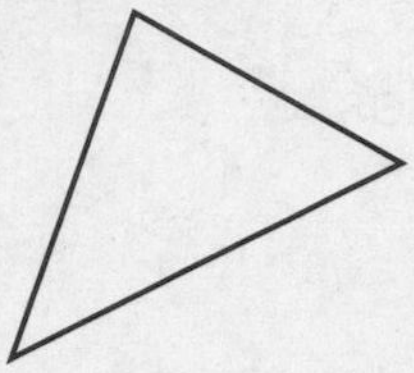

______

7. 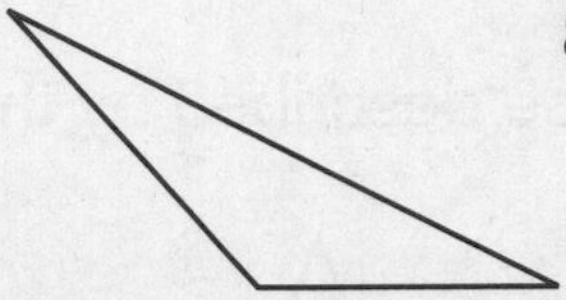

______

8. 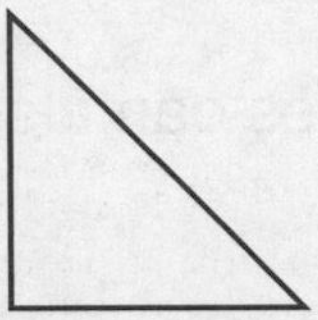

______

9. Writing to Explain Can a triangle have 2 right angles? Explain.

______

______

______

10. Reasoning What is the least number of acute angles that a triangle can have?

______

11. Which pair of triangle names identifies the figure?

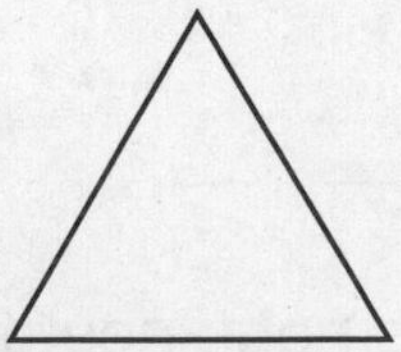

- ○ Equilateral triangle, acute triangle
- ○ Equilateral triangle, right triangle
- ○ Scalene triangle, acute triangle
- ○ Isosceles triangle, obtuse triangle

Name ____________________

Quadrilaterals

Quadrilaterals are polygons with four sides. Quadrilaterals can be further classified by the relationships of their sides. Below are some special quadrilaterals.

1. 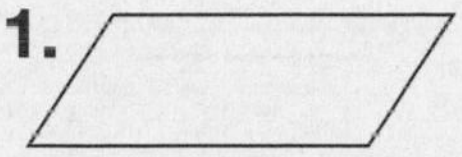
2. 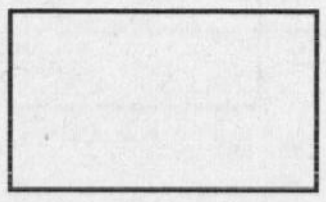
3. 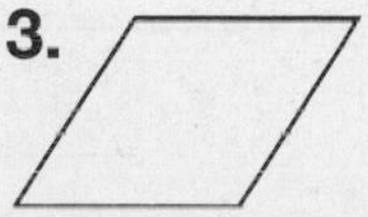
4. 
5. 

Parallelogram
Opposite sides are equal and parallel.

Rectangle
Parallelogram with 4 right angles.

Rhombus
Parallelogram with 4 equal sides.

Square
A rhombus with 4 right angles.

Trapezoid
Exactly one pair of parallel sides.

Write as many names as possible for each quadrilateral.

1. 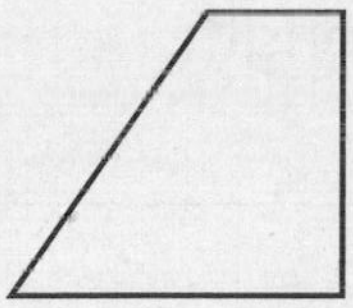

____

____

2. 

____

____

3. 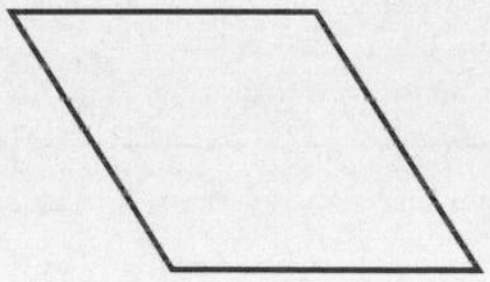

____

____

4. 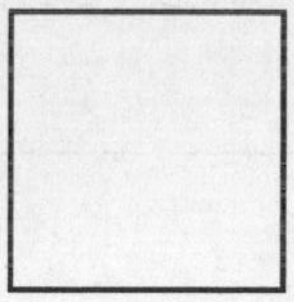

____

____

5. **Reasoning** Is a trapezoid also a parallelogram? Explain why or why not.

____

____

____

Name ______________________

Practice
5-7

Quadrilaterals

Write as many special names as possible for each quadrilateral.

1. 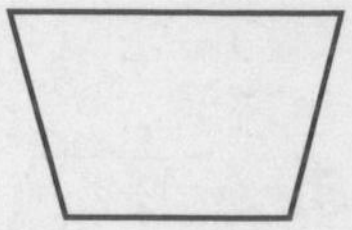
2. 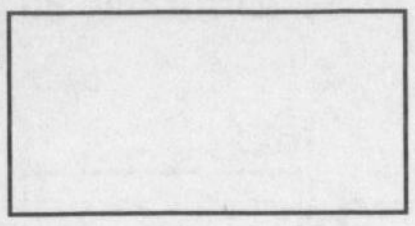
3. 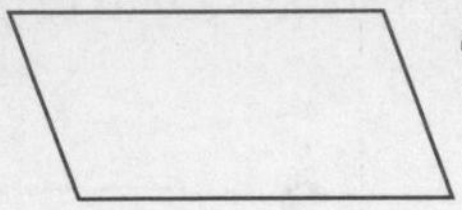
4. 
5. 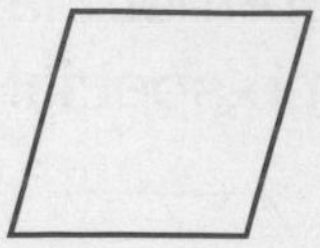

In **6–9**, write the name that best describes the quadrilateral. Draw a picture to help.

6. A parallelogram with 4 equal sides, but no right angles.

____

7. A rectangle with 4 right angles and all sides the same length.

____

8. A figure that is not a parallelogram, with one pair of parallel sides.

____

9. A parallelogram with 4 right angles with different lengths and widths.

____

10. Writing to Explain Can a rectangle also be a rhombus?

____

____

____

11. Which of the following correctly names the figure?

- ○ Rhombus
- ○ Trapezoid
- ○ Parallelogram
- ○ Rectangle

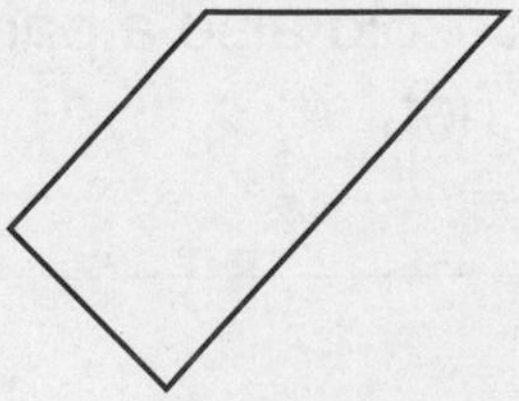

Name ______________________________

Problem Solving: Make and Test Generalizations

A generalization is a statement that has drawn a conclusion about something. For example, look at these three figures.

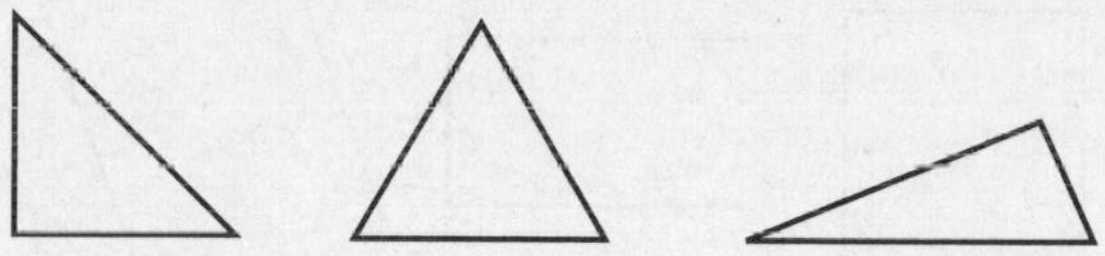

Make a generalization: The figures are all acute triangles. The triangle on the left has a right angle, making it a right triangle. This generalization is not true.

Try another generalization: The figures are all triangles. Each of the figures is a polygon with 3 sides. This generalization is correct.

Make and test a generalization for each set of polygons.

1.

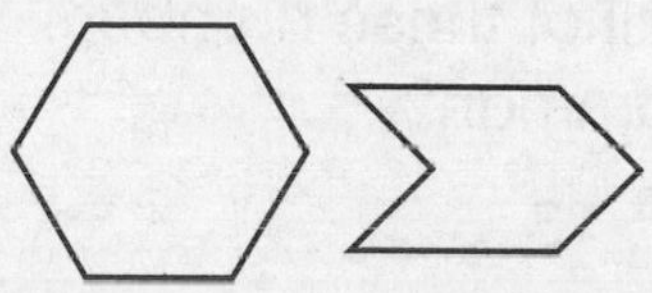

2.

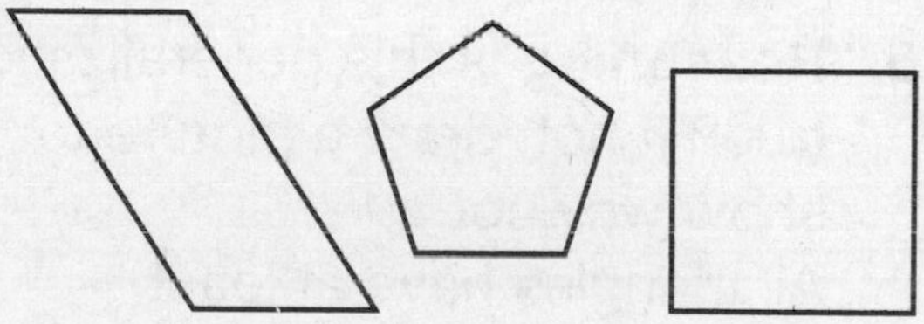

3.

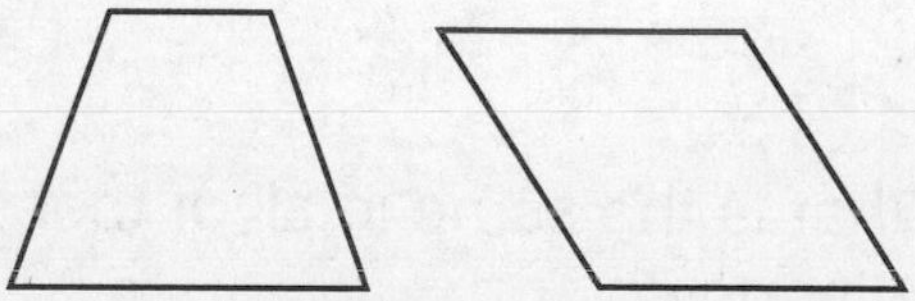

4.

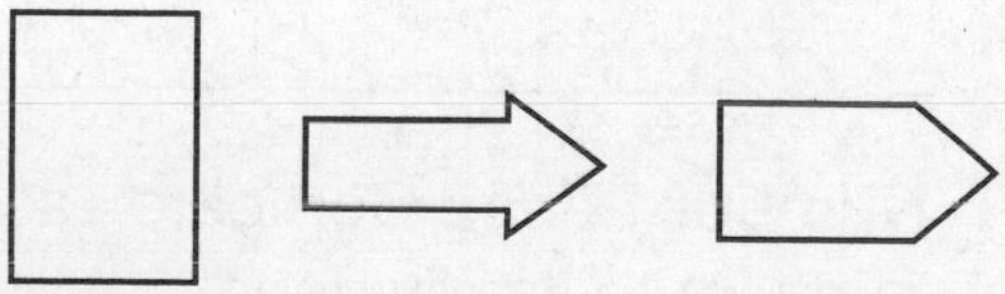

Name ______________________

Problem Solving: Make and Test Generalizations

In **1–4**, make a generalization for each set of polygons.

1. 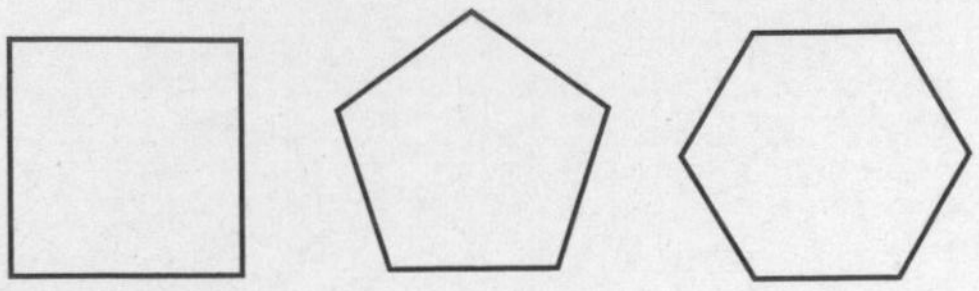

2. 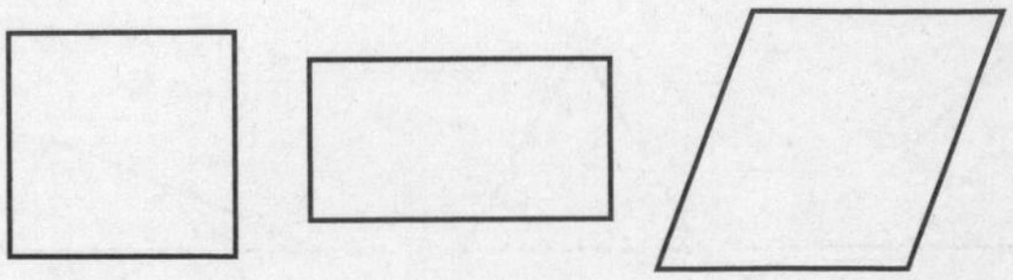

3. 

4. 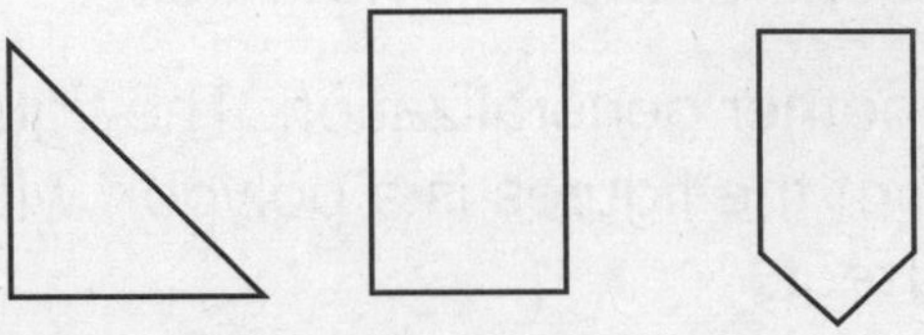

5. **Reasoning** Is this generalization true? If not, draw a picture to show why not.
All triangles have at least 2 acute angles.

6. What do all of these numbers have in common?
3, 5, 7, 11, 13

7. **Number Sense** Compare each quotient to its dividend.
$42 \div 6 = 7$
$8 \div 1 = 8$
$12 \div 12 = 1$
Make a generalization about dividends and quotients for whole numbers.

8. What is the same in all of these polygons?

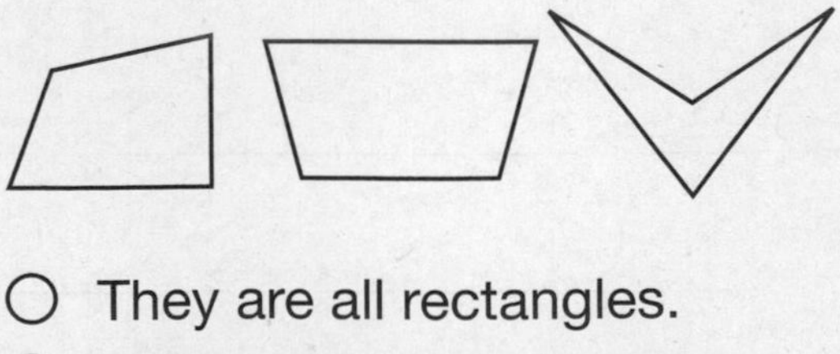

- ○ They are all rectangles.
- ○ They are all rhombuses.
- ○ They are all quadrilaterals.
- ○ They all have right angles.

Name ______________________________

Multiplication as Repeated Addition

Each group below has the same number of squares. There are 5 groups of 4 squares. There are a total of 20 squares.

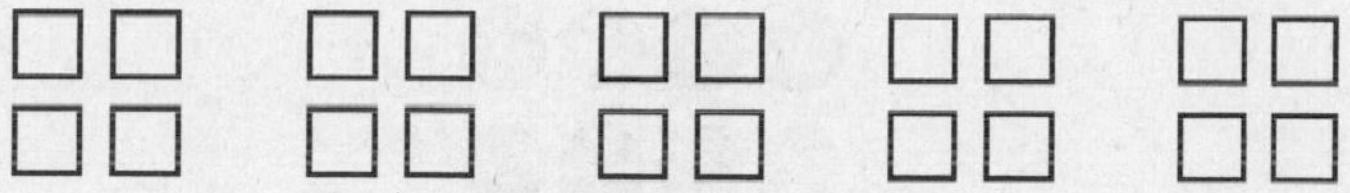

Here is the addition sentence for this problem: 4 + 4 + 4 + 4 + 4 = 20

Here is the multiplication sentence for this problem: 5 × 4 = 20

Complete the addition and multiplication sentences.

1. 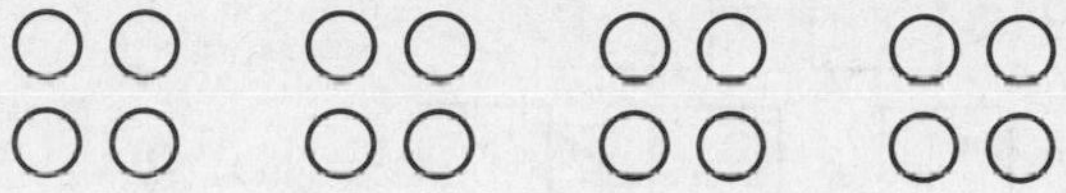

4 groups of _____   4 + 4 + 4 + 4 = _____   4 × _____ = 16

2. 

_____ groups of 7   _____ + _____ + _____ + _____ = 28

7 × _____ = _____

Write each addition sentence as a multiplication sentence.

3. 1 + 1 + 1 + 1 + 1 = 5 ______________________________

4. 8 + 8 + 8 = 24 ______________________________

Write each multiplication sentence as an addition sentence.

5. 5 × 5 = 25 ______________________________

6. 6 × 2 = 12 ______________________________

7. Writing to Explain Juan says, "When you put together unequal groups, you can only add." Is he correct? Explain.

____

Name ____________________

Practice
6-1

Multiplication as Repeated Addition

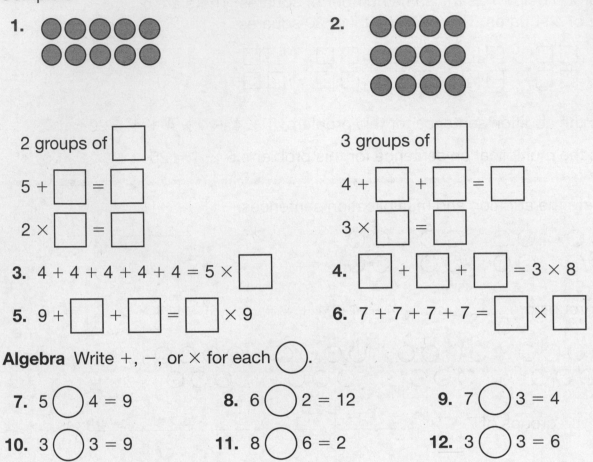

Complete.

1.

2 groups of □

5 + □ = □

2 × □ = □

2.

3 groups of □

4 + □ + □ = □

3 × □ = □

3. 4 + 4 + 4 + 4 + 4 = 5 × □

4. □ + □ + □ = 3 × 8

5. 9 + □ + □ = □ × 9

6. 7 + 7 + 7 + 7 = □ × □

Algebra Write +, −, or × for each ◯.

7. 5 ◯ 4 = 9

8. 6 ◯ 2 = 12

9. 7 ◯ 3 = 4

10. 3 ◯ 3 = 9

11. 8 ◯ 6 = 2

12. 3 ◯ 3 = 6

13. Number Sense Marlon has 4 cards, Jake has 4 cards, and Sam has 3 cards. Can you write a multiplication sentence to find how many cards they have in all? Explain.

____

____

14. Write a Problem Draw a picture that shows equal groups. Then write an addition sentence and a multiplication sentence for your picture.

15. Which is equal to 6 + 6 + 6 + 6?

○ 6 × 3 ○ 3 × 6 ○ 4 × 6 ○ 6 × 5

Name ______________________________

Arrays and Multiplication

An array shows objects in equal rows. This array shows 3 rows of 6 pennies.

The multiplication sentence for this array is $3 \times 6 = 18$.

You can use the Commutative Property of Multiplication to multiply the numbers in any order:
$3 \times 6 = 18$ and $6 \times 3 = 18$.

Write a multiplication sentence for each array.

1. 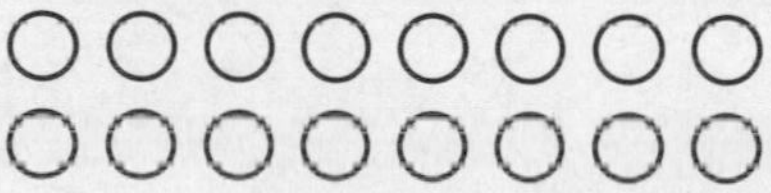

   ____

2. 

   ____

Complete each multiplication sentence. You may use counters or draw a picture to help.

3. $3 \times 4 = 12$ ______ $\times 3 = 12$
4. $5 \times 2 = 10$ $2 \times$ ______ $= 10$
5. **Number Sense** How can you use the Commutative Property to know that

    is equal to  ?

   ____

   ____

   ____

Name ______________________________

Practice
6-2

Arrays and Multiplication

Write a multiplication sentence for each array.

1. 

____

2. 

____

3. 

____

Draw an array to find each multiplication fact. Write the product.

4. $3 \times 6 =$ ______

5. $4 \times 7 =$ ______

Complete each multiplication sentence.
Use counters or draw an array to help.

6. $3 \times \square = 21$

$7 \times \square = 21$

7. $4 \times 9 = \square$

$9 \times 4 = \square$

8. $5 \times 6 = \square$

$6 \times 5 = \square$

9. $4 \times 7 = 28$

$7 \times 4 = \square$

10. $6 \times 8 = 48$

$8 \times 6 = \square$

11. $9 \times 5 = 45$

$5 \times 9 = \square$

12. Writing to Explain If you know that $7 \times 8 = 56$, how can you use the Commutative Property of Multiplication to find the product of 8×7?

____

____

____

____

13. Which of the following is equal to 8×4?

○ 4×8 ○ $4 + 8$ ○ $8 - 4$ ○ $8 + 4$

Name ______________________

Reteaching
6-3

Using Multiplication to Compare

Multiplication can tell how many times greater one group is than another.

Erica has 3 apples. Scott has 4 times as many apples. How many apples does Scott have?

Draw Erica's apples.

$3 \times 1 = 3$

Draw Scott's apples.

$3 \times 1 = 3$

$3 \times 2 = 6$

$3 \times 3 = 9$

$3 \times 4 = 12$

Scott has 12 apples, which is 4 times as many apples as Erica.

Find each amount. You may use drawings or counters to help.

1. 4 times as many as 2 ________
2. 3 times as many as 6 ________
3. 5 times as many as 4 ________
4. 3 times as many as 7 ________
5. 2 times as many as 8 ________
6. 4 times as many as 4 ________
7. **Geometry** A triangle, , has 3 sides. Draw a figure that has twice as many sides as a triangle.

Name ______________________

Practice
6-3

Using Multiplication to Compare

Find each amount. You may use drawings or counters to help.

1. 2 times as many as 5 ______

2. 3 times as many as 7 ______

3. 4 times as many as 6 ______

4. 3 times as many as 9 ______

5. twice as many as 8 ______

6. 5 times as many as 3 ______

7. 4 times as many as 7 ______

8. 5 times as many as 6 ______

9. 4 times as many as 3 ______

10. **Reasoning** John has 5 computer games. Julian has twice as many computer games as John. How many computer games do they have in all? ______

11. George Washington is on the $1 bill. Abraham Lincoln is on the bill that is worth 5 times as much as the $1 bill. What bill is Abraham Lincoln on? ______

12. Paula has twice as many guests this week as she did last week. Last week she had 7 guests. How many guests does she have this week? ______

13. John F. Kennedy is on the coin that is worth 5 times as much as a dime. What coin is John F. Kennedy on?

○ nickel ○ quarter ○ half-dollar ○ dollar

Name ___________________________________

Reteaching
6-4

Writing Multiplication Stories

When you write a multiplication story you should:

- Always end the story with a question.
- Draw a picture to show the main idea.

Example:
Write a multiplication story for 5×9.

Josephine has 5 friends over for a snack. She gives each friend 9 grapes. How many grapes did Josephine give all together?

Josephine gave 45 grapes all together.

Write a multiplication story for each exercise. Draw a picture to find each product.

1. 4×3

____

____

2. 5×2

____

____

3. 4×6

____

____

4. **Number Sense** Leshon has seven $5 bills. Write a multiplication sentence to show how much money Leshon has. ____________________

Name ____________________

Writing Multiplication Stories

Write a multiplication story for each.

Draw a picture to find each product.

1. 3×6

2. 2×8

3. 4×3

Write a multiplication story for each picture.

4. 

5. 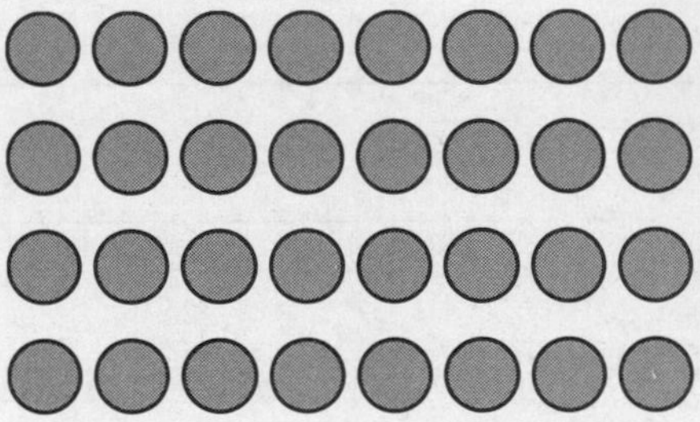

6. **Algebra** Hot dog buns come in packages of 8. Mrs. Wilson has a total of 40 hot dog buns. Draw a picture to find how many packages of hot dog buns Mrs. Wilson has.

7. There are 9 players on a baseball team. At the park, 4 teams are playing. How many baseball players are playing at the park?

○ 27 ○ 32 ○ 36 ○ 40

Name ______________________

Reteaching **6-5**

Problem Solving: Writing to Explain

David is making 3 pancakes for each person in his family. Today, there are 6 family members at breakfast. How many pancakes does he need to make? Explain how you can solve this problem.

You can make a table to solve this problem.

As the number of people increases by 1, the number of pancakes David needs to make increases by 3.

People	1	2	3	4	5	6
Pancakes	3	6	9	12	15	18
		3 + 3 = 6	6 + 3 = 9	9 + 3 = 12	12 + 3 = 15	15 + 3 = 18

David needs to make 18 pancakes.

1. Marcia got on an elevator on the fourth floor. She went down 2 floors. Then she went up 6 floors. Then she went down 3 floors. What floor is Marcia on now?

   ______

2. **Writing to Explain** How did you determine your answer to Exercise 1?

   ____

   ____

   ____

3. Look at the numbers below.
   75, 74, 72, 69, 65, ■, ■

   a. Describe the pattern in the list of numbers.

   ____

   ____

   ____

   b. What are the next two numbers in the pattern?

   ______

4. Ms. Skidmore is setting up basketball teams. There are 5 players on each team.

   a. Complete the table below.

Teams	1	2	3	4	5
Players	5	10	15		

   b. Explain how the number of players changes as the number of teams changes.

   ____

Name ______________________

Practice 6-5

Writing to Explain

1. Look at the numbers below.
13, 15, 19, 25, ■, ■

a. Describe the pattern in the list of numbers.

____

____

____

b. Explain how you can find the next two numbers. What are the next two numbers?

____

____

2. Mr. Wilson is setting up volleyball teams. There are 6 players on a team.

a. Explain how the number of players changes as the number of teams changes.

____

____

____

b. Complete the table below.

Teams	1	2	3	4	5
Players	6	12	18		

3. **Algebra** The table below shows the amount of money that Louise earns in allowance each week.

a. Complete the table.

Louise's Allowance

Number of Weeks	Allowance
1	$8
2	$16
3	$24
4	
5	

b. How did the table help you to find the pattern?

____

____

4. Diana's piano practice schedule is shown below.

a. Complete the table.

Diana's Piano Practice Schedule

Day	Minutes
Monday	45
Tuesday	50
Wednesday	55
Thursday	
Friday	

b. If she continues the pattern, for how many minutes will Diana practice Saturday?

____

Name ______________________________

2 and 5 as Factors

When you multiply by 2, you can use a doubles fact.
For example, 2 × 3 is the same as adding 3 + 3.

You can use a pattern to multiply by 5.

2s Facts		5s Facts	
2 × 0 = 0	2 × 5 = 10	5 × 0 = 0	5 × 5 = 25
2 × 1 = 2	2 × 6 = 12	5 × 1 = 5	5 × 6 = 30
2 × 2 = 4	2 × 7 = 14	5 × 2 = 10	5 × 7 = 35
2 × 3 = 6	2 × 8 = 16	5 × 3 = 15	5 × 8 = 40
2 × 4 = 8	2 × 9 = 18	5 × 4 = 20	5 × 9 = 45

Each multiple of 2 ends in 0, 2, 4, 6, or 8. All multiples of 2 are even.

Each multiple of 5 ends in 0 or 5.

Find each product.

1. 3 × 2 = ______ **2.** 4 × 2 = ______ **3.** 6 × 2 = ______

4. 4 × 5 = ______ **5.** 3 × 5 = ______ **6.** 7 × 5 = ______

7. 5 × 2 = ______ **8.** 6 × 5 = ______ **9.** 8 × 2 = ______

10. 9 × 5

11. 2 × 7

12. 2 × 2

13. 5 × 5

14. 0 × 2

15. What is 9 times 2? ______ **16.** What is 5 times 8? ______

17. Writing to Explain Is 25 a multiple of 2 or 5? How do you know?

____

____

Name ____________________

Practice 7-1

2 and 5 as Factors

Find each product.

1. 2×5 ______ **2.** 4×5 ______ **3.** 3×2 ______ **4.** 8×5 ______ **5.** 7×2 ______

6. 9×2 **7.** 6×5 **8.** 5×9 **9.** 2×6 **10.** 5×5

11. Multiply 7 and 5. ______

12. Find 8 times 2. ______

Algebra Compare. Use <, >, or =.

13. 3×5 ◯ 4×5

14. 6×3 ◯ 6×2

15. 8×2 ◯ 2×8

16. 6×5 ◯ 5×6

17. 4×2 ◯ 5×2

18. 7×5 ◯ 5×6

19. Tara walks 2 miles each day. How many miles does she walk in a week?

______

20. There are 5 days in each school week. How many school days are there in 9 weeks?

______

21. Writing to Explain How can adding doubles help you to multiply by 2? Give an example in your explanation.

______

______

______

______

22. If the ones digit of a number greater than 1 is 0, what multiple or multiples must that number have?

○ 2 only ○ 5 only ○ 2 and 5 ○ Neither 2 or 5

Name ______________________________

9 as a Factor

You can use two patterns to help you remember 9s facts.

9s Facts
9 × 0 = 0
9 × 1 = 9
9 × 2 = 18
9 × 3 = 27
9 × 4 = 36
9 × 5 = 45
9 × 6 = 54
9 × 7 = 63
9 × 8 = 72
9 × 9 = 81

1. The tens digit will be 1 less than the factor being multiplied by 9.

2. The sum of the digits of the product will always be 9, unless the other factor is 0.

Find 9 × 7.

The tens digit must be 1 less than 7.
The tens digit is 6.

The sum of the digits must be 9.
9 − 6 = 3, so the ones digit is 3.

The product is 63.

Find each product.

1. 9 × 3 = ________ **2.** 2 × 9 = ________ **3.** 1 × 9 = ________

4. 5 × 9 = ________ **5.** 5 × 8 = ________ **6.** 6 × 9 = ________

7. 2 × 7 = ________ **8.** 0 × 9 = ________ **9.** 4 × 9 = ________

10. $\begin{array}{r} 9 \\ \times 9 \\ \hline \end{array}$ **11.** $\begin{array}{r} 9 \\ \times 5 \\ \hline \end{array}$ **12.** $\begin{array}{r} 8 \\ \times 9 \\ \hline \end{array}$ **13.** $\begin{array}{r} 7 \\ \times 9 \\ \hline \end{array}$ **14.** $\begin{array}{r} 9 \\ \times 2 \\ \hline \end{array}$

15. Multiply 6 and 9. ________ **16.** Multiply 0 and 9. ________

17. **Writing to Explain** Look at the table of 9s facts. Do you see another number pattern in the multiples of 9? Explain.

____

____

Name ____________________

Practice
7-2

9 as a Factor

Find each product.

1. 9×4 ______ **2.** 7×9 ______ **3.** 9×9 ______ **4.** 9×8 ______ **5.** 5×3 ______

6. $\begin{array}{r} 9 \\ \times 5 \\ \hline \end{array}$ **7.** $\begin{array}{r} 2 \\ \times 9 \\ \hline \end{array}$ **8.** $\begin{array}{r} 6 \\ \times 9 \\ \hline \end{array}$ **9.** $\begin{array}{r} 2 \\ \times 7 \\ \hline \end{array}$ **10.** $\begin{array}{r} 8 \\ \times 9 \\ \hline \end{array}$

11. Multiply 4 and 9. ______ **12.** Find 3 times 9. ______

Algebra Complete. Use +, −, or ×.

13. $2 \times 9 = 10 \square 8$ **14.** $20 + 16 = 9 \square 4$ **15.** $9 \times 5 = 50 \square 5$

16. $9 \times 8 = 70 \square 2$ **17.** $10 \square 1 = 1 \times 9$ **18.** $9 \square 3 = 20 + 7$

19. Paula's hair was put into 9 braids. Each braid used 3 beads. How many beads were used in all?

____

20. A baseball game has 9 innings. A doubleheader is 2 games in the same day. How many innings are there in a doubleheader?

____

21. **Write a Problem** Write a multiplication story for 9×8. Include the product in your story.

____

____

22. Which number below is a multiple of 9?

○ 35 ○ 46 ○ 54 ○ 65

Name ______________________

Multiplying with 0 and 1

Zero and 1 have special multiplication properties.

The Identity (One) Property of Multiplication		The Zero Property of Multiplication	
When you multiply a number and 1, the product is that number.		When you multiply a number and 0, the product is 0.	
Examples:		Examples:	
$4 \times 1 = 4$	$16 \times 1 = 16$	$5 \times 0 = 0$	$123 \times 0 = 0$
$1 \times 9 = 9$	$13 \times 1 = 13$	$17 \times 0 = 0$	$0 \times 58 = 0$
$251 \times 1 = 251$	$1 \times 48 = 48$	$0 \times 51 = 0$	$74 \times 0 = 0$

1. $1 \times 2 =$ ______ **2.** $0 \times 3 =$ ______ **3.** $4 \times 1 =$ ______

4. $8 \times 0 =$ ______ **5.** $6 \times 1 =$ ______ **6.** $1 \times 7 =$ ______

7. $\begin{array}{r} 1 \\ \times\ 7 \\ \hline \end{array}$ **8.** $\begin{array}{r} 6 \\ \times\ 0 \\ \hline \end{array}$ **9.** $\begin{array}{r} 8 \\ \times\ 1 \\ \hline \end{array}$

10. $\begin{array}{r} 10 \\ \times\ \ 0 \\ \hline \end{array}$ **11.** $\begin{array}{r} 1 \\ \times\ 2 \\ \hline \end{array}$ **12.** $\begin{array}{r} 0 \\ \times\ 9 \\ \hline \end{array}$

Complete each number sentence. Write <, >, or = for each ◯.

13. 8×2 ◯ 4×4 **14.** 19×1 ◯ 37×0 **15.** 7×2 ◯ $13 + 1$

Complete each number sentence. Write × or + for each ◯.

16. 5 ◯ 0 = 5 **17.** 5 ◯ 1 = 6 **18.** 1 ◯ 5 = 5

19. Write a Problem Write a multiplication sentence that shows the Zero Property of Multiplication. Explain why it shows this property.

____

Name ______________________

Practice
7-3

Multiplying with 0 and 1

Find each product.

1. 1×4 ______ **2.** 0×5 ______ **3.** 6×1 ______ **4.** 0×3 ______ **5.** 5×1 ______

6. $\begin{array}{r} 1 \\ \times 1 \\ \hline \end{array}$ **7.** $\begin{array}{r} 0 \\ \times 9 \\ \hline \end{array}$ **8.** $\begin{array}{r} 1 \\ \times 8 \\ \hline \end{array}$ **9.** $\begin{array}{r} 6 \\ \times 1 \\ \hline \end{array}$ **10.** $\begin{array}{r} 7 \\ \times 0 \\ \hline \end{array}$

11. Multiply 1 and 7. ______

12. Find 0 times 8. ______

Algebra Complete. Write <, >, or = for each ◯.

13. 1×6 ◯ 3×0 **14.** 5×0 ◯ 1×7 **15.** 1×3 ◯ 3×1

Algebra Complete. Write ×, +, or − for each ☐.

16. 1 ☐ $7 = 7$ **17.** 8 ☐ $0 = 8$ **18.** 6 ☐ $1 = 5$

19. Sara keeps 4 boxes under her bed. Each box is for holding a different type of seashell. There are 0 shells in each box. Write a multiplication sentence to show how many shells Sara has in all.

____

20. Writing to Explain Is the product of 0×0 the same as the sum of $0 + 0$? Explain.

____

____

21. Geometry A pentagon has 5 sides. Lonnie made a design with one pentagon. How many sides does Lonnie's design have?

______

22. Which multiplication problem below has the greatest product?

○ 5×1 ○ 6×0 ○ 0×7 ○ 8×0

Name ______________________

Reteaching
7-4

10 as a Factor

The table shows the multiplication facts for 10.

10s Facts	
10 × 0 = 0	10 × 5 = 50
10 × 1 = 10	10 × 6 = 60
10 × 2 = 20	10 × 7 = 70
10 × 3 = 30	10 × 8 = 80
10 × 4 = 40	10 × 9 = 90

All multiples of 10 end with zero, such as 110; 2,350; and 467,000.

Find 10 × 5.

To find the answer, you can skip count or you can add a zero after the 5.

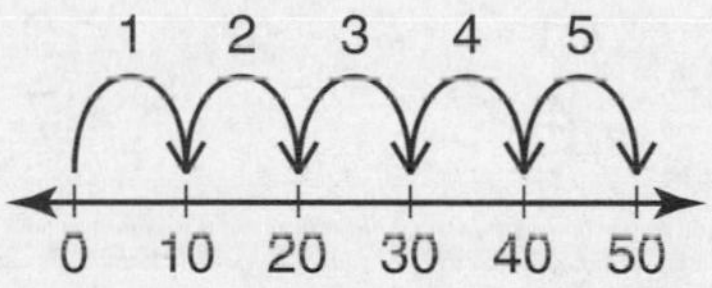

or

Tens	Ones
	5

× 10 =

Tens	Ones
5	0

5 × 10 = 50

1. 10 × 2 = ______ **2.** 5 × 10 = ______ **3.** 10 × 8 = ______

4. 2 × 8 = ______ **5.** \$10 × 6 = ______ **6.** 7 × 5 = ______

7. \$10 × 4 = ______ **8.** 9 × 2 = ______ **9.** 8 × 9 = ______

10. 10 × 3

11. \$4 × 5

12. 2 × 2

13. \$10 × 5

14. \$8 × 5

15. 10 × 4

16. Critical Thinking When you multiply a whole number by 10, what is always true about the ones place in the product?

____

Name ______________________________

10 as a Factor

Find each product.

1. 3×10 ______ **2.** 7×10 ______ **3.** 10×5 ______ **4.** 7×5 ______ **5.** 10×8 ______

6. 9×10 ______ **7.** 6×1 ______ **8.** 10×2 ______ **9.** 9×7 ______ **10.** 4×10 ______

11. 1×10 ______ **12.** 6×10 ______ **13.** 5×4 ______ **14.** 10×10 ______ **15.** 10×3 ______

16. 8×5 **17.** 10×9 **18.** 10×8 **19.** 10×4 **20.** 10×7

21. 10×6 **22.** 5×2 **23.** 10×1 **24.** 10×5 **25.** 9×0

26. Mary Ann earns $10 each day walking the neighborhood dogs. How much will she earn in 7 days?

______

27. A game of basketball requires 10 players. At the park, there are 5 games being played. How many total players are at the park?

______

28. **Strategy Practice** Mr. Keyes made four rows of 10 cookies. Seven of the cookies in the first row were eaten. How many cookies remain?

______

29. Which is not a multiple of 10?

○ 30 ○ 55
○ 70 ○ 90

Name ______________________________

Reteaching

7-5

Problem Solving: Two-Question Problems

Sometimes you need the answer to one question to help you answer another question.

Ms. Williams bought 3 pizzas for $8 each. She gave the cashier $30. How much change did she receive?

First, find the cost of the pizzas.

_______ in all

$8	$8	$8

$\$8 \times 3 = \$24$

The pizzas cost $24.

Next, find the change.

$30 in all

$24	___

$\$30 - \$24 = \$6$

Ms. Williams received $6 in change.

1a. Ray bought a pair of sunglasses for $22 and a hat for $19. How much money did the items cost?

_______ in all

$22	$19

1b. Ray gave the cashier a $50 bill. How much change should Ray receive?

$50 in all

$41	___

2. Writing to Explain Cindy bought 4 lunch specials for $7 each. She gave the cashier $40. How much change should Cindy receive? Explain how you found your answer.

____

____

____

____

Name ______________________

Practice 7-5

Problem Solving: Two-Question Problems

Use the answer from the first problem to solve the second problem.

1a. Lynette bought a book for $13 and a DVD for $22. How much money did the items cost?

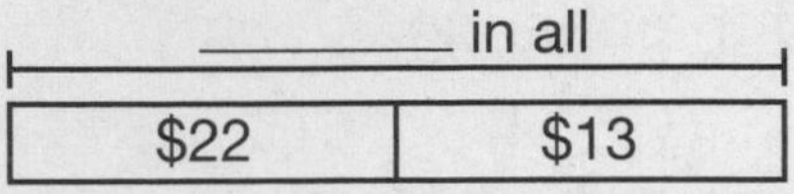

1b. Suppose Lynette paid the cashier with a $50 bill. How much change should Lynette get?

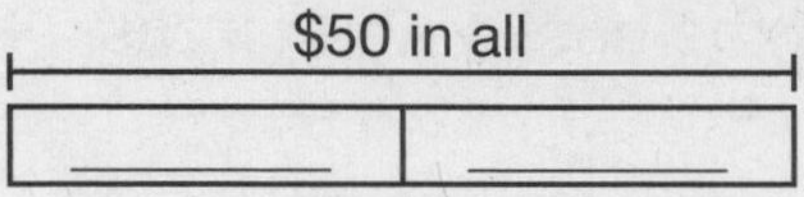

2a. Melissa bought 2 T-shirts for $9 each. How much money did Melissa spend on T-shirts?

____

b. Melissa had $32 in her purse. How much money does she have left?

____

3a. Curt bought 3 tickets to the movies for $8 each. How much money did Curt spend on movie tickets?

____

b. Curt also bought a large popcorn for $5. How much money did Curt spend all together?

____

4. Lenny bought 4 packs of baseball cards for $3 each. He paid the cashier with a $20 bill. How much change will Lenny receive?

- ○ $7
- ○ $8
- ○ $12
- ○ $13

5. Write a Problem Write two problems that can be solved by using the answer from the first problem to solve the second problem.

____

____

____

____

____

____

Name ______________________________

3 as a Factor

You can use an array to show 3s facts.

3s Facts

$3 \times 0 = 0$	$3 \times 5 = 15$
$3 \times 1 = 3$	$3 \times 6 = 18$
$3 \times 2 = 6$	$3 \times 7 = 21$
$3 \times 3 = 9$	$3 \times 8 = 24$
$3 \times 4 = 12$	$3 \times 9 = 27$

Multiply 2×3 using arrays.

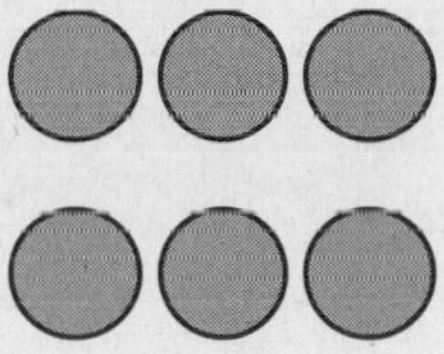

$2 \times 3 = 6$

You can also use a 2s and a 1s fact to find a 3s fact.

Find 7×3.

a. Find a 2s fact with 7: $2 \times 7 = 14$

b. Find a 1s fact with 7: $1 \times 7 = 7$

c. Add the facts: $14 + 7 = 21$

Find each product.

1. 3×2 ________ **2.** 3×4 ________ **3.** 3×5 ________ **4.** 3×1 ________ **5.** 3×9 ________

6. 6×9 ________ **7.** 7×3 ________ **8.** 0×3 ________ **9.** 8×5 ________ **10.** 3×3 ________

11. Number Sense How can you use a 2s fact and a 1s fact to find 3×8?

____

____

Name ______________________

Practice
8-1

3 as a Factor

Find the product.

1. 1×3 ______
2. 3×7 ______
3. 6×3 ______
4. 8×3 ______
5. 10×5 ______

6. 3×2 ______
7. 4×3 ______
8. 3×0 ______
9. 2×7 ______
10. 3×3 ______

11. 5×3
12. 10×3
13. 12×3
14. 3×9
15. 11×3

16. A bicycle store also sells tricycles. It has 6 tricycles in stock. How many wheels do the tricycles have in all?

______

17. There were 5 people who bought tickets to a football game. They bought 3 tickets each. How many tickets were bought all together?

______

18. **Number Sense** What addition sentence is equal to 4×3?

______

19. **Geometry** How many small squares are in the figure below?

20. **Reasonableness** Maria said $7 \times 3 = 21$. Connie said $3 \times 7 = 21$. Who is correct? Explain.

______
______
______

21. Which number below is a multiple of 3?

○ 16 ○ 20 ○ 24 ○ 28

Name ______________________________

Reteaching
8-2

4 as a Factor

If you know a 2s multiplication fact, you can find a 4s multiplication fact.

4s Facts

$4 \times 0 = 0$	$4 \times 5 = 20$
$4 \times 1 = 4$	$4 \times 6 = 24$
$4 \times 2 = 8$	$4 \times 7 = 28$
$4 \times 3 = 12$	$4 \times 8 = 32$
$4 \times 4 = 16$	$4 \times 9 = 36$

You can double a 2s fact or add a 2s fact by itself to find a 4s fact.

When you double an array of 2×1, you get an array of 4×1.

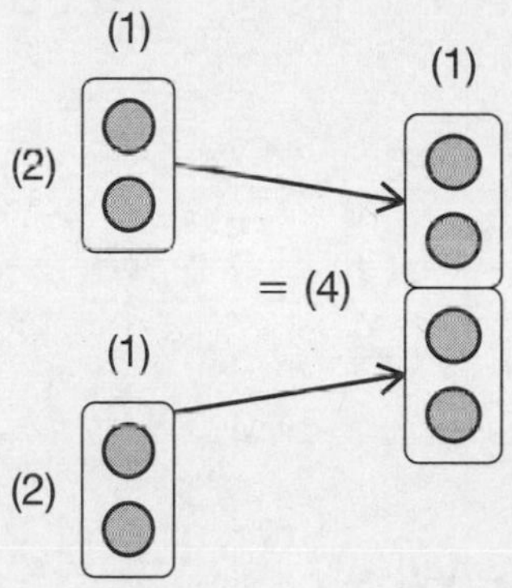

Find 4×3 by doubling a 2s fact.

a. Find a 2s fact with 3 as a factor.

$2 \times 3 = 6$

b. Double it.

$6 \times 2 = 12$

Find 4×3 by adding a 2s fact by itself.

a. Find a 2s fact with 3 as a factor.

$2 \times 3 = 6$

b. Add the fact to itself.

$6 + 6 = 12$

Find each product.

1. 4×6 ________ **2.** 8×4 ________ **3.** 6×5 ________ **4.** 9×4 ________ **5.** 4×1 ________

6. 4×3 ________ **7.** 4×7 ________ **8.** 12×2 ________ **9.** 0×4 ________ **10.** 4×4 ________

11. Number Sense How can you use 2×8 to find 4×8?

____

____

Name ______________________

Practice
8-2

4 as a Factor

Find the product.

1. 2×4 ______

2. 4×5 ______

3. 3×4 ______

4. 4×4 ______

5. 5×8 ______

6. 4×6 ______

7. 1×4 ______

8. 3×9 ______

9. 0×4 ______

10. 4×7 ______

11. 10×4

12. 11×4

13. 12×4

14. 4×9

15. 8×4

16. **Number Sense** What multiplication fact can you double to find 4×7?

______

17. Each square table can seat 4 people. How many people can sit at 8 square tables?

______

18. Jillian sold 4 books of raffle tickets. Each book had 12 tickets. How many tickets did Jillian sell all together?

______

19. The soccer team has practice 4 times each week during the season. If the season is 10 weeks long, how many practices do they have?

______

20. **Explain It** If you know that $4 \times 5 = 20$, how can you use the Commutative Property to find 5×4?

______

______

______

21. Aaron changed the tires on 5 cars. Each car had 4 tires. How many tires did Aaron change?

○ 12 ○ 16 ○ 20 ○ 24

Name ______________________

Reteaching 8-3

6 and 7 as Factors

You can use multiplication facts that you already know to find other multiplication facts.

6s Facts

6 × 0 = 0	6 × 5 = 30
6 × 1 = 6	6 × 6 = 36
6 × 2 = 12	6 × 7 = 42
6 × 3 = 18	6 × 8 = 48
6 × 4 = 24	6 × 9 = 54

You can use a 3s fact to find a 6s fact. Find the 3s fact and then add the product to itself.

Find 6 × 9.

a. Find the 3s fact with 9: 3 × 9 = 27.

b. Add the product to itself: 27 + 27 = 54.

7s Facts

7 × 0 = 0	7 × 5 = 35
7 × 1 = 7	7 × 6 = 42
7 × 2 = 14	7 × 7 = 49
7 × 3 = 21	7 × 8 = 56
7 × 4 = 28	7 × 9 = 63

You can use a 2s and a 5s fact to find a 7s fact.

Find 7 × 5.

a. Find the 2s fact with 5: 2 × 5 = 10.

b. Find the 5s fact with 5: 5 × 5 = 25.

c. Add the products: 10 + 25 = 35.

Find each product.

1. 2 × 7 ______ **2.** 6 × 7 ______ **3.** 7 × 9 ______ **4.** 6 × 4 ______ **5.** 6 × 8 ______

6. 7 × 7 ______ **7.** 6 × 2 ______ **8.** 8 × 7 ______ **9.** 3 × 7 ______ **10.** 6 × 6 ______

11. 5 × 6 **12.** 7 × 4 **13.** 6 × 9 **14.** 7 × 3

15. Number Sense Harold says, "To find 6 × 8, I can use the facts for 5 × 4 and 1 × 4." Do you agree? Explain.

____

____

Name ______________________________

Practice
8-3

6 and 7 as Factors

Find the product.

1. 5×6 ______ **2.** 6×3 ______ **3.** 6×8 ______ **4.** 3×7 ______ **5.** 7×10 ______

6. 7×4 ______ **7.** 6×4 ______ **8.** 5×7 ______ **9.** 7×8 ______ **10.** 6×6 ______

11. $\begin{array}{r} 7 \\ \times\ 6 \\ \hline \end{array}$ **12.** $\begin{array}{r} 10 \\ \times\ 6 \\ \hline \end{array}$ **13.** $\begin{array}{r} 12 \\ \times\ 7 \\ \hline \end{array}$ **14.** $\begin{array}{r} 7 \\ \times\ 7 \\ \hline \end{array}$ **15.** $\begin{array}{r} 12 \\ \times\ 6 \\ \hline \end{array}$

16. **Number Sense** What multiplication fact can be found by using the arrays for 2×9 and 5×9?

______

17. Raul's science class is hatching chicken eggs. If the eggs take 3 weeks to hatch, how many days will it be until they hatch?

______

18. Emily cut 7 apples into slices. There are 6 slices from each apple. How many apple slices does she have in all?

______

19. At a barbeque there are 6 tables set up. Each table can seat 12 people. How many people can sit at the tables all together?

______

20. **Writing to Explain** How could you use $5 \times 6 = 30$ to find the product of 6×6?

____

____

____

21. It takes 7 minutes for Barry to ride his bicycle one mile. How long would it take Barry to ride his bicycle 4 miles?

○ 21 minutes ○ 24 minutes ○ 27 minutes ○ 28 minutes

Name ______________________

8 as a Factor

You can double a 4s fact to multiply with 8.

8s Facts

8 × 0 = 0	8 × 5 = 40
8 × 1 = 8	8 × 6 = 48
8 × 2 = 16	8 × 7 = 56
8 × 3 = 24	8 × 8 = 64
8 × 4 = 32	8 × 9 = 72

Find 8 × 6.

a. Find 4 × 6 = 24.

b. Add the product to itself: 24 + 24 = 48

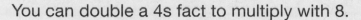

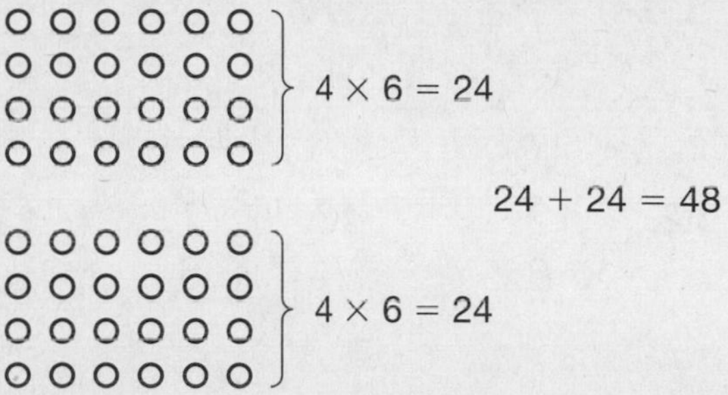

So, 8 × 6 = 48.

Find each product.

1. 2 × 8 ______ **2.** 4 × 8 ______ **3.** 8 × 5 ______ **4.** 9 × 7 ______ **5.** 8 × 8 ______

6. 0 × 8 ______ **7.** 6 × 7 ______ **8.** 9 × 8 ______ **9.** 1 × 8 ______ **10.** 6 × 8 ______

11. A cup is equal to 8 fluid ounces. How many fluid ounces are there in 5 cups?

______

12. Explain It How can you use 4s facts to find 7 × 8? Give the product in your explanation.

____

____

Name ____________________

8 as a Factor

Find the product.

1. 1×8 ______ **2.** 8×0 ______ **3.** 4×6 ______ **4.** 2×8 ______ **5.** 8×7 ______

6. 8×3 ______ **7.** 4×8 ______ **8.** 8×9 ______ **9.** 8×5 ______ **10.** 8×8 ______

11. 10×8 **12.** 12×8 **13.** 7×6 **14.** 8×3 **15.** 9×8

16. An octopus has 8 arms. At the zoo, there are 3 octopuses in one tank. How many arms do the octopuses have altogether? ______

17. Number Sense How can you use 4×7 to find 8×7? Find the product.

____

____

18. Explain It José said all of the multiples of 8 are also multiples of 2. Jamila said that all of the multiples of 8 are also multiples of 4. Who is correct? Explain.

____

____

19. A package of fruit juice contains 8 boxes. How many boxes are there in 5 packages? ______

20. What is the next number in the pattern below?
16, 24, 32, 40, 48 ______

21. Each package of rolls contains 8 rolls. Ted bought 6 packages. How many rolls did he buy in all?

○ 42 ○ 48 ○ 49 ○ 54

Name ____________________

Reteaching
8-5

Multiplying with 3 Factors

You can use the Associative Property of Multiplication to multiply three factors. The Associative Property states that the way the factors are grouped does not change the product.

The Associative Property of Multiplication is applied like the Associative Property of Addition.

Addition	**Multiplication**
$4 + 3 + 3 = 4 + (3 + 3)$	$4 \times 3 \times 3 = 4 \times (3 \times 3)$
$4 + 6$	4×9
10	36

Find the product that is easy to find. Then multiply by the third number.

Find each product. You may draw a picture to help.

1. $3 \times 2 \times 1$ ________ **2.** $2 \times 3 \times 5$ ________ **3.** $3 \times 3 \times 2$ ________ **4.** $7 \times 3 \times 2$ ________

5. $4 \times 2 \times 7$ ________ **6.** $3 \times 4 \times 5$ ________ **7.** $2 \times 2 \times 6$ ________ **8.** $2 \times 5 \times 7$ ________

9. There are 6 boxes in each row of fruit juice. Each package has 2 rows. Mrs. Stokes bought 3 packages. How many boxes of fruit juice did Mrs. Stokes buy? Write a number sentence with your answer.

____

____

10. **Writing to Explain** How do you know that $4 \times 2 \times 2$ is the same as 4×4? Explain.

____

Name ______________________

Multiplying with 3 Factors

Find the product. You many draw a picture to help.

1. $2 \times 3 \times 3$ ______ **2.** $2 \times 2 \times 4$ ______ **3.** $8 \times 2 \times 2$ ______ **4.** $6 \times 2 \times 3$ ______

5. $3 \times 3 \times 4$ ______ **6.** $5 \times 2 \times 5$ ______ **7.** $5 \times 4 \times 2$ ______ **8.** $4 \times 2 \times 3$ ______

Find the missing number.

9. $4 \times 4 \times 3 = 48$,
so $4 \times (4 \times 3) = \square$

10. $(5 \times 2) \times 8 = \square$

11. Sarah and Amanda each have 2 bags with 4 marbles in each. How many marbles do they have all together?

______

12. Jesse bought 2 sheets of stamps. On each sheet there are 5 rows of stamps with 6 stamps in each row. How many stamps did Jesse buy?

______

13. Reasonableness Is the product of $6 \times 2 \times 4$ less than 50? Explain.

____

____

14. Which number makes this number sentence true?

$8 \times 2 \times 4 = 8 \times (\blacksquare \times 4)$

○ 2 ○ 4 ○ 8 ○ 64

15. Write three ways to find $3 \times 2 \times 4$.

____

____

Name ______________________________

Reteaching
8-6

Problem Solving: Multiple-Step Problems

Enzo's puts 3 meatballs in each of its meatball subs. Carlos's uses 2 times as many meatballs for its meatball subs. Mr. Kerwin orders 4 meatball subs from Carlos's. How many meatballs will be in his subs?

Find and solve the hidden question.

How many meatballs does Carlos's put in each meatball sub?

______ meatballs in a sub

3	3

$3 \times 2 = 6$

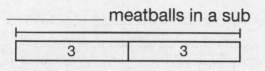

Carlos's puts 6 meatballs in each of its meatball subs.

Use the answer to the hidden question to solve the problem.

______ meatballs in all

6	6	6	6

$6 \times 4 = 24$

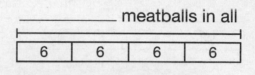

Mr. Kerwin will have 24 meatballs all together in his 4 meatball subs.

1. Meredith bought a book for $8, a magazine for $5, and bottled water for $2. She paid with a $20 bill. How much change should she get?

Tip: Find the total cost of the three items.

______ in all

$8	$5	$2

$20 in all

$15	______

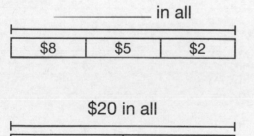

2. Sue bought 3 T-shirts for $8 each. She paid with a $50 bill. How much change should she get?

______

3. **Writing to Explain** What steps did you take to answer Exercise 2?

____

____

____

____

____

Name ______________________________

Problem Solving: Multiple-Step Problems

Use the pictures for **1–4**.

1. Teri bought 3 boxes of pencils. She paid with a $20 bill. How much change did she receive?

Tip First find the cost of the pencils.

__________ in all

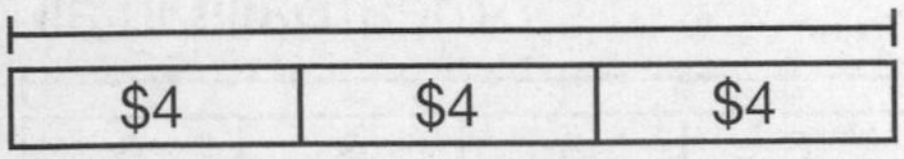

$20 in all

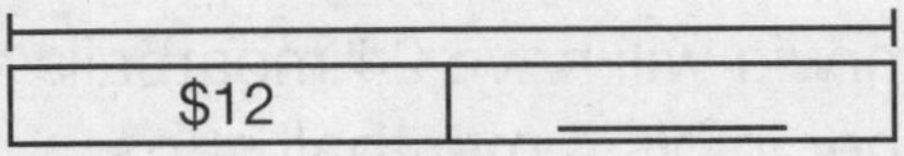

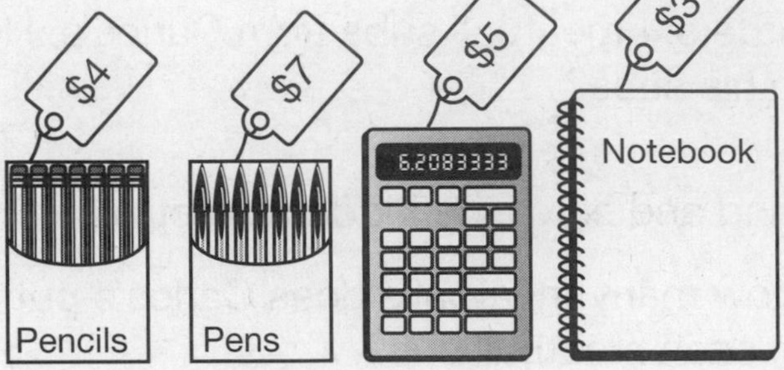

2. Martin bought 3 boxes of pens and a calculator. How much money did he spend all together?

Tip First find the cost of the pens.

____

3. Joey bought 2 notebooks and 2 boxes of pencils. How much money did he spend all together?

____

4. Allie bought 3 notebooks and 2 boxes of pens. She paid with $40. How much change did she receive?

____

5. Write a Problem Write a real-world problem involving multiple steps. Then solve your problem.

____

____

____

____

6. Number Sense Bert has $50 in his wallet. Then he buys 2 CDs for $13 each. How much money does he have left?

○ $12 ○ $24 ○ $26 ○ $37

Name ______________________________

Division as Sharing

Division shows how many items are in each group or how many equal groups there are.

There are 15 counters that are going to be put into 5 groups. How many counters will be in each group?

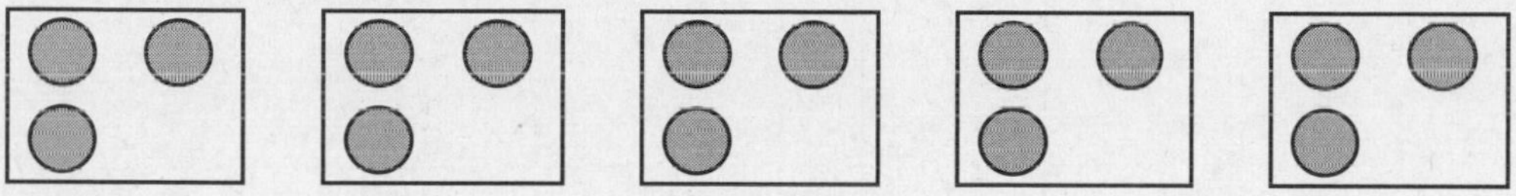

There are 15 counters. There are 5 groups.
There are 3 counters in each group.
So, $15 \div 5 = 3$.

Draw a picture to solve. Use counters if needed.

1. 12 tennis balls, 4 cans
How many tennis balls in each can?

____

2. 20 cookies, 5 bags
How many cookies in each bag?

____

3. 16 apples, 2 baskets
How many apples in each basket?

____

4. 20 fingers, 4 hands
How many fingers on each hand?

____

5. One box contains 12 granola bars. Two bars are in each package. How many packages are in each box of granola bars?

____

6. **Number Sense** Could you divide 14 shirts into two equal groups? Why or why not?

____

____

Name ______________________

Practice
9-1

Division as Sharing

Draw a picture to solve. Use counters if needed.

1. 24 people, 4 rows
How many people in each row?

______

2. 18 marbles, 2 people
How many marbles for each person?

______

3. 25 apples, 5 trees
How many apples on each tree?

______

4. 21 books, 3 shelves
How many books on each shelf?

______

Complete each division sentence.

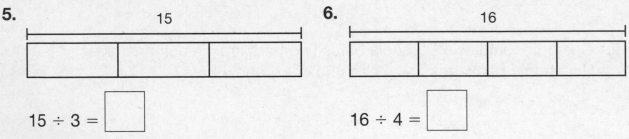

5.

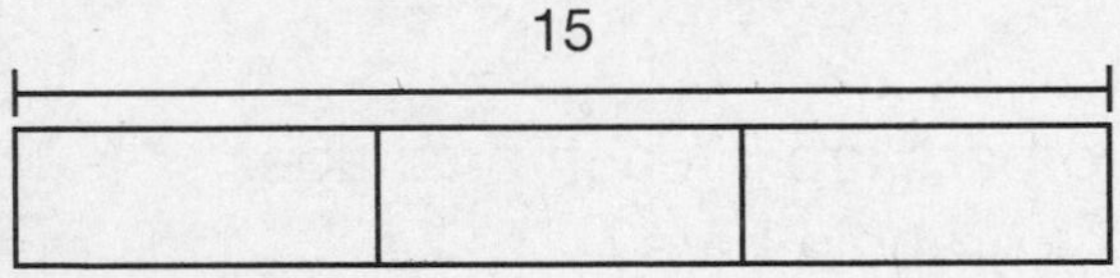

$15 \div 3 = \square$

6.

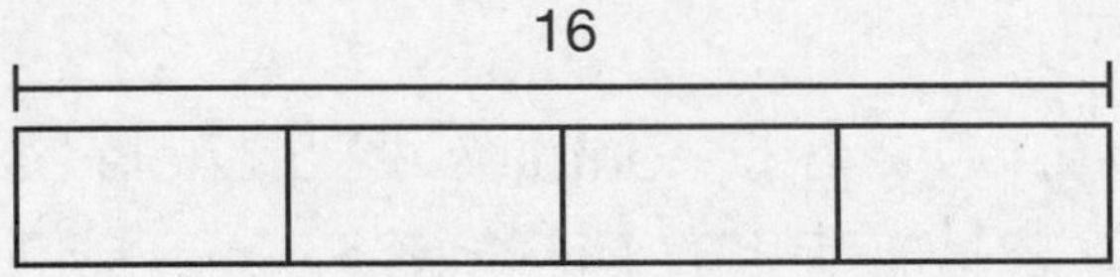

$16 \div 4 = \square$

7. **Writing to Explain** Ron and Pam each have 20 pennies. Ron will put his pennies into 4 groups. Pam will put her pennies into 5 groups. Who will have more pennies in each group? Explain.

____

____

8. There are 28 days in February. There are 7 days in a week. How many weeks are there in February?

○ 3 ○ 4 ○ 5 ○ 6

Name ______________________________

Division as Repeated Subtraction

You can think of division as repeated subtraction.

Emily has 20 raffle tickets. There are 5 tickets in each book.
How many books of raffle tickets does Emily have?

Start with 20 tickets. Subtract 5.	$20 - 5 = 15$
Subtract 5 more tickets.	$15 - 5 = 10$
Subtract 5 more tickets.	$10 - 5 = 5$
Subtract 5 more tickets.	$5 - 5 = 0$
You have reached 0.	

You have subtracted 5 four times.
So, $20 \div 5 = 4$.

Emily has 4 books of raffle tickets.

Draw a picture to solve. Use counters if needed.

1. 10 markers
   5 markers in each box
   How many boxes?
   ______

2. 8 hamsters
   2 hamsters in each cage
   How many cages?
   ______

3. 16 books
   4 books on each shelf
   How many shelves?
   ______

4. 18 players
   3 players on each team
   How many teams?
   ______

5. Annie had 16 balloons. She shares them equally with Connie.
   How many balloons does each girl have now?
   ______

6. **Writing to Explain** Show how you can use repeated subtraction to find how many groups of 7 are in 28.
   Then write the division sentence for the problem.
   ____
   ____

Name ____________________

Practice 9-2

Division as Repeated Subtraction

Draw a picture to solve. Use counters if needed.

1. 18 pens
3 pens in each box
How many boxes?

______

2. 24 students
3 students on each team
How many teams?

______

3. 35 stickers
5 stickers on each sheet
How many sheets?

______

4. 30 leaves
6 leaves painted on each vase
How many vases?

______

5. **Number Sense** What division sentence means the same as the following subtraction sentences?

$12 - 4 = 8$
$8 - 4 = 4$
$4 - 4 = 0$

______

6. Tandem bicycles are ridden by 2 people. If 14 people rented tandem bicycles, how many bicycles were rented?

______

7. **Writing to Explain** Tamara says that $15 \div 3 = 5$. Is she correct? Explain.

______

______

______

8. Keisha has to carry 32 boxes to her room. She can carry 4 boxes on each trip. How many trips will she take?

○ 6 ○ 7 ○ 8 ○ 9

Name ____________________

Reteaching
9-3

Writing Division Stories

Eddie was asked to write a division story using 12 ÷ 4.

Eddie wrote his story this way.

Cami has 12 crayons and some cans.
She puts 4 crayons into each can.

How many cans did Cami use?

Think of a situation where the larger number can be put into groups.

Write your question.

You can show Eddie's story this way.

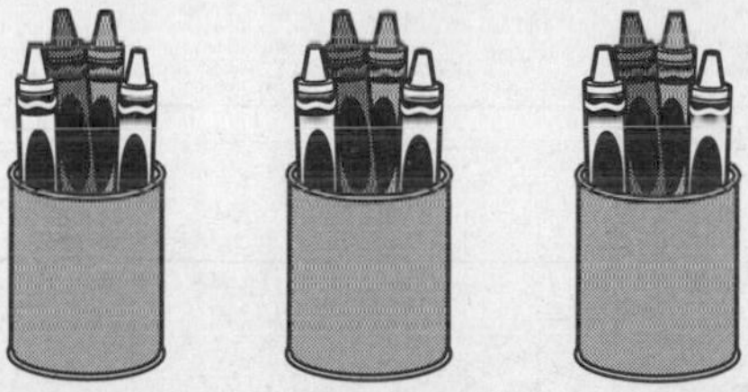

Cami used 3 cans.

Write a division story for each number sentence. Then use counters or draw a picture to solve.

1. 10 ÷ 2 = ☐

2. 21 ÷ 3 = ☐

3. 18 ÷ 3 = ☐

4. 16 ÷ 4 = ☐

5. Writing to Explain Sheila wrote a division story. She asked how many equal groups 24 flowers could be put into. What information must she give about the groups?

Name ____________________

Practice 9-3

Writing Division Stories

Write a division story for each number sentence. Then use counters or draw a picture to solve.

1. 54 ÷ 6 = ☐

2. 36 ÷ 9 = ☐

3. 42 ÷ 7 = ☐

4. 25 ÷ 5 = ☐

5. There are 40 relatives at a party. There are 5 tables that each seat the same number of people. How many people can sit at each table?

____

6. A softball pitcher needs to get 3 outs in an inning. If a pitcher gets 21 outs, how many innings did she pitch?

____

7. **Writing to Explain** There are 16 people at a party. They want to set up relay teams with exactly 3 people each. Can they do it? Explain.

8. Which division sentence will give an answer that is not in equal groups?

○ 26 ÷ 4 ○ 35 ÷ 7 ○ 42 ÷ 6 ○ 45 ÷ 5

Name ______________________________

Reteaching
9-4

Problem Solving: Act It Out and Draw a Picture

Sometimes, drawing a picture will help you solve a problem. It will help you "see" the problem and perhaps the solution.

Some orange juice spilled on a tile floor and covered up part of the floor. The tile floor was in the shape of a rectangle. There were 40 square tiles in the whole floor. How many tiles were in each row?

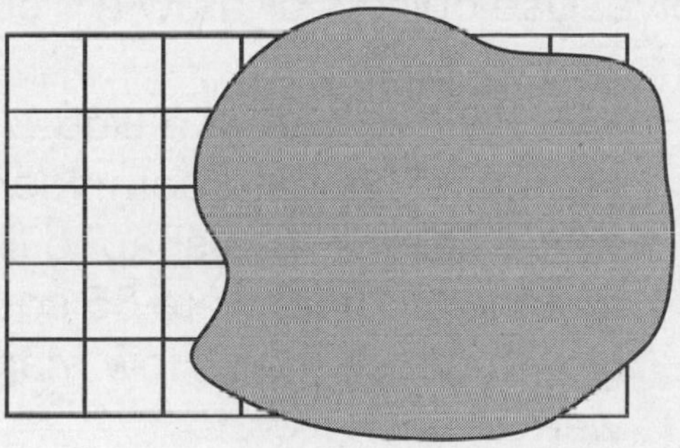

Draw a picture to show what you know.

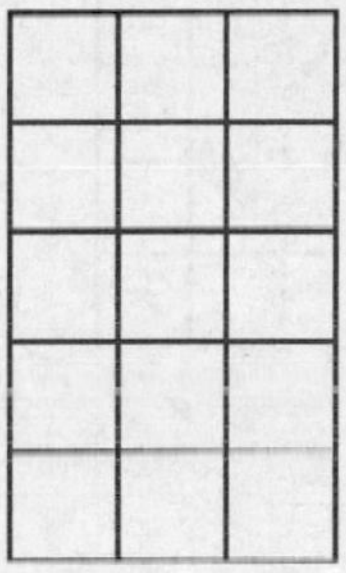

Finish the picture to solve the problem.

There should be 40 tiles in all.

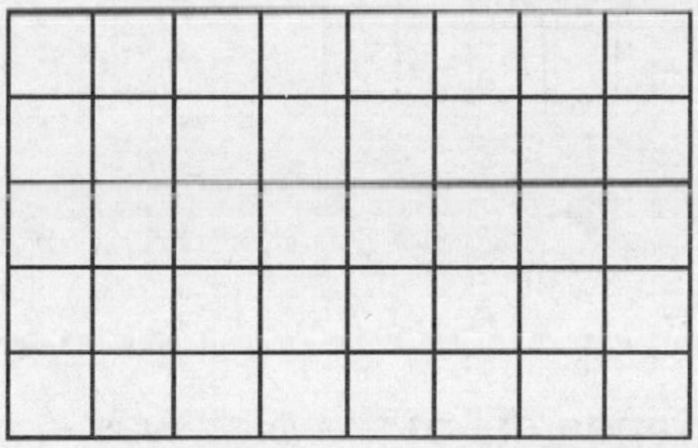

So there are 8 tiles in each row.

Solve. Use objects or draw a picture.

1. Mr. Robbins spilled stain on part of a tiled floor. The whole section of floor was shaped like a rectangle. There were 45 squares in the section. How many squares were in each row?

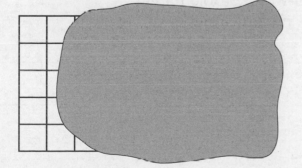

____

2. Kate is painting a wall. She painted over part of a section of 30 square tiles. The whole section of tiles was shaped like a rectangle. How many rows of tiles were in the whole section?

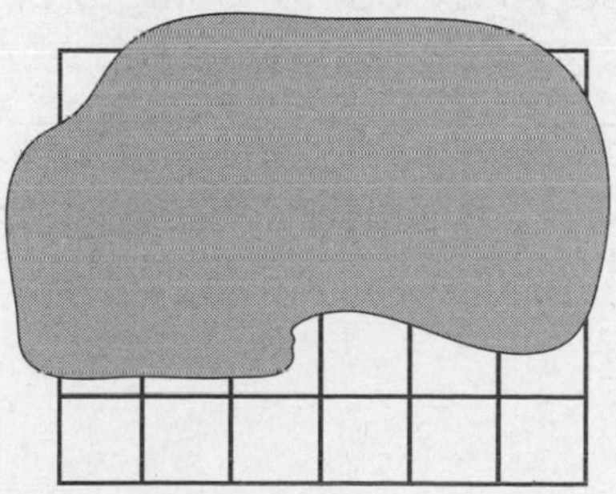

____

Name ____________________

Problem Solving: Act It Out and Draw a Picture

Solve. Use objects or draw a picture.

1. Ron painted part of a tiled section of his bathroom floor. The whole section was shaped like a rectangle. There were 35 square tiles in the section. How many tiles were in each row?

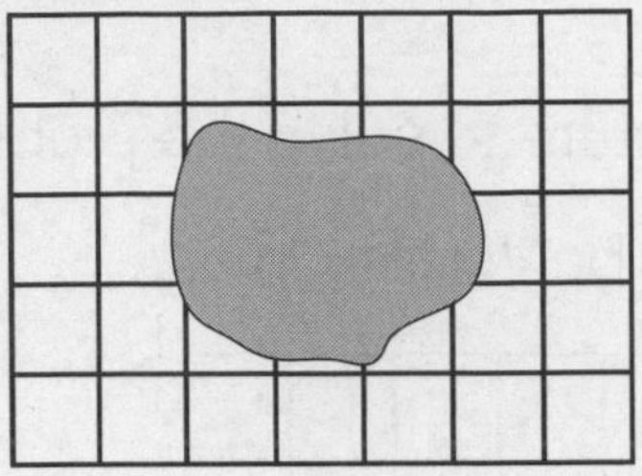

____

2. Some syrup spilled on a checkerboard style table. The syrup covered some of the tiles. There were 36 squares on the table. How many of the squares had syrup on them?

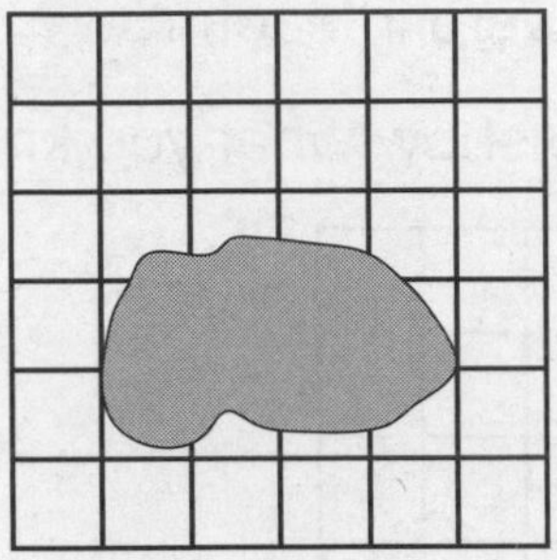

____

3. Dress rehearsal of the play was attended by 142 people. Opening night was attended by 238 people. How many people saw the two shows in all?

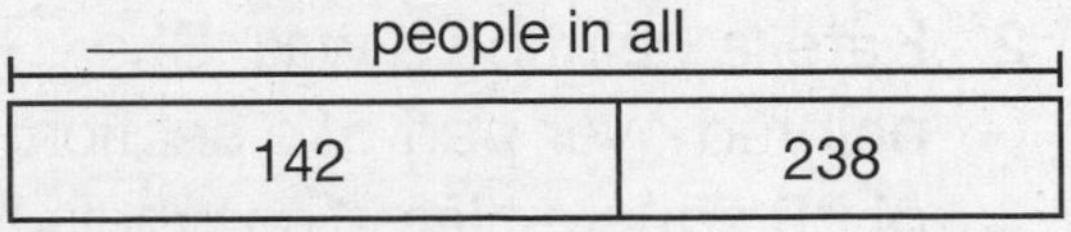

4. Carol and Deanna drove 320 miles all together this weekend. They drove 196 miles Sunday. How many miles did they drive Saturday?

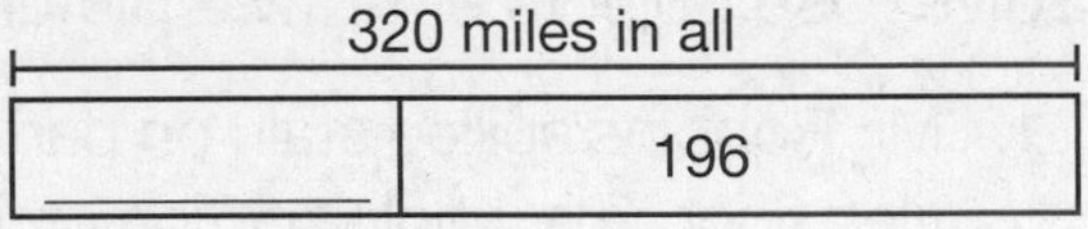

5. **Write a Problem** Write and solve a real-world problem that you can solve by using objects or drawing a picture.

____

____

Name ______________________

Reteaching
10-1

Relating Multiplication and Division

You can use multiplication facts to understand division.
Fact families show how multiplication and division are related.

Here is the fact family for 3, 8, and 24:

$3 \times 8 = 24$ $24 \div 3 = 8$

$8 \times 3 = 24$ $24 \div 8 = 3$

Complete. Use counters or draw a picture to solve.

1. $3 \times \square = 6$

$6 \div 3 = \square$

2. $7 \times \square = 14$

$14 \div 7 = \square$

3. $5 \times \square = 20$

$20 \div 5 = \square$

4. $4 \times \square = 24$

$24 \div 4 = \square$

5. **Number Sense** What other number is a part of this act family? 3, 4, ______

6. There are 28 days in 4 weeks. What fact family would you use to find the number of days in 1 week?

____

7. There are 12 in. in 1 ft. What fact family would you use to find the number of inches in 2 ft?

____

Name ______________________

Practice
10-1

Relating Multiplication and Division

Complete. Use counters or draw a picture to help.

1. $5 \times \square = 15$

$15 \div 5 = \square$

2. $6 \times \square = 24$

$24 \div 6 = \square$

3. $7 \times \square = 35$

$35 \div 7 = \square$

4. $5 \times \square = 25$

$25 \div 5 = \square$

5. $3 \times \square = 12$

$12 \div 3 = \square$

6. $3 \times \square = 27$

$27 \div 3 = \square$

7. Number Sense Write a fact family for 3, 6, and 18.

____

____

8. Patrick purchased 12 books. He needed 4 books for each of his projects at school. How many projects did he have?

______

9. Draw a Picture Draw an array. Then write a fact family to describe your array.

____

____

10. Writing to Explain Evan told his class that the people in his family have 14 legs all together. Quinton said that there must be 7 people in Evan's family. Is Quinton correct? Explain.

____

____

11. Which number makes this number sentence true? $■ \div 6 = 8$

○ 2 ○ 14 ○ 24 ○ 48

Name ____________________

Reteaching
10-2

Fact Families with 2, 3, 4, and 5

You can use multiplication facts to help you find division facts.

Darren and Molly have 16 sheets of paper. Each will get the same number of sheets of paper. How many will each get?

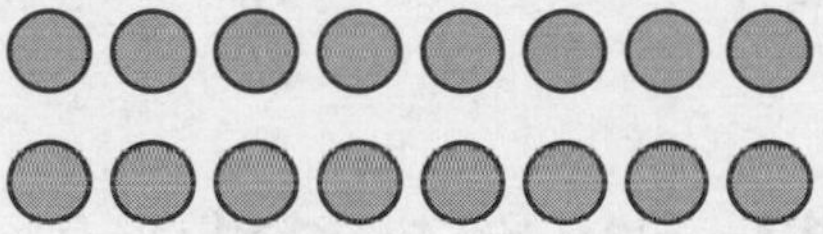

Peter has 24 pennies. He puts the pennies into 4 equal piles. How many pennies are in each pile?

What You Think	What You Write	What You Think	What You Write
2 times what number equals 16? $2 \times \mathbf{8} = 16$	$16 \div 2 = \mathbf{8}$ Darren and Molly will each get 8 sheets of paper.	4 times what number equals 24? $4 \times \mathbf{6} = 24$	$24 \div 4 = \mathbf{6}$ Peter has 6 pennies in each pile.

Find each quotient.

1. $14 \div 2$ ______ **2.** $35 \div 5$ ______ **3.** $15 \div 3$ ______ **4.** $32 \div 4$ ______ **5.** $24 \div 3$ ______

6. 2)12 **7.** 3)27 **8.** 5)25 **9.** 4)20 **10.** 4)40

11. Number Sense Write a fact family using the numbers 5, 6, and 30.

____

____

Name ______________________

Practice 10-2

Fact Families with 2, 3, 4, and 5

Find each quotient.

1. 14 ÷ 2 ____ **2.** 12 ÷ 3 ____ **3.** 16 ÷ 4 ____ **4.** 30 ÷ 5 ____ **5.** 21 ÷ 3 ____

6. $2\overline{)20}$ **7.** $4\overline{)32}$ **8.** $5\overline{)40}$ **9.** $3\overline{)18}$ **10.** $4\overline{)32}$

11. Find 18 divided by 3. ____

12. Divide 60 by 6. ____

13. Find 35 divided by 5. ____

Algebra Find each missing number.

14. 45 ÷ ☐ = 5 **15.** 30 ÷ 3 = ☐ **16.** ☐ ÷ 2 = 7

Number Sense Write < or > to compare.

17. 5 × 2 ◯ 8 ÷ 2 **18.** 3 × 6 ◯ 6 ÷ 3 **19.** 4 + 8 ◯ 4 × 8

20. Gabriella and 4 friends shared a pack of 15 glue sticks equally. How many glue sticks did each person get?

____

21. Erica counted 45 fingers when the students were asked who wants to play kickball. How many hands went up?

____

22. Writing to Explain Franklin says that if he divides 50 by 5, he will get 10. Jeff says he should get 9. Who is correct? Explain.

____

____

23. Which fact does not belong in the same fact family as 24 ÷ 4 = 6?

○ 4 × 6 = 24 ○ 6 + 4 = 10 ○ 24 ÷ 6 = 4 ○ 6 × 4 = 24

Name ______________________

Fact Families with 6 and 7

Multiplication facts can help you to find division facts when 6 or 7 is the divisor.

Find 35 ÷ 7.

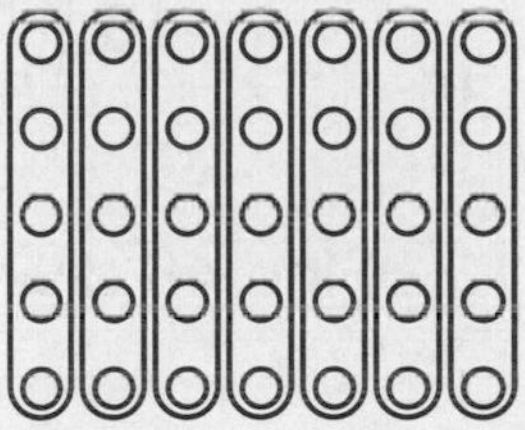

There are 48 marbles. They come in packages of 6. How many packages of marbles are there?

What You Think	What You Write	What You Think	What You Write
What number times 7 equals 35? $7 \times \mathbf{5} = 35$	$35 \div 7 = \mathbf{5}$	What number times 6 equals 48? $6 \times \mathbf{8} = 48$	$48 \div 6 = \mathbf{8}$ There are 8 packages of marbles.

Find each quotient.

1. 30 ÷ 6 ______ **2.** 28 ÷ 7 ______ **3.** 36 ÷ 6 ______ **4.** 21 ÷ 7 ______ **5.** 42 ÷ 6 ______

6. $7\overline{)49}$ **7.** $6\overline{)54}$ **8.** $7\overline{)70}$ **9.** $6\overline{)48}$ **10.** $7\overline{)56}$

11. Number Sense Name a number that can be equally divided by 6 and 7.

____

12. Reasoning Using 6 as one of the numbers, write a fact family with only two facts.

____

Name ______________________

Practice 10-3

Fact Families with 6 and 7

Find each quotient.

1. $24 \div 6$ ______ **2.** $42 \div 7$ ______ **3.** $36 \div 4$ ______ **4.** $63 \div 7$ ______ **5.** $40 \div 5$ ______

6. $6\overline{)48}$ **7.** $7\overline{)49}$ **8.** $2\overline{)12}$ **9.** $6\overline{)36}$ **10.** $3\overline{)27}$

11. Find 70 divided by 7. ______ **12.** Divide 66 by 6. ______ **13.** Find 48 divided by 6. ______

14. **Journal** How can you use a multiplication fact to find a division fact?

____

____

____

15. Sierra's karate class lasts 56 days. How many weeks does the class last? ______

16. **Writing to Explain** Wendell has a box with 36 cherries. He divides the cherries equally among 5 friends and himself. Bonnie received 6 cherries. She thinks she should have received one more. Is she correct? Explain.

____

____

____

17. Mr. Kline brought 30 boxes of fruit juice to a soccer game. Fruit juice comes in packages of 6. How many packages did Mr. Kline bring? ______

18. Katie bought 42 baseball cards. The cards come in packs of 7. How many packs of cards did Katie buy?

○ 5 ○ 6 ○ 7 ○ 8

Name ______________________________

Reteaching
10-4

Fact Families with 8 and 9

Multiplication facts can help you to find division facts when 8 or 9 is the divisor.

There are 32 counters. There are 8 counters in each row. How many rows are there?

There are 45 counters. There are 9 rows. How many counters are in each row?

What You Think	What You Write	What You Think	What You Write
8 times what number equals 32? $8 \times \mathbf{4} = 32$	$32 \div 8 = \mathbf{4}$ There are 4 rows of counters.	9 times what number equals 45? $9 \times \mathbf{5} = 45$	$45 \div 9 = \mathbf{5}$ There are 5 counters in each row.

Find each quotient.

1. $54 \div 9$ ______ **2.** $24 \div 8$ ______ **3.** $56 \div 8$ ______ **4.** $36 \div 9$ ______ **5.** $63 \div 9$ ______

6. $9\overline{)72}$ **7.** $8\overline{)48}$ **8.** $8\overline{)40}$ **9.** $8\overline{)80}$ **10.** $9\overline{)81}$

11. Number Sense What multiplication fact could you use to find a number that can be divided equally by 8 and 9?

____

Name ______________________

Practice
10-4

Fact Families with 8 and 9

Find each quotient.

1. $48 \div 8$ ____ **2.** $18 \div 9$ ____ **3.** $49 \div 7$ ____ **4.** $64 \div 8$ ____ **5.** $45 \div 9$ ____

6. $6\overline{)42}$ **7.** $8\overline{)72}$ **8.** $9\overline{)36}$ **9.** $5\overline{)15}$ **10.** $8\overline{)56}$

11. Find 81 divided by 9. ____ **12.** Divide 40 by 8. ____ **13.** Find 90 divided by 9. ____

Algebra Write < or > to compare.

14. $63 \div 9$ ◯ 8 **15.** $32 \div 8$ ◯ 8 **16.** $54 \div 9$ ◯ 5

17. **Reasoning** It costs \$7 for a matinee and \$8 for an evening movie. With \$56, would you be able to buy more matinee tickets or evening tickets? Explain.

____

____

18. Teri scored 64 points in the first 8 basketball games she played in. She scored the same number of points in each game. How many points did she score in each game? ____

19. **Writing to Explain** Adam made 19 paper cranes Monday and 8 more Tuesday. He gave 9 friends an equal number of cranes. How many cranes did each friend receive? Explain how you found your answer.

____

____

____

20. A short story consists of 81 pages. Andrea will read 9 pages each day. How many days will it take Andrea to finish the story?

○ 6 ○ 7 ○ 8 ○ 9

Name ______________________

Reteaching
10-5

Dividing with 0 and 1

There are special rules to follow when dividing by 1 or 0.

Rule	Example	What You **Think**	What You **Write**
When any number is divided by 1, the quotient is that number.	$7 \div 1 = ?$	1 times what number = 7? $1 \times 7 = 7$ So, $7 \div 1 = 7$	$7 \div 1 = 7$ or $1\overline{)7}$ with quotient 7
When any number (except 0) is divided by itself, the quotient is 1.	$8 \div 8 = ?$	8 times what number = 8? $8 \times 1 = 8$ So, $8 \div 8 = 1$	$8 \div 8 = 1$ or $8\overline{)8}$ with quotient 1
When zero is divided by a number (except 0), the quotient is 0.	$0 \div 5 = ?$	5 times what number = 0? $5 \times 0 = 0$ So, $0 \div 5 = 0$	$0 \div 5 = 0$ or $5\overline{)0}$ with quotient 0
You cannot divide a number by 0.	$9 \div 0 = ?$	0 times what number = 9? There is no number that works, so $9 \div 0$ cannot be done.	$9 \div 0$ cannot be done

Find each quotient.

1. $25 \div 1$ ______ **2.** $9 \div 9$ ______ **3.** $0 \div 8$ ______ **4.** $6 \div 6$ ______ **5.** $4 \div 1$ ______

6. $1\overline{)7}$ **7.** $12\overline{)12}$ **8.** $17\overline{)0}$ **9.** $5\overline{)5}$ **10.** $1\overline{)9}$

Compare. Use <, >, or =.

11. $15 \div 1$ ◯ $15 \div 15$

12. $0 \div 12$ ◯ $12 \div 12$

Name ______________________

Practice 10-5

Dividing with 0 and 1

Find each quotient.

1. $0 \div 6$ ____
2. $8 \div 8$ ____
3. $6 \div 1$ ____
4. $0 \div 5$ ____
5. $9 \div 9$ ____

6. $1\overline{)5}$
7. $4\overline{)0}$
8. $6\overline{)6}$
9. $1\overline{)8}$
10. $1\overline{)3}$

11. $3\overline{)24}$
12. $6\overline{)42}$
13. $8\overline{)72}$
14. $5\overline{)30}$
15. $7\overline{)63}$

16. Find 0 divided by 2. ____
17. Divide 7 by 1. ____
18. Find 4 divided by 4. ____

Algebra Write <, >, or = to compare.

19. $6 \div 6$ ◯ $8 \div 8$
20. $0 \div 5$ ◯ $5 \div 5$
21. $9 \div 1$ ◯ $7 \div 1$

22. Tickets for rides cost \$1 each at the fair. Bob has \$6 to buy tickets. How many tickets can Bob buy? ____

23. **Reasoning** Nikki is the goalie on her soccer team. She has allowed 0 goals in 8 games. How many goals has she allowed in each game? ____

24. **Writing to Explain** Why is $10 - 0 = 10$, but $0 \div 10 = 0$? Explain.

____

____

____

25. Which has the greatest quotient?

◯ $6 \div 6$ ◯ $5 \div 1$ ◯ $0 \div 3$ ◯ $8 \div 8$

Name ______________________________

Problem Solving: Draw a Picture and Write a Number Sentence

You can draw a picture to help you divide.

Neil has 54 CDs. He has the CDs equally placed among 6 shelves. How many CDs can go on each shelf?

Draw a diagram to show the problem. Make 6 rows with the same number of CDs until you reach 54.

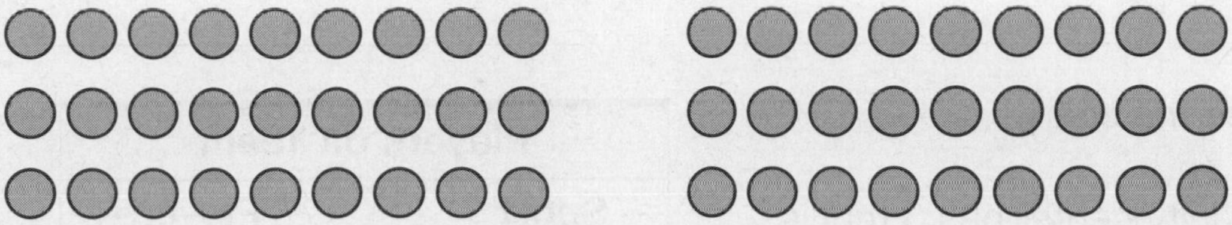

Write a number sentence: $54 \div 6 = 9$.

Check your answer by using multiplication: $6 \times 9 = 54$.

Neil can put 9 CDs on each shelf.

Draw a diagram to show what you know.
Then write a number sentence and solve.

1. There are 5 cars taking students to a museum. Each car can seat 4 students. How many students can go to the museum?

____

2. There are 16 players competing in the beach volleyball tournament. There are 8 teams competing. How many players are on each team?

____

3. **Writing to Explain** Sandy said she could use addition to answer question 1. How could this be done?

____

____

Name ___

Problem Solving: Draw a Picture and Write a Number Sentence

In **1** and **2**, draw a diagram to show what you know. Then write a number sentence and solve.

1. Maria bought 5 cans of tennis balls. Each can contained 3 tennis balls. How many tennis balls did Maria buy all together?

___

2. In Ms. Ramirez's class there are 28 students. They sit in 4 rows. How many students are in each row?

___

In **3** and **4**, use the chart.

Players on Team	
Sport	**Players**
Tennis	2
Basketball	5
Softball	10

3. A community center has 3 tennis teams and 5 basketball teams. No one is on both teams. How many athletes are there?

___

4. **Number Sense** Fabio said that there are 3 times as many people on a basketball team as on a tennis team. Is he correct? Explain why or why not.

___

___

___

Write a number sentence and solve. Use this information for **5** and **6**.

Marshall sleeps 8 hours each day.

5. How many hours does Marshall sleep in one week? ___

6. How many hours is Marshall awake each day? ___

7. Tricia spent $12 to rent ice skates. She rented them for 4 hours. Which number sentence can you write to find how much it costs to rent skates for one hour?

○ $\$12 - \$4 = \blacksquare$ ○ $\$12 + \$4 = \blacksquare$ ○ $\$12 \times 4 = \blacksquare$ ○ $\$12 \div 4 = \blacksquare$

Name ____________________

Repeating Patterns

Patterns can grow or patterns can repeat.
Repeating patterns can use numbers or shapes.
You can extend a pattern by finding its rule.

Repeating Patterns with Shapes

Use this pattern. What is the next shape?

Assign each shape a number. When a shape repeats use the same number.

1 2 3 1 2 3 1

The next shape is the second shape.

Repeating Patterns with Numbers

Use the pattern below. What is the 12th number in this pattern?

4, 7, 3, 5, 4, 7, 3, 5, 4, 7, ...

Find the pattern.
The pattern is 4, 7, 3, 5, and then it repeats.

Extend the pattern until reaching the 12th number.

4, 7, 3, 5, 4, 7, 3, 5, 4, 7, 3, 5

The 12th number is 5.

---

1. Draw the next three shapes in the pattern.

____

2. What are the next three numbers in the pattern below?
5, 8, 3, 1, 5, 8, 3, 1, 5, 8

____

3. **Explain It** In the pattern above, how could you find the 15th number? What is that number?

____

____

____

Name ______________________________

Practice
11-1

Repeating Patterns

Draw the next three shapes to continue the pattern.

1. 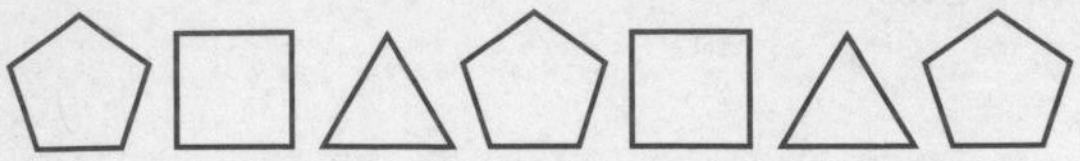

____

2. 

____

Write the next three numbers to continue the pattern.

3. 4, 6, 2, 8, 4, 6, 2, 8, 4

____

4. 3, 3, 5, 3, 3, 5, 3, 3, 5

____

5. Draw a Picture What is the 12th shape in the pattern below?

____

6. Strategy Practice Penny has made a pattern of shapes on her bedroom walls. She drew a rectangle, 2 circles, a rectangle, and then 2 more circles until she drew 24 circles. How many shapes did she draw in all?

____

7. Mrs. Washington placed students in a line. The order was 1 boy, 2 girls, 2 boys, and continued. Was the 10th student a boy or a girl?

____

8. What is the 15th number in the pattern below?
3, 6, 5, 2, 3, 6, 5, 2

○ 2 ○ 3 ○ 5 ○ 6

Name ____________________________________

Number Sequences

A number sequence is a pattern that increases or decreases while following a rule.

What are the next three numbers in this pattern?

36, 42, 48, 54, ...

Step 1	**Step 2**
Find the pattern.	Use the rule to extend the pattern.
You can subtract to find the pattern.	The pattern is "add 6." Start with 54.
$54 - 48 = 6$	$54 + 6 = 60$
$48 - 42 = 6$	$60 + 6 = 66$
$42 - 36 = 6$	$66 + 6 = 72$
Each number is 6 more than the number before it. So, the rule is "add 6."	So, the next three numbers are 60, 66, and 72.

Find the next three numbers in each pattern.
Write the rule for the pattern.

1. 35, 40, 45, ■, ■, ■
____

2. 43, 39, 35, ■, ■, ■
____

3. 32, 39, 46, ■, ■, ■
____

4. 13, 21, 29, ■, ■, ■
____

5. 75, 65, 55, ■, ■, ■
____

6. 51, 45, 39, ■, ■, ■
____

7. **Critical Thinking** How can you use subtraction to complete an addition pattern? Use Exercise 3 as an example.

____

____

____

Name ______________________

Practice
11-2

Number Sequences

Find the missing numbers in each pattern. Write the rule for the pattern.

1. 19, 23, 27, ■, ■

2. 32, 26, 20, ■, ■

3. 125, 150, 175, ■, ■

4. 8, 15, ■, ■, 36

5. 90, 80 ■, ■, 50

6. 84, 69, 54, ■, ■

7. 30, 50, ■, 90, ■

8. 65, 56, ■, 38, ■

9. 35, ■, 57, 68, ■

10. **Reasoning** The house numbers on Carr Memorial Avenue follow a pattern. The first four houses on the left side of the street are numbered 8, 14, 20, and 26. How many more houses are on the left side of the street with numbers less than 50?

11. Noreen is beginning an exercise program. The first week she exercises 25 minutes each day. The second week she exercises 30 minutes a day and the third week she increases it to 35 minutes a day. If the pattern continues, how long will she exercise each day in the fifth week?

12. **Journal** What do you need to do to extend a pattern?

13. John said that 52 is part of the pattern below. Mary said that 66 is part of the pattern below. Who is correct?
18, 26, 34, 42, …

- ○ Neither is correct.
- ○ Both are correct.
- ○ Only John is correct.
- ○ Only Mary is correct.

Name ______________________

Extending Tables

A table is an organized way to show a pattern.

Weeks	Days
1	7
3	21
5	35
6	42
8	?

Each pair of values follows a rule. If you can find the rule, you can extend the table.

What is the missing number in this table?

Step 1

Find the pattern.

The first 4 weeks are shown. You can divide to find the pattern.

$42 \div 6 = 7$
$35 \div 5 = 7$
$21 \div 3 = 7$
$7 \div 1 = 7$

There are 7 days in one week.

Step 2

Use the rule to find the missing number.

Multiply the days in 1 week by the number of weeks.

$8 \times 7 = 56$

The missing number is 56.

Complete each table.

1.

Cars	Wheels
1	4
2	8
3	
4	16
8	32

2.

Old Price	New Price
$63	$53
$48	$38
	$31
$37	$27
$26	$16

3.

Weight of Salad in Ounces	6	10	14	18
Total Weight of Container in Ounces	9	13	17	

Name ______________________________

Practice 11-3

Extending Tables

Find the missing numbers.

1.

Number of Cats	Number of Legs
1	4
2	
3	12
4	16
	32

2.

Money Earned	Money Saved
$25	$15
$32	$22
$43	
	$47
$73	$63

3.

Touchdowns	Points
1	6
2	12
3	
	36
8	48

For **4** and **5**, use the table at the right.

T-shirts	Cost
1	$8
3	$24
5	$40

4. How much money would 9 T-shirts cost?

____

5. Strategy Practice How much more money do 10 T-shirts cost than 6 T-shirts? Explain how you determined your answer.

____

____

6. Number Sense Bob has 3 bookshelves that hold a total of 27 books. He adds a fourth shelf and now has 36 books. If he adds 2 more shelves, how many books can he have total?

____

7. What is the missing number in the table below?

In	3	5	8	15
Out	9	11	14	

○ 21 ○ 25 ○ 30 ○ 45

Name ___

Reteaching

11-4

Writing Rules for Situations

When working with tables, it is important to find the rule. The rule tells how to calculate one of the numbers in a pair. The rule must work for every pair of values.

Old Price	New Price
$15	$10
$22	$17
$28	$23
$37	$32
$51	$46

Each pair of values follows a rule. If you can find the rule, you can extend the table.

Step 1

Find the pattern. Check the first pair of numbers to see how the first number changed to become the second number.

15 − 10 = 5

The rule of the first pair of numbers is "subtract 5."

Step 2

See if the rule works for all the values.

22 − 17 = 5　　37 − 32 = 5

28 − 23 = 5　　51 − 46 = 5

The rule "subtract 5" works for every pair of values.

Find the missing numbers in each table.
Write the rule for the table.

1.

Earned	Spent
$21	$14
$30	$23
$42	
$48	$41
$59	

___

2.

Teams	Players
3	27
8	72
6	
9	
2	18

___

3.

Tickets	Cost
2	$1
6	$3
12	
10	$5
20	

___

4. **Reasonableness** Joe said that by using the information in Exercise 2 there would be 250 players if there were 25 teams. Is that reasonable? Explain.

___

___

Name ______________________________

Practice
11-4

Writing Rules for Situations

Find the missing numbers in each table.
Write the rule for the table.

1.

Max's Age	Carol's Age
7	13
10	
14	20
18	24
	31

____

2.

Tricycles	Wheels
5	15
3	9
7	
	27
2	6

____

3.

Old Price	New Price
$25	$18
$16	$9
	$32
$53	$46
$72	

____

For **4** and **5**, use the table at the right.

Players	Teams
24	4
48	8
36	6
30	5

4. The table shows the number of players on a volleyball team. What is the rule of the table?

____

5. **Explain It** If there are 16 teams, how many players will there be? Explain how you found your answer.

____

____

6. How many miles can Nick travel in 5 hours? 6 hours?

Hours	1	2	3	4
Miles	60	120	180	240

____

7. The table shows how many CDs Jim and Ken own after joining a CD club. What is the rule?

Jim	8	12	20	30
Ken	16	20	28	38

○ Add 8
○ Multiply by 2
○ Subtract 8
○ Divide by 2

Name ______________________

Reteaching
11-5

Translating Words to Expressions

You can use phrases that are given in a problem to determine which sign to use. This will help you to solve word problems. Below are examples of addition, subtraction, multiplication, and division phrases.

Word phrase	Numerical expression
3 hours studied Monday and 2 more today	$3 + 2$
6 DVDs fewer than 15	$15 - 6$
6 times the \$5 earned	$6 \times \$5$
15 people in 3 equal rows	$15 \div 3$

Write a numerical expression for each word phrase.

1. 16 less than 35

____

2. 12 more than 17

____

3. 4 times as many as 7

____

4. 18 that are in 2 equal groups

____

5. **Write a Problem** Write a problem in words involving the number of pages in a book. Then write the numerical expression that you would need to use to solve your problem.

____

____

Name ______________________

Practice 11-5

Translating Words to Expressions

Write a numerical expression for each word phrase.

1. a total of 21 that is split into 3 equal groups

____

2. the difference when 9 is taken away from 24

____

3. the sum of 32 and 27

____

4. the product of 7 and 5

____

5. 3 times as old as 6 years old

____

6. 15 CDs more than 12 CDs

____

7. 32 carrots shared equally by 8 people

____

8. $20 paid from $50

____

There are 12 people on a bus. Write a numerical expression for the number of people described in each word phrase.

9. 4 people leave the bus

____

10. 6 people get on the bus

____

11. half of the people leave the bus

____

12. twice as many people get on the bus

____

13. **Geometry** A figure has 3 more sides than a pentagon. Write an expression for the number of sides the new figure has.

____

14. Kim has 20 books each on 4 shelves. Which number sentence shows how to find how many books in all?

- ○ $20 + 4$
- ○ $20 - 4$
- ○ 20×4
- ○ $20 \div 4$

Name ____________________

Problem Solving: Act It Out and Use Reasoning

Izzie has 12 coins. Four of the coins are quarters. He has 2 more dimes than nickels. How many of each coin does he have?

You can use logical reasoning to find the answer. You may be able to determine information that is not told.

What do I know?	What do I need to find out?	What can I determine from the information?
Izzie has 12 coins. 4 of the coins are quarters. Izzie has 2 more dimes than nickels.	How many dimes does Izzie have? How many nickels does Izzie have?	If 4 of the 12 coins are quarters, Izzie has a total of 8 dimes and nickels.

You can act it out to find how many dimes and nickels Izzie has.

Take 8 two-color counters. Find combinations so that one color will have 2 more than the other. If you try 4 and 4, the difference is 0, so try 5 and 3. It works.

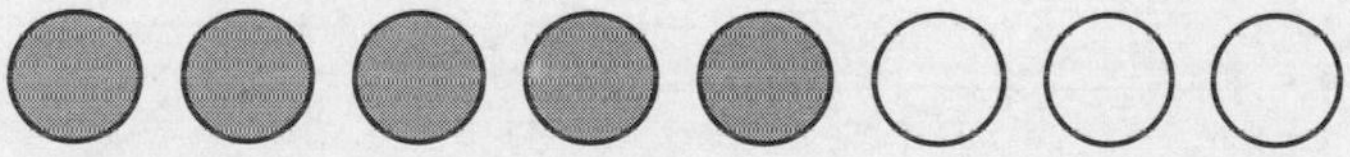

So, Izzie has 4 quarters, 5 dimes, and 3 nickels.

Solve. Find the number of each kind of object in the collection.

1. Kim's Music Video Collection

13 videos in all
4 concert videos
3 more rap videos than pop videos

Concert videos = ☐

Rap videos = ☐

Pop videos = ☐

2. Molly's Art Collection

5 paintings
3 more sculptures than mosaics
16 pieces in all

Paintings = ☐

Sculptures = ☐

Mosaics = ☐

Name ____________________

Practice
11-6

Problem Solving: Act It Out and Use Reasoning

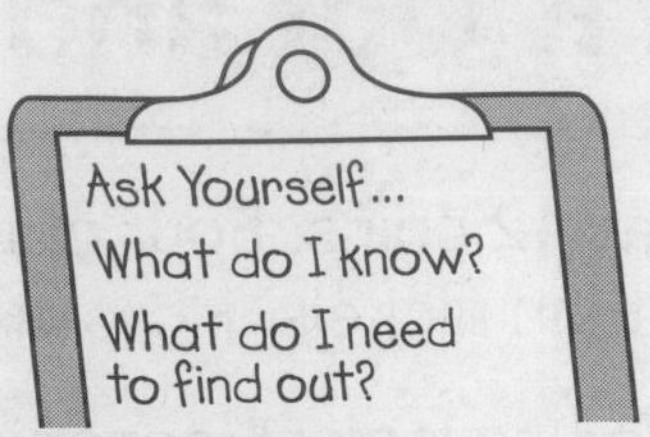
Ask Yourself...
What do I know?
What do I need to find out?

Solve. Find the number of each kind of object in the collection.

1. **Sue's Card Collection**

   8 packs of baseball cards
   3 fewer packs of hockey cards than football cards
   17 packs in all

   Baseball cards = ☐

   Hockey cards = ☐

   Football cards = ☐

2. **Drew's DVD Collection**

   7 comedy DVDs
   4 more drama DVDs than horror DVDs
   15 DVDs in all

   Comedy DVDs = ☐

   Drama DVDs = ☐

   Horror DVDs = ☐

3. **Strategy Practice** Mike is 8 years older than Kyle. Kyle is 6 years old. The sum of Mike's, Kyle's, and Jamal's ages is 23. How many years old is Jamal?

   ____

4. Miranda has 24 CDs in her collection. Of those CDs, 10 are pop CDs. She has 6 more country CDs than jazz CDs. How many country CDs does Miranda have?

   ____

5. Curt has 12 models in all. Three of the models are airplanes. Curt has 5 more models of cars than boats. How many models of cars does Curt have?

   ____

6. Stevie, Lindsey, and Christine are the lead singers in a band. They will sing 18 songs. Lindsey will sing 8 songs. Christine will sing 6 fewer songs than Stevie. How many songs will Stevie sing?

   ○ 2 ○ 4 ○ 6 ○ 8

Name ______________________

Reteaching
12-1

Dividing Regions into Equal Parts

A whole can be divided into equal parts in different ways.

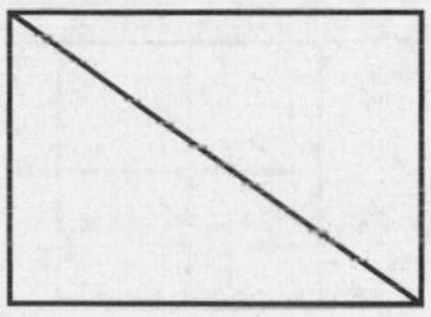
2 equal parts
halves

3 equal parts
thirds

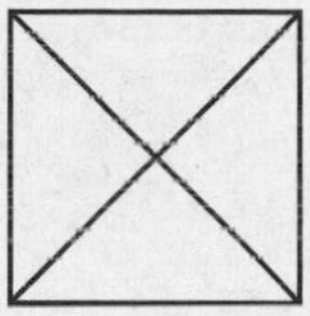
4 equal parts
fourths

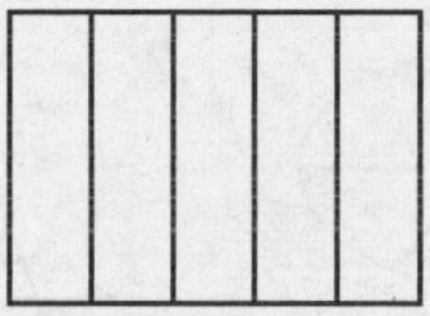
5 equal parts
fifths

6 equal parts
sixths

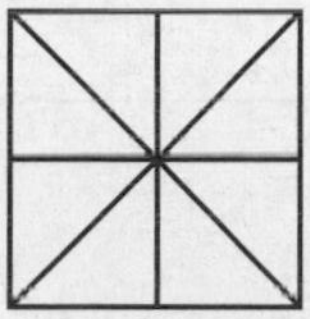
8 equal parts
eighths

10 equal parts
tenths

12 equal parts
twelfths

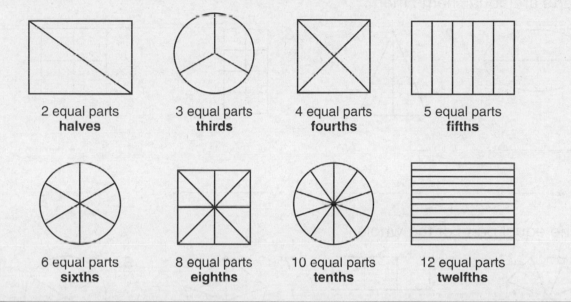

Tell if each shows equal parts or unequal parts.
If the parts are equal, name them.

1. 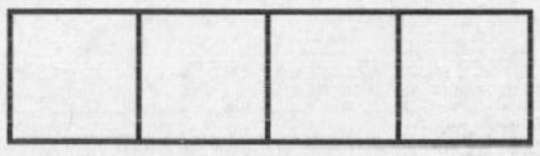

____

2. 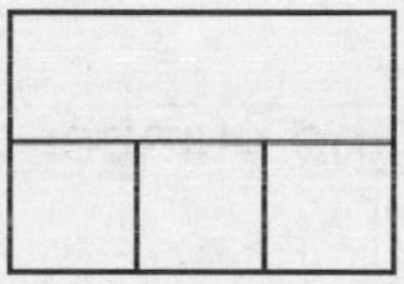

____

3. 

____

Name the equal parts of the whole.

4. 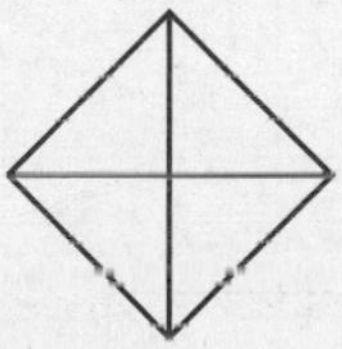

____

5. 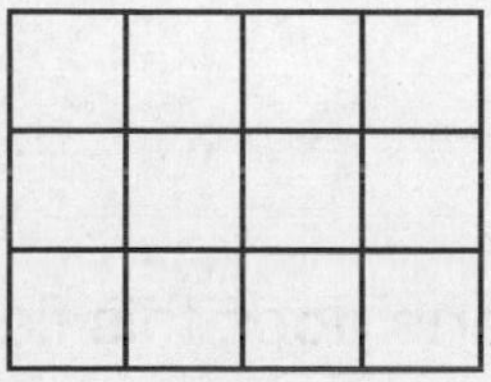

____

6. 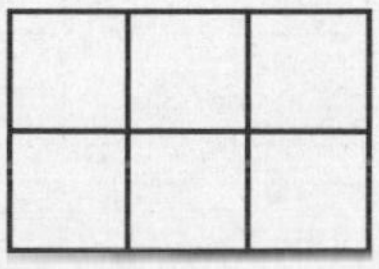

____

7. Using grid paper, draw a picture of a whole that is divided into thirds.

8. Reasoning How many equal parts are there when you divide a figure into fifths? ______________

Name ______________________________

Practice 12-1

Dividing Regions into Equal Parts

Tell if each shows equal or unequal parts.
If the parts are equal, name them.

1. 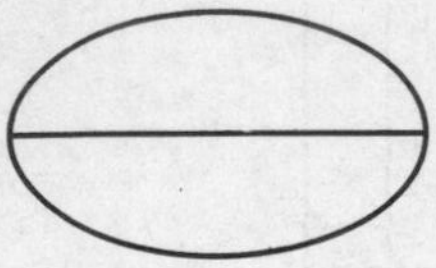

______

______

2. 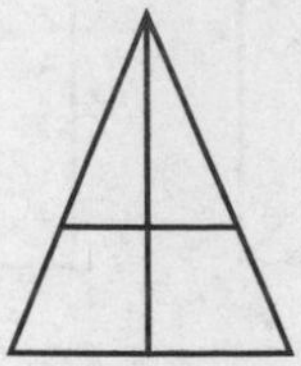

______

______

3. 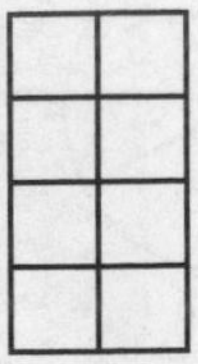

______

______

4. 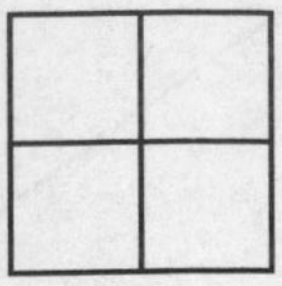

______

______

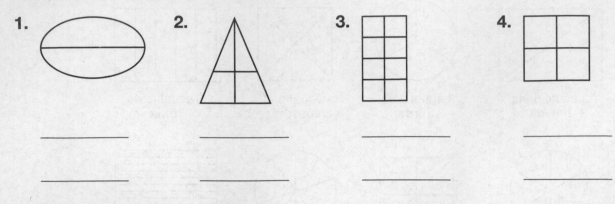

Name the equal parts of the whole.

5. 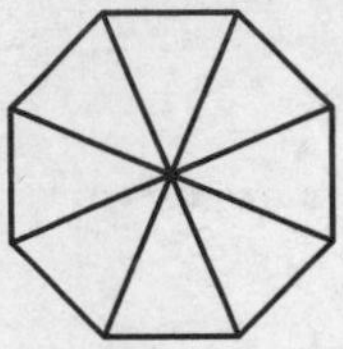

______

6. 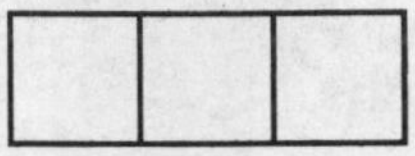

______

7. 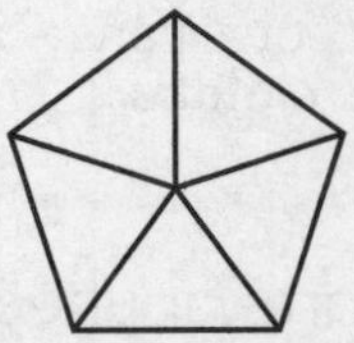

______

8. 

______

Use the grid to draw a region showing the number of equal parts named.

9. tenths

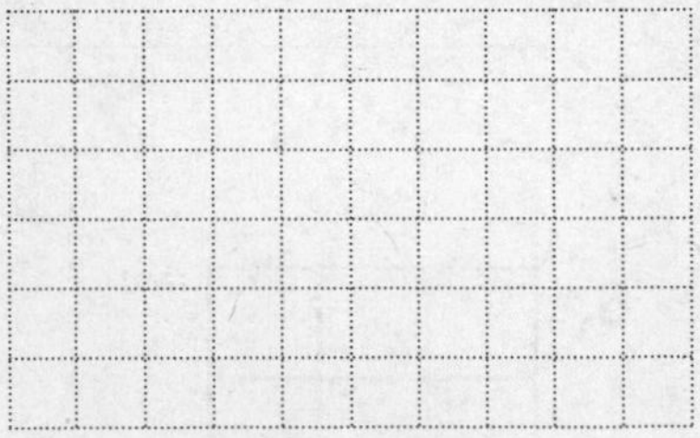

10. sixths

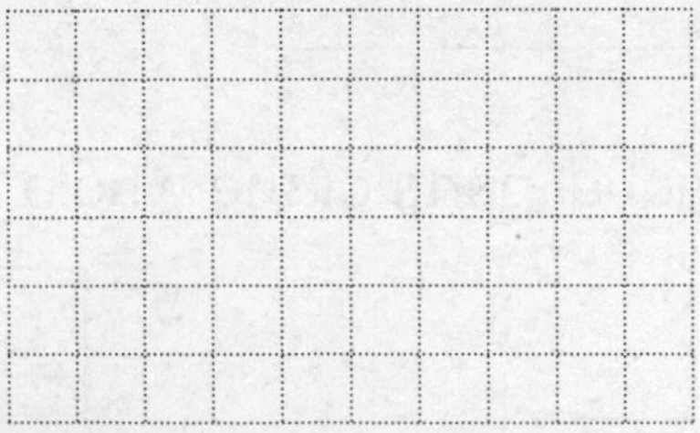

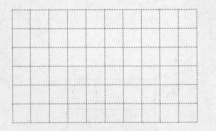

11. Geometry How many equal parts does this figure have?

______

12. Which is the name of 12 equal parts of a whole?

○ halves ○ tenths ○ sixths ○ twelfths

Name ____________________

Reteaching
12-2

Fractions and Regions

A fraction can be used to name part of a whole.

The denominator names the number of equal parts.

The numerator names the number of parts being considered.

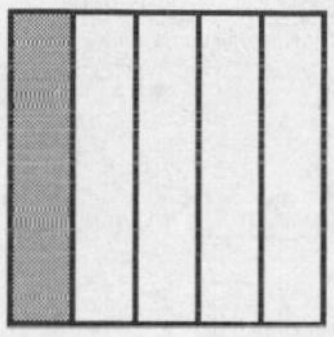

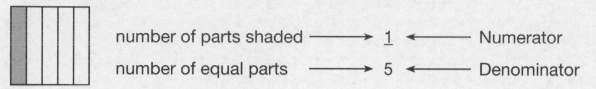

number of parts shaded ⟶ 1 ⟵ Numerator

number of equal parts ⟶ 5 ⟵ Denominator

One fifth of the rectangle is shaded.

Here are some other fractions to represent parts of a whole.

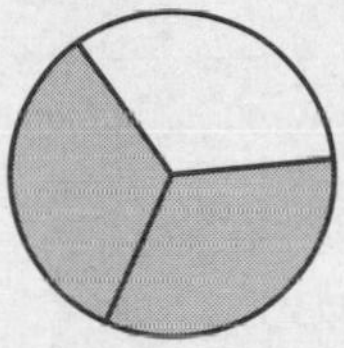

$\frac{2}{3}$ of the circle is shaded.

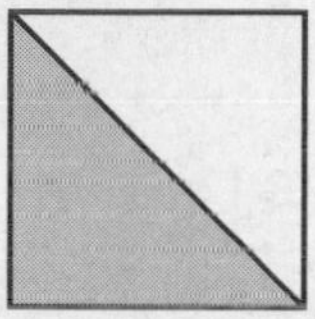

$\frac{1}{2}$ of the square is shaded.

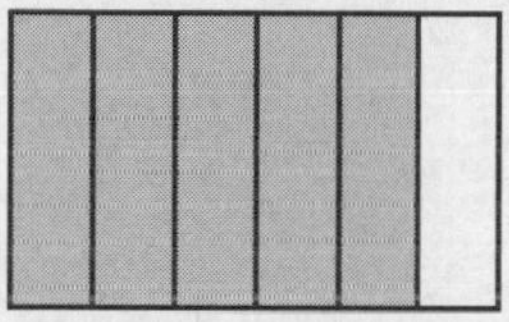

$\frac{5}{6}$ of the rectangle is shaded.

Write the fraction of each figure that is shaded.

1. 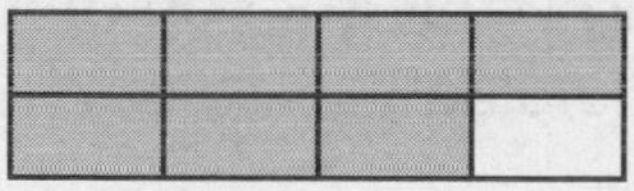

____

2. 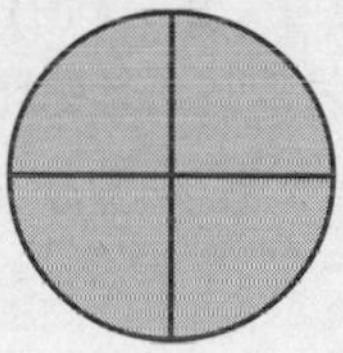

____

3. 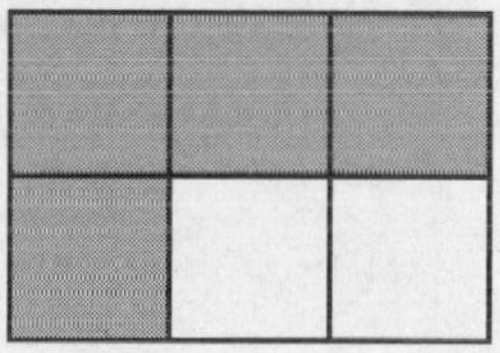

____

4. 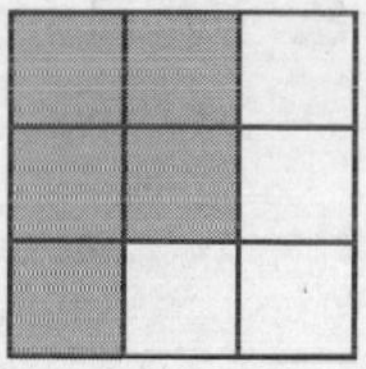

____

Draw a figure to show each fraction.

5. $\frac{1}{3}$

6. $\frac{5}{12}$

7. $\frac{3}{5}$

8. **Reasoning** A shape is $\frac{1}{7}$ shaded. What fraction is not shaded?

____

Name ______________________________

Fractions and Regions

Write the fraction of each figure that is shaded.

1. 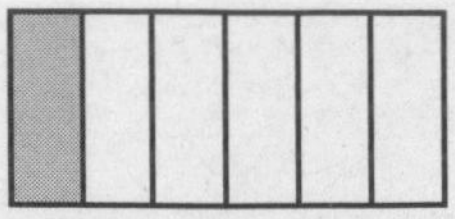 ________

2. 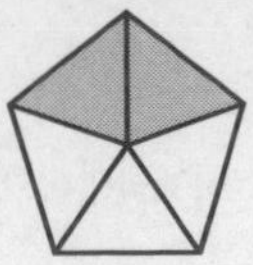 ________

3.  ________

4. 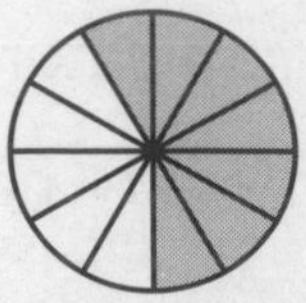 ________

Draw a picture to show each fraction.

5. $\frac{3}{8}$

6. $\frac{1}{4}$

7. $\frac{4}{5}$

In **8** and **9**, use the information below.

Three parts of a rectangle are red. Two parts are blue.

8. What fraction of the rectangle is red?

____

9. **Reasoning** What fraction of the rectangle is blue?

____

10. **Draw a Picture** A banner is made of 8 equal parts. Five of the parts contain stars. Three of the parts contain hearts. Draw the banner.

11. How can you write the fraction $\frac{4}{6}$ in word form?

○ fourth sixth ○ four sixes ○ four sixths ○ fourth six

Name ______________________

Reteaching **12-3**

Fractions and Sets

A fraction can name part of a group.

What fraction of the marbles are black?

$\frac{3}{8}$ ← Number of black marbles / Total number of marbles

$\frac{3}{8}$ of the marbles are black.

---

1. What fraction of the toys are balls? ______

2. What fraction of the fruits are oranges? ______

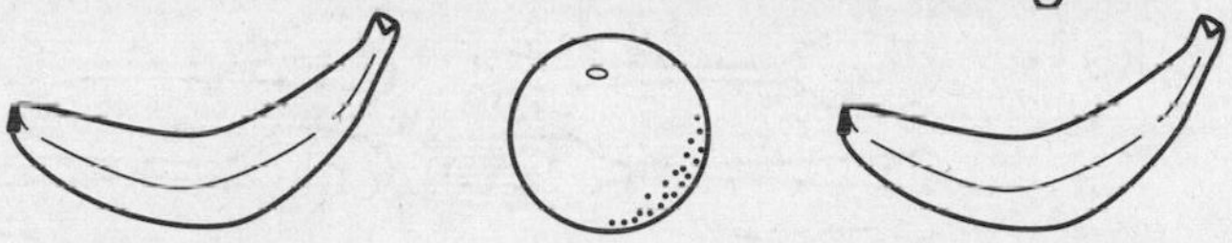

3. What fraction of the blocks have letters on them? ______

4. What fraction of the days of the week begin with the letter *T*? ______

For **5** and **6** draw a picture to show each fraction of a set.

5. $\frac{3}{5}$ of the squares are shaded.

6. $\frac{2}{3}$ of the balls are footballs.

7. Reasoning Out of 6 cats, 2 are tan. What fraction of cats are not tan? ______

Name ______________________________

Practice
12-3

Fractions and Sets

In **1–3**, write the fraction of the counters that are shaded.

1. 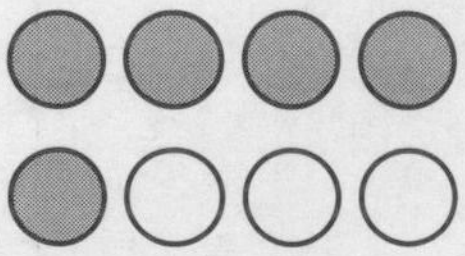

______

2. 

______

3. 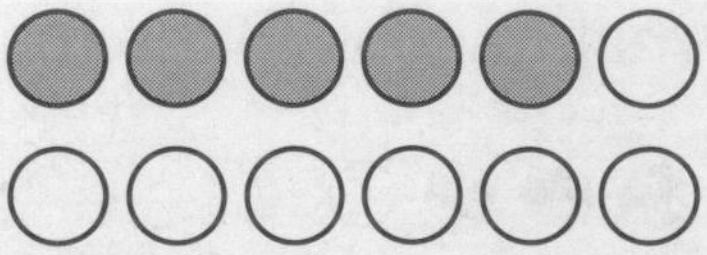

______

Draw a picture of the set described.

4. 4 shapes, $\frac{3}{4}$ of the shapes are squares

5. 6 shapes, $\frac{1}{6}$ of the shapes are circles

6. 10 shapes, $\frac{7}{10}$ of the shapes are triangles

In **7** and **8**, use the utensils to answer the questions.

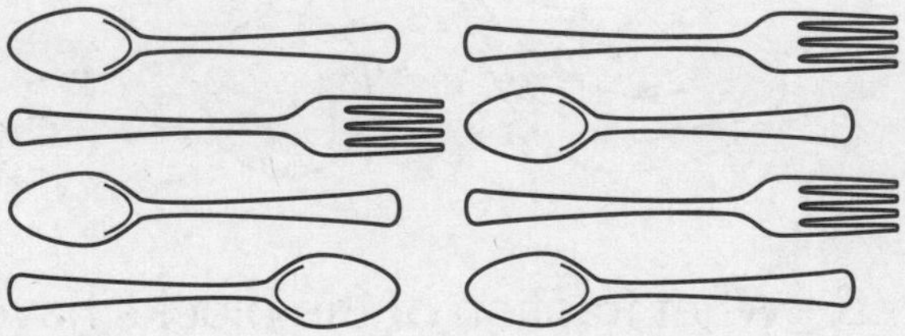

7. What fraction of the utensils are forks?

______

8. What fraction of the utensils are spoons?

______

9. **Number Sense** Johnny bought 5 movie tickets and spent \$44. Of the tickets he bought, $\frac{3}{5}$ were children's tickets that cost \$8 each. The other tickets were adult tickets. How much does one adult ticket cost?

______

10. Pamela has 4 pink ribbons, 3 green ribbons, and 2 blue ribbons. What fraction of Pamela's ribbons are green?

○ $\frac{3}{9}$ ○ $\frac{3}{6}$ ○ $\frac{3}{5}$ ○ $\frac{3}{4}$

Name ______________________________

Fractions and Length

A fraction can name part of the length of an object.

What part of this line segment is black?

You can use fraction strips to find the part of the whole.

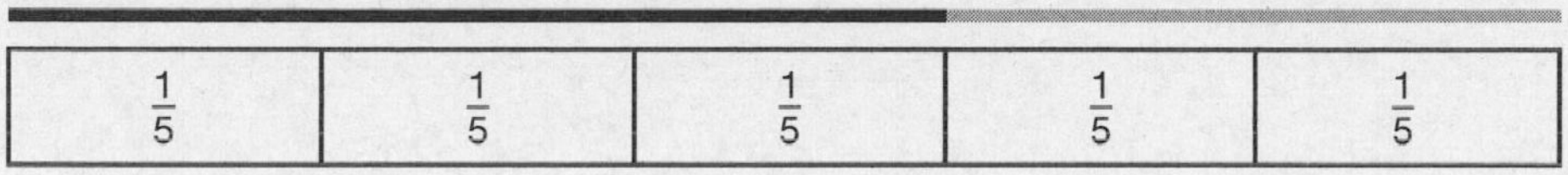

The line segment is $\frac{3}{5}$ black. The line segment is $\frac{2}{5}$ gray.

What fraction of the length of the 1 strip do the other strips show?

1.

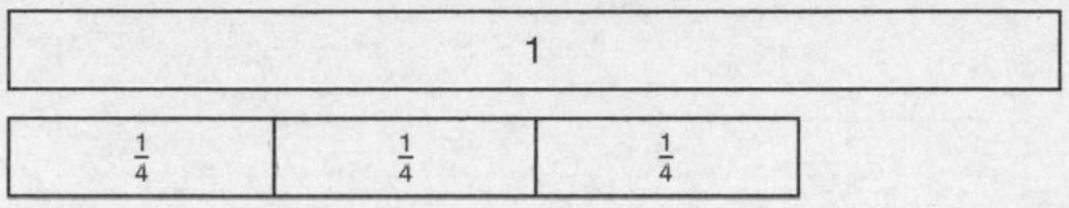

____

2.

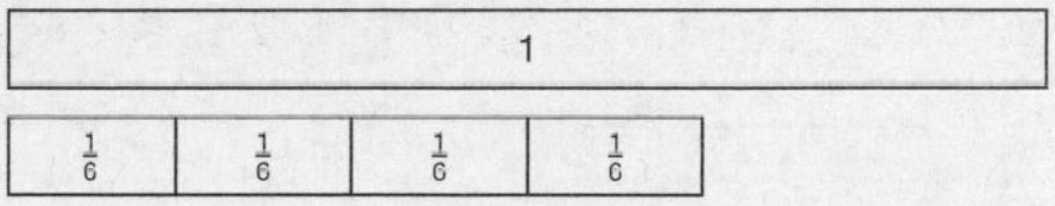

____

3.

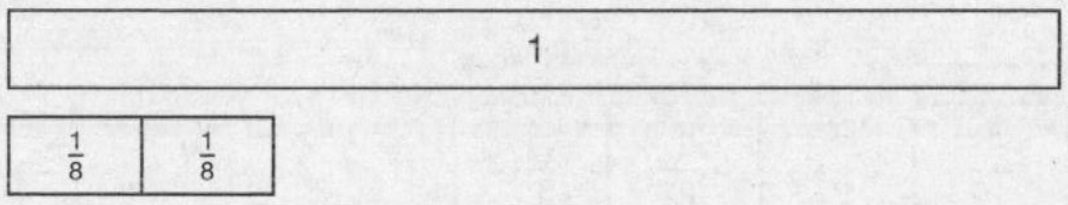

____

4.

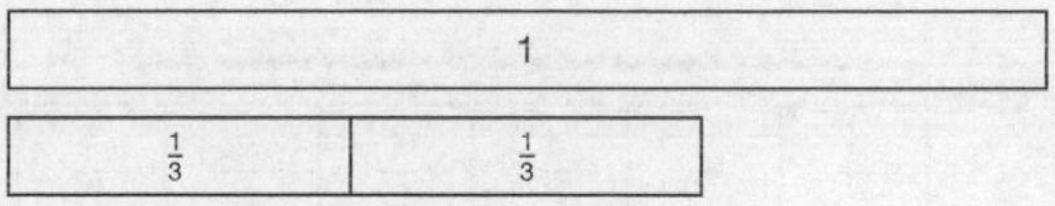

____

5. What fraction of the line segment is black? __________

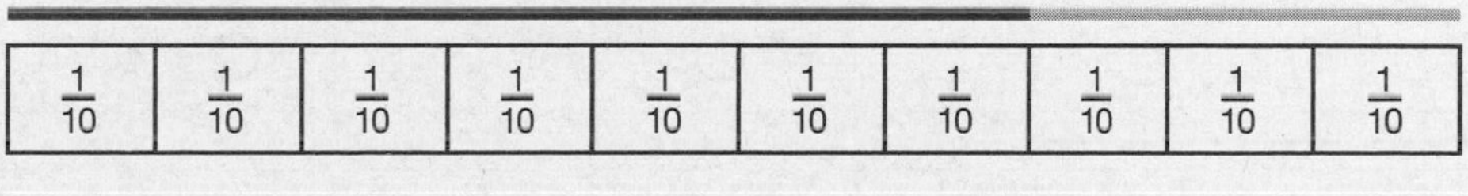

6. Reasoning A figure is part blue and part red.

It is $\frac{5}{8}$ red. What part of the figure is blue? __________

Name ______________________________

Practice 12-4

Fractions and Length

What fraction of the length of the 1 strip do the other strips show?

1. 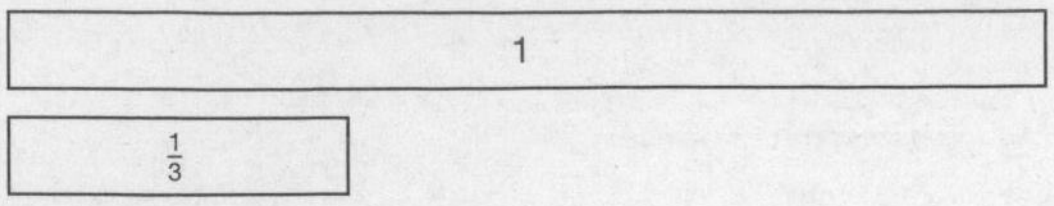

______

2. 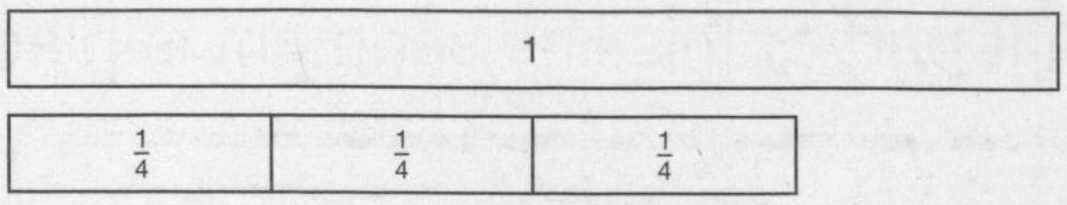

______

3. 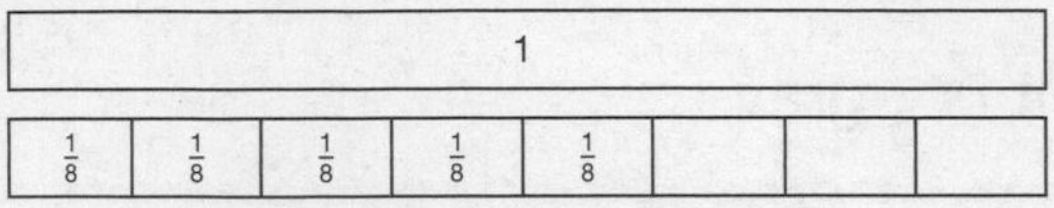

______

4. 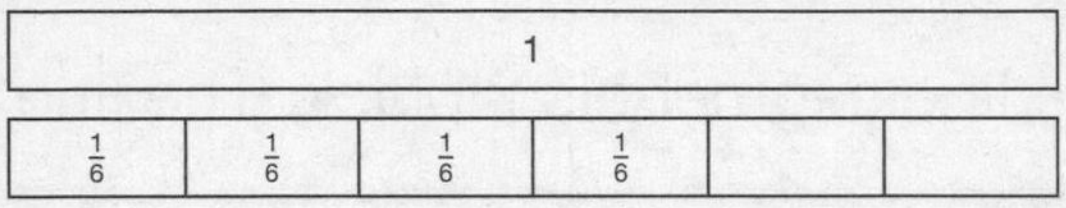

______

In **5** and **6**, what fraction of each length of yarn is black?

5. 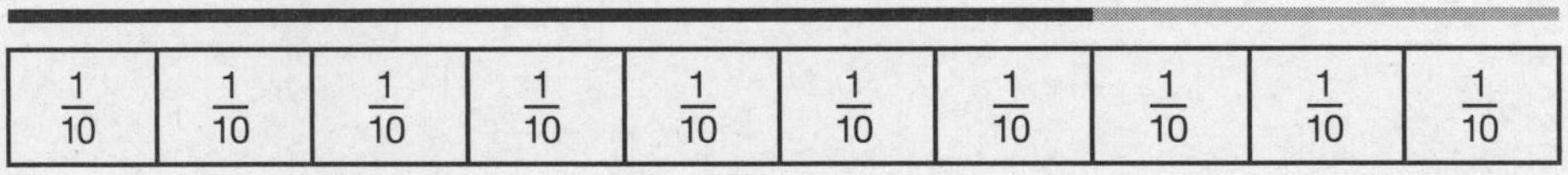

______

6. 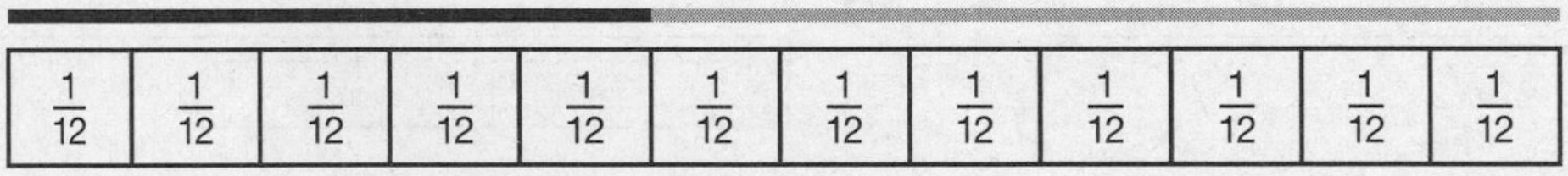

______

7. Explain It What is the purpose of using fraction strips and a 1 strip?

____

____

____

____

____

8. About $\frac{7}{10}$ of Earth's surface is covered by water. About what fraction of Earth's surface is not covered by water?

○ $\frac{3}{4}$ ○ $\frac{2}{3}$

○ $\frac{1}{2}$ ○ $\frac{3}{10}$

Name ____________________

Reteaching
12-5

Using Models to Compare Fractions

You can compare fractions by using fraction strips.

Linda and Patti have the same number of raffle tickets to sell. Linda has sold $\frac{3}{5}$ of her raffle tickets. Patti has sold $\frac{2}{3}$ of her raffle tickets. Who sold more of her raffle tickets: Linda or Patti?

Use fraction strips to represent each fraction.

Line up the fraction strips on the left.

Linda
Patti
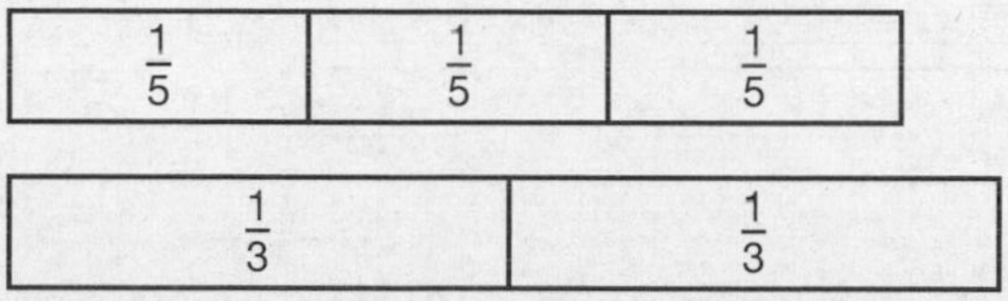

The fraction strips that stretch farther to the right are greater. If the right side lines up, the fractions are equal.

So, $\frac{3}{5} < \frac{2}{3}$. Patti sold more of her raffle tickets than Linda sold of hers.

Compare. Write >, <, or =.

1.
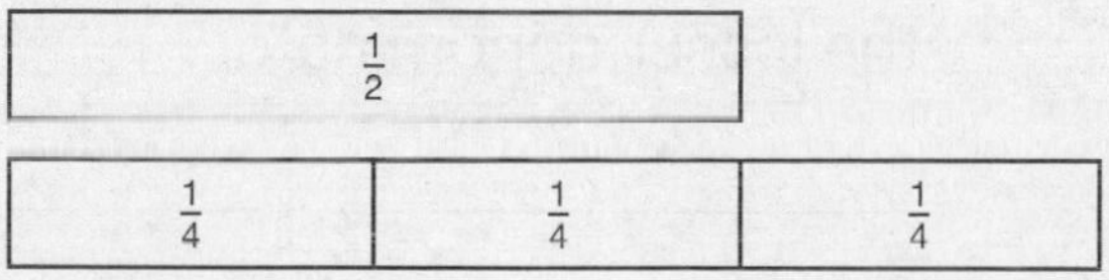

$\frac{1}{2}$ ◯ $\frac{3}{4}$

2.
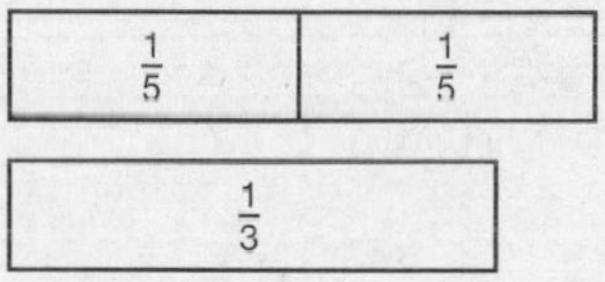

$\frac{2}{5}$ ◯ $\frac{1}{3}$

3.
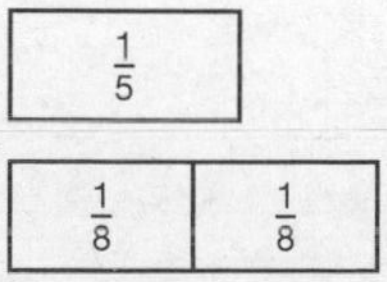

$\frac{2}{8}$ ◯ $\frac{1}{4}$

4.
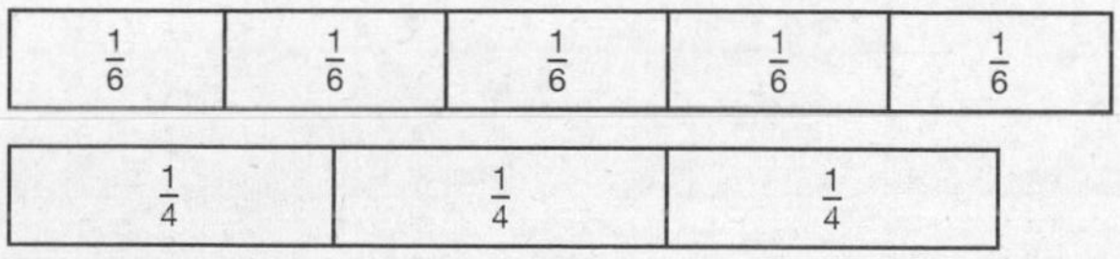

$\frac{5}{6}$ ◯ $\frac{3}{4}$

5. Explain It Why is it important to line up the fraction strips on the left?

____

____

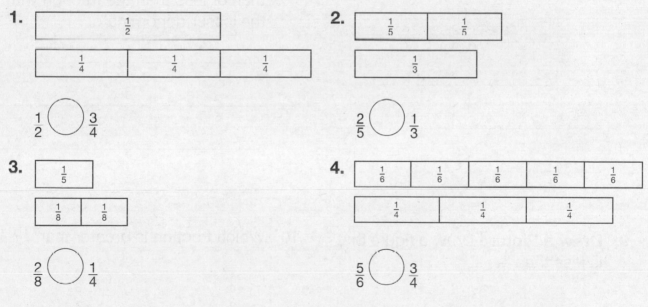

Name ____________________

Practice
12-5

Using Models to Compare Fractions

Compare. Write >, <, or =.

1. 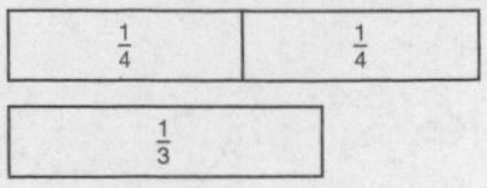

$\frac{2}{4}$ ◯ $\frac{1}{3}$

2. 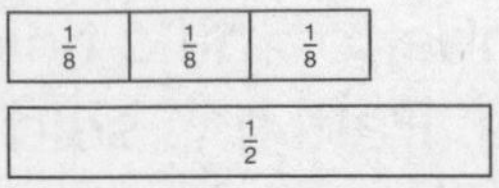

$\frac{3}{8}$ ◯ $\frac{1}{2}$

3. 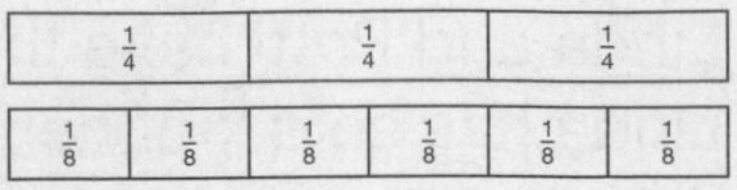

$\frac{3}{4}$ ◯ $\frac{6}{8}$

4. 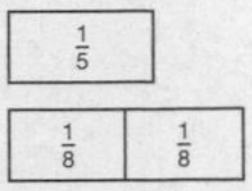

$\frac{1}{5}$ ◯ $\frac{2}{8}$

5. 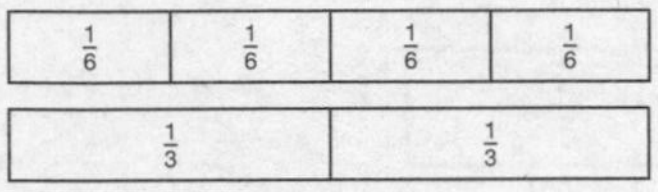

$\frac{4}{6}$ ◯ $\frac{2}{3}$

6. 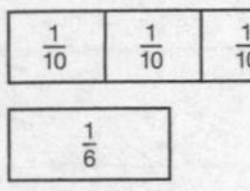

$\frac{3}{10}$ ◯ $\frac{1}{6}$

7. Number Sense Your body consists of $\frac{7}{10}$ water. Is more than $\frac{1}{2}$ your body water? Explain.

____

____

____

____

____

8. Two fractions have the same numerator, but different denominators. Is the fraction with the greater denominator greater than or less than the fraction with the lesser denominator?

____

____

____

____

9. Draw a Picture Draw a figure that is less than $\frac{1}{6}$.

10. Which fraction is greater than $\frac{1}{2}$?

◯ $\frac{1}{4}$

◯ $\frac{2}{6}$

◯ $\frac{3}{8}$

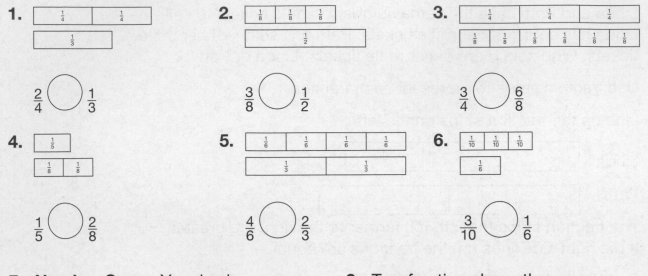

◯ $\frac{3}{4}$

Name ______________________________

Finding Equivalent Fractions

Equivalent fractions are fractions that name the same amount. Equivalent fractions have different numerators and denominators, but their values are equal.

You can find equivalent fractions by using fraction strips.

$$\frac{1}{4} = \frac{\blacksquare}{8}$$

Find how many $\frac{1}{8}$s are equal to $\frac{1}{4}$. The denominator is 8 so use $\frac{1}{8}$ strips.

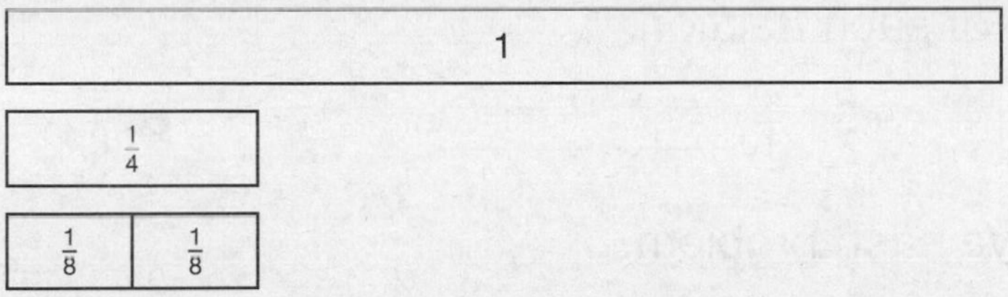

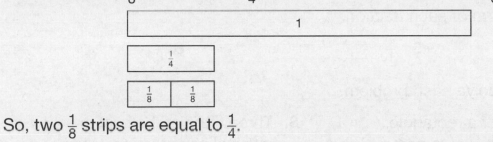

So, two $\frac{1}{8}$ strips are equal to $\frac{1}{4}$.

$$\frac{1}{4} = \frac{2}{8}$$

Another name for $\frac{1}{4}$ is $\frac{2}{8}$.

Complete each number sentence.

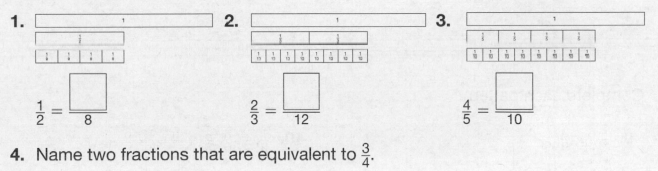

1. 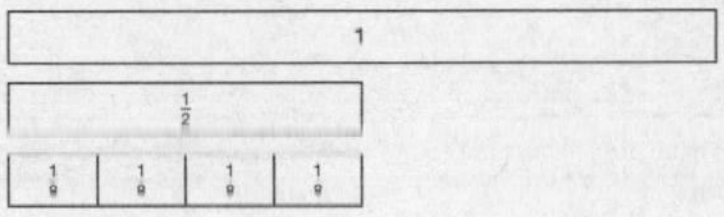

$\frac{1}{2} = \frac{\square}{8}$

2. 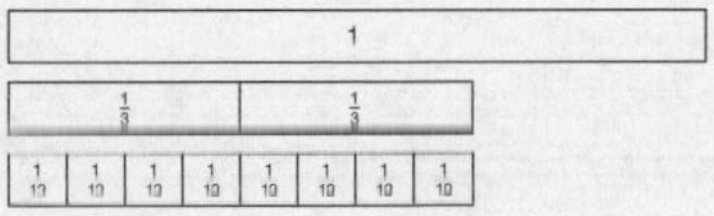

$\frac{2}{3} = \frac{\square}{12}$

3. 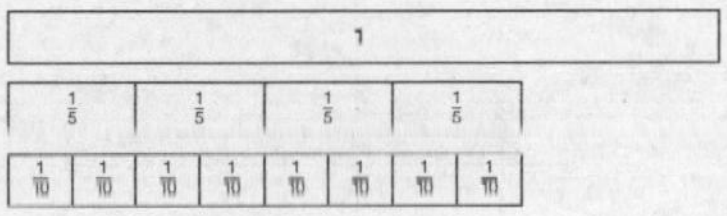

$\frac{4}{5} = \frac{\square}{10}$

4. Name two fractions that are equivalent to $\frac{3}{4}$.

____

____

5. **Reasoning** Larry and Willa are each reading the same book. Larry has read $\frac{2}{3}$ of the book. Willa said that she has read $\frac{4}{6}$ of the book, so she read more. Is Willa correct? Explain.

____

____

____

Name ____________________

Finding Equivalent Fractions

Complete each number sentence.

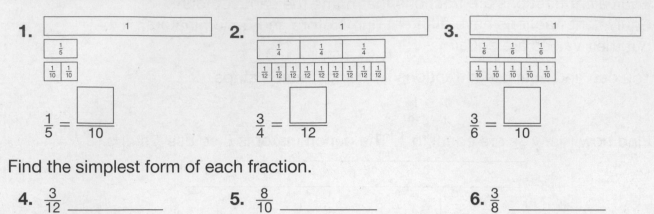

1.

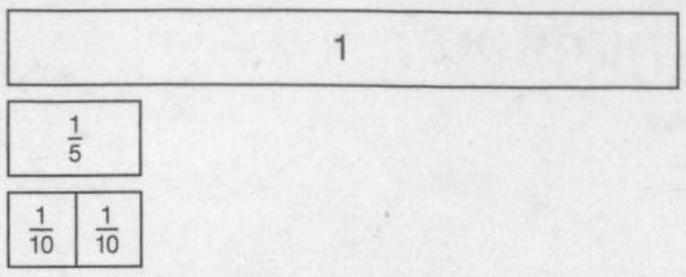

$\frac{1}{5} = \frac{\square}{10}$

2.

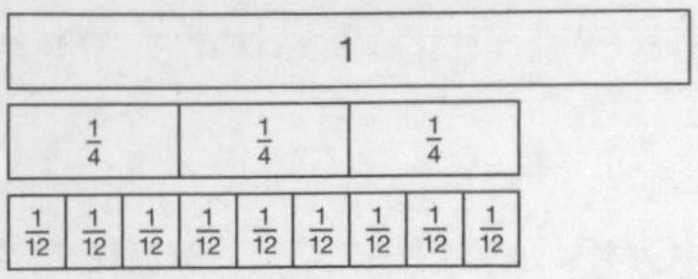

$\frac{3}{4} = \frac{\square}{12}$

3.

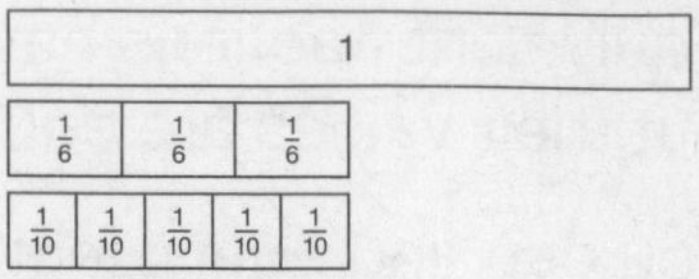

$\frac{3}{6} = \frac{\square}{10}$

Find the simplest form of each fraction.

4. $\frac{3}{12}$ ____________

5. $\frac{8}{10}$ ____________

6. $\frac{3}{8}$ ____________

Name a fraction to solve each problem.

7. Rob colored $\frac{1}{4}$ of a rectangle. What is another way to name $\frac{1}{4}$?

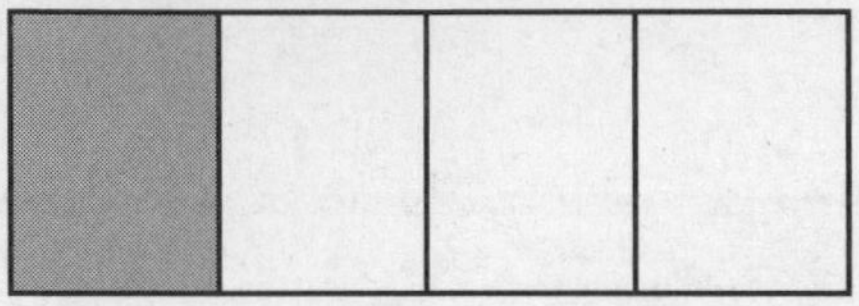

____

8. Three fifths of the cast in a musical have to sing. What fraction of the cast does not have to sing?

____

Complete each pattern.

9. $\frac{1}{3}, \frac{2}{6}, \frac{3}{9}, \frac{4}{\square}$

10. $\frac{1}{2}, \frac{2}{4}, \frac{3}{6}, \frac{4}{8}, \frac{5}{\square}, \frac{6}{\square}$

11. Journal When using fraction strips, how do you know that two fractions are equivalent?

____

____

____

____

____

12. Samuel has read $\frac{5}{6}$ of his assignment. Judy has read $\frac{10}{12}$ of her assignment. Their assignments were the same size. Which sentence is true?

- ○ Samuel read more than Judy.
- ○ Judy read more than Samuel.
- ○ They read the same amount.
- ○ They will both finish the assignment at the same time.

Name ____________________

Reteaching
12-7

Using Equivalent Fractions

You can use equivalent fractions to compare fractions with unlike denominators.

Which symbol makes this sentence true?

$\frac{1}{3}$ ◯ $\frac{3}{6}$

Compare using fraction strips.

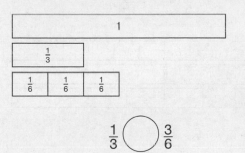

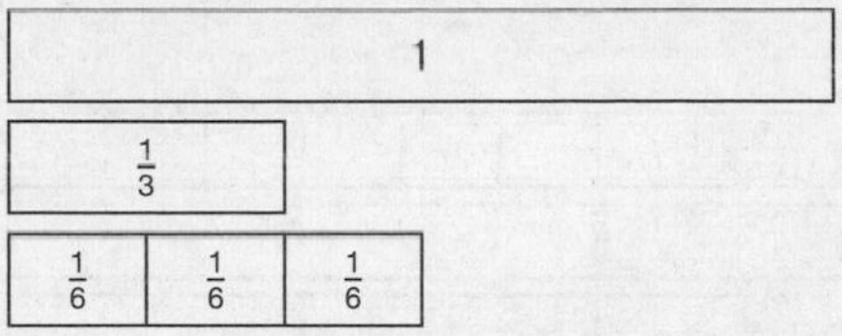

$\frac{1}{3}$ ◯ $\frac{3}{6}$

Use equivalent fractions.

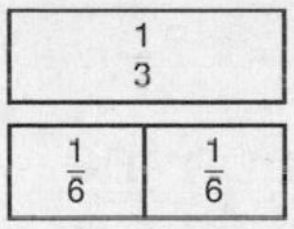

$\frac{1}{3}$ ◯ $\frac{2}{6}$

Now compare.

$\frac{2}{6} < \frac{3}{6}$, so $\frac{1}{3} < \frac{3}{6}$

Compare. Write >, <, or =.

1. $\frac{5}{8}$ ◯ $\frac{1}{2}$

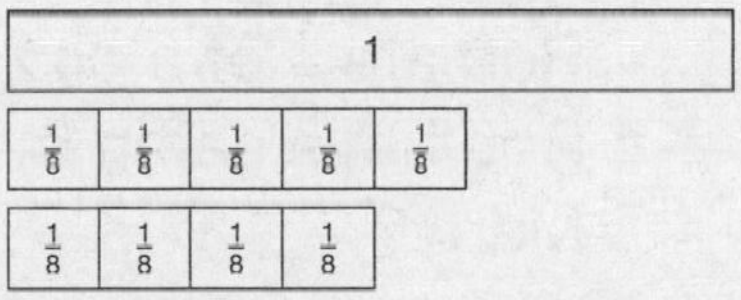

$\frac{4}{8}$

2. $\frac{3}{6}$ ◯ $\frac{2}{3}$

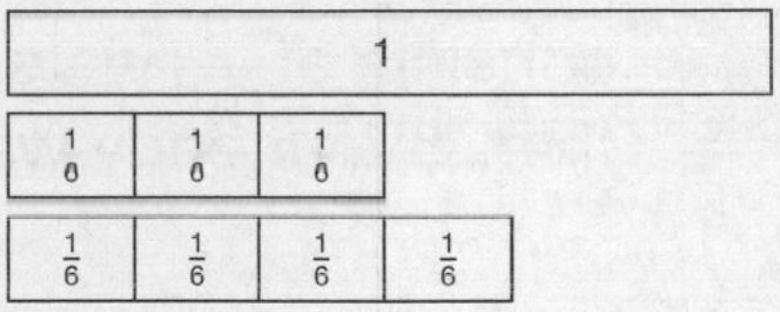

$\frac{4}{6}$

3. $\frac{4}{12}$ ◯ $\frac{2}{6}$

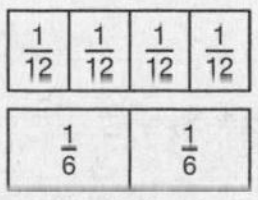

4. $\frac{3}{4}$ ◯ $\frac{1}{2}$

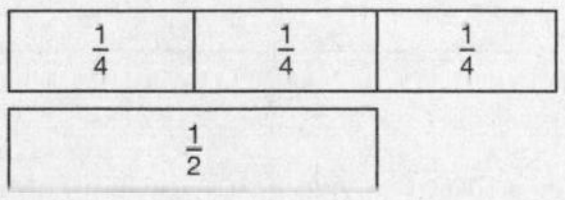

5. **Number Sense** Chris is eating a pizza divided into 12 slices. Mark is eating the same size pizza, but his is divided into 4 slices. They each ate the same number of slices. Mark ate 2 slices. How many slices did Chris eat?

____

Name ______________________________

Using Equivalent Fractions

Compare. Write >, <, or =. You may use fraction strips or drawings to help.

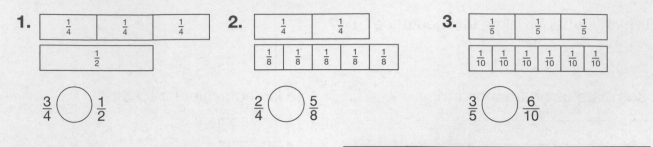

1.

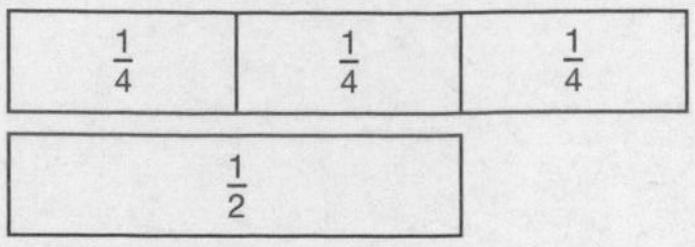

$\frac{3}{4}$ ◯ $\frac{1}{2}$

2.

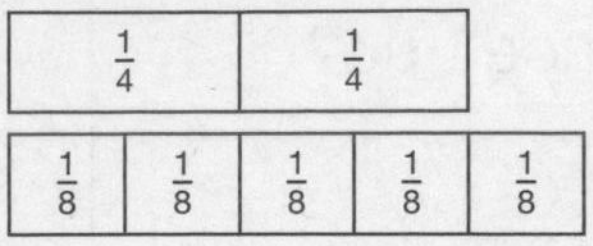

$\frac{2}{4}$ ◯ $\frac{5}{8}$

3.

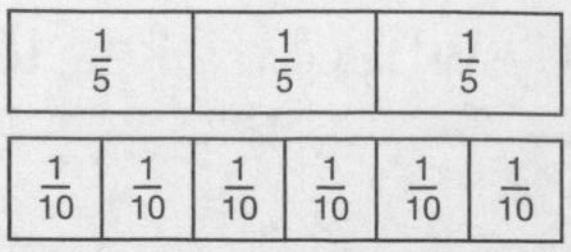

$\frac{3}{5}$ ◯ $\frac{6}{10}$

Three pieces of wood are each the same size. The shaded parts show how much of each of the boards was left after Deb used some of the pieces.

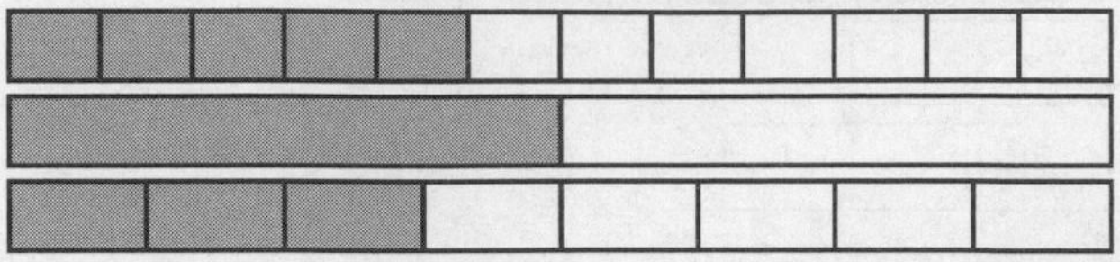

Compare. Write >, <, or =.

4. $\frac{5}{12}$ ◯ $\frac{1}{2}$

5. $\frac{1}{2}$ ◯ $\frac{3}{8}$

6. $\frac{5}{12}$ ◯ $\frac{3}{8}$

7. Reasonableness Your body consists of $\frac{7}{10}$ water. Is more than $\frac{1}{2}$ your body water? Explain.

____

8. Reasoning Marty ate $\frac{1}{4}$ of a pizza. Rob ate $\frac{1}{5}$ of a pizza. How could Rob have eaten more pizza than Marty?

____

____

____

9. Which fraction is greater $\frac{2}{3}$ or $\frac{9}{12}$? Explain.

____

____

____

10. Which fraction is equal to $\frac{1}{3}$?

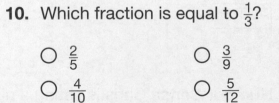

○ $\frac{2}{5}$ ○ $\frac{3}{9}$

○ $\frac{4}{10}$ ○ $\frac{5}{12}$

Name ______________________

Reteaching
12-8

Problem Solving: Make a Table and Look for a Pattern

Unger Soda hired 20 testers to try their new celery soda. Seven of the testers did not like the taste of the new soda. Suppose that pattern continues. If 100 people were hired all together, how many would not like the taste of the soda?

Make a table. Then write the information that you know. Find a pattern to extend the table until you find the results for 100 testers.

Doesn't Like	7	14	21	28	35
Total Testers	20	40	60	80	100

Increases by 7.
Increases by 20.

So, 35 people out of 100 will not like the taste of the Unger's celery soda.

Complete each table to solve.

1. Ms. Lee is buying bags of mixed dumplings. There are 40 dumplings in each bag. In each bag are 10 pork dumplings. If Ms. Lee buys 200 dumplings, how many will be pork dumplings?

Pork Dumplings	10				
Total Dumplings	40				

2. Packages of mixed socks contain 12 pairs of socks. In each package, there are 5 pairs of white socks. How many pairs of white socks would there be in 60 pairs of socks?

Pairs of White Socks	5				
Total Pairs of Socks	12				

3. Explain It Look back at Exercise 2. What pattern do you see?

____

____

____

____

4. Write a Problem Write a problem that can be solved by making a table and using a pattern. Then solve the problem.

____

____

____

Name ______________________________

Practice
12-8

Problem Solving: Make a Table and Look for a Pattern

Complete each table to solve.

1. Roses at a flower shop are sold in packages of 12. Each package contains 4 red roses. How many red roses will you get if you buy 60 roses?

Red Roses	4				
Total Roses	12				

2. There are 20 lollipops in each package of Yum's Lollipops. Each package contains 4 grape lollipops. How many grape lollipops will you get if you buy 100 lollipops?

Grape Lollipops	4				
Total Lollipops	20				

3. There are 9 bottles of salsa in a gift pack of Pedro's Salsa. In each gift pack, 2 of the bottles are extra spicy. Suppose someone buys 45 bottles. How many of the bottles will be extra spicy?

Extra Spicy Bottles	2				
Total Bottles	9				

4. **Reasoning** Look back at Exercise 3. Suppose Jackie bought 27 bottles.

   a. How many of the bottles would not be extra spicy?

   ____

   b. How many more bottles are not extra spicy than are extra spicy?

   ____

5. In a package of 25 colored pencils, 8 are red. If you bought 125 pencils, how many would be red?

Red Pencils	8				
Total Pencils	25				

6. **Write a Problem** Write a problem that can be solved by making a table and using a pattern. Then solve the problem.

____

____

____

Name ______________________________

Reteaching
13-1

Using Models to Add Fractions

You can use fraction strips to add fractions.

Add $\frac{3}{10} + \frac{2}{10}$.

Step 1

Place three $\frac{1}{10}$ fraction strips to the left of two $\frac{1}{10}$ fraction strips.

$\frac{1}{10}$	$\frac{1}{10}$	$\frac{1}{10}$	$\frac{1}{10}$	$\frac{1}{10}$

How many $\frac{1}{10}$ fraction strips?

____

Step 2

Write the sum in simplest form.

$\frac{1}{10}$	$\frac{1}{10}$	$\frac{1}{10}$	$\frac{1}{10}$	$\frac{1}{10}$
$\frac{1}{2}$				

$\frac{5}{10} = \frac{1}{2}$

So, $\frac{3}{10} + \frac{2}{10} = \frac{1}{2}$

Write the sum in simplest form. You may use fraction strips or draw a picture to help.

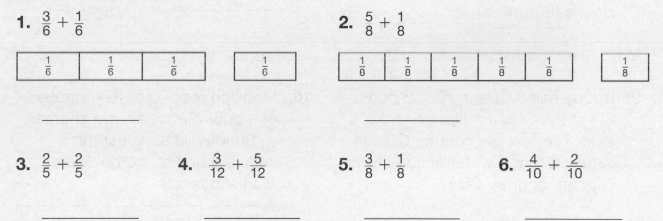

1. $\frac{3}{6} + \frac{1}{6}$

$\frac{1}{6}$	$\frac{1}{6}$	$\frac{1}{6}$	$\frac{1}{6}$

____

2. $\frac{5}{8} + \frac{1}{8}$

$\frac{1}{8}$	$\frac{1}{8}$	$\frac{1}{8}$	$\frac{1}{8}$	$\frac{1}{8}$	$\frac{1}{8}$

____

3. $\frac{2}{5} + \frac{2}{5}$ ______________

4. $\frac{3}{12} + \frac{5}{12}$ ______________

5. $\frac{3}{8} + \frac{1}{8}$ ______________

6. $\frac{4}{10} + \frac{2}{10}$ ______________

7. Explain It How do you know whether you have to write a sum in simplest form?

____

Name ____________________

Practice
13-1

Using Models to Add Fractions

Add. Write the sum in simplest form. You may draw a picture to help.

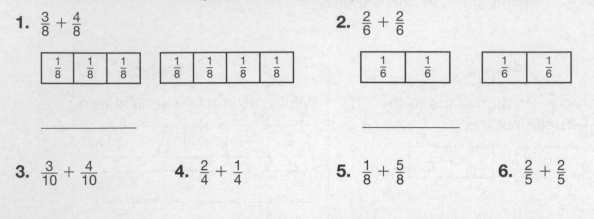

1. $\frac{3}{8} + \frac{4}{8}$

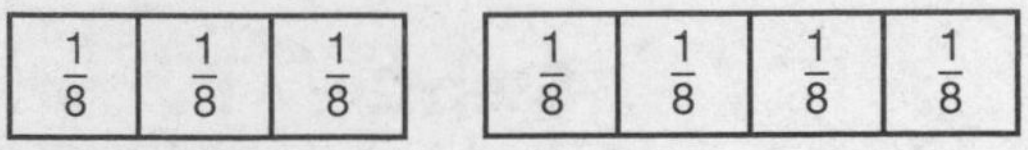

____

2. $\frac{2}{6} + \frac{2}{6}$

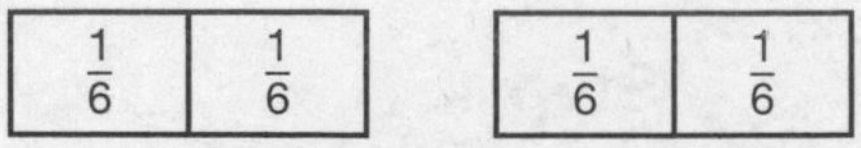

____

3. $\frac{3}{10} + \frac{4}{10}$ ____________

4. $\frac{2}{4} + \frac{1}{4}$ ____________

5. $\frac{1}{8} + \frac{5}{8}$ ____________

6. $\frac{2}{5} + \frac{2}{5}$ ____________

7. Marlon and Ricky ate a pizza that was divided into eighths. Marlon ate $\frac{2}{8}$ and Ricky ate $\frac{2}{8}$ of the pizza. How much of the pizza did they eat in all? Write your sum in simplest form.

____

8. **Write a Problem** Write an addition problem that has $\frac{9}{10}$ as the sum.

____

____

____

9. Buddy has 8 CDs in his CD book. Six of the CDs are classic rock CDs. The rest are country CDs. In simplest form, what fraction of the CDs are country CDs?

____

10. Madison read $\frac{4}{10}$ of the chapters of a book Saturday and another $\frac{2}{10}$ Sunday. In simplest form, what fraction of the book did Madison read?

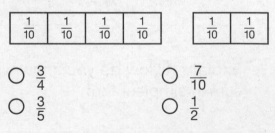

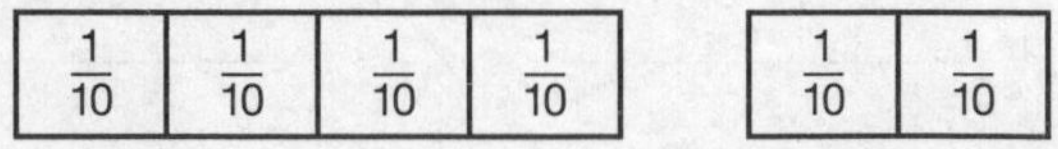

○ $\frac{3}{4}$
○ $\frac{7}{10}$
○ $\frac{3}{5}$
○ $\frac{1}{2}$

11. Of Tami's pets $\frac{2}{6}$ are dogs and $\frac{3}{6}$ are cats. What fraction of Tami's pets are dogs or cats?

____

Name ______________________________

Adding Fractions

When you add fractions with like denominators, add the numerators. The denominator remains the same.

Add $\frac{4}{12} + \frac{2}{12}$.

Add with fraction strips.

$\frac{1}{12}$	$\frac{1}{12}$	$\frac{1}{12}$	$\frac{1}{12}$		$\frac{1}{12}$	$\frac{1}{12}$

Count the number of fraction strips.

$$\frac{4}{12} + \frac{2}{12} = \frac{6}{12}$$

$\frac{1}{12}$	$\frac{1}{12}$	$\frac{1}{12}$	$\frac{1}{12}$	$\frac{1}{12}$	$\frac{1}{12}$
$\frac{1}{2}$					

$$\frac{4}{12} + \frac{2}{12} = \frac{1}{2}$$

Add the numerators.

$$\frac{4}{12} + \frac{2}{12} = \frac{4+2}{12} = \frac{6}{12}$$

Write the sum in simplest form.

$$\frac{6}{12} \div \frac{6}{6} = \frac{1}{2}$$

$$\frac{4}{12} + \frac{2}{12} = \frac{1}{2}$$

Add. Write the sum in simplest form.

1. $\frac{3}{5} + \frac{1}{5}$ ________

2. $\frac{4}{8} + \frac{3}{8}$ ________

3. $\frac{1}{2} + \frac{1}{2}$ ________

4. $\frac{3}{10} + \frac{2}{10}$ ________

5. $\frac{5}{12} + \frac{3}{12}$ ________

6. $\frac{4}{9} + \frac{2}{9}$ ________

7. $\frac{4}{7} + \frac{2}{7}$ ________

8. $\frac{3}{8} + \frac{3}{8}$ ________

9. $\frac{2}{6} + \frac{4}{6}$ ________

10. **Number Sense** How do two fractions have a sum of exactly 1?

____

____

Name ______________________

Practice 13-2

Adding Fractions

Add. Write each sum in simplest form.

1. $\frac{3}{8} + \frac{5}{8}$ ________

2. $\frac{2}{7} + \frac{3}{7}$ ________

3. $\frac{2}{9} + \frac{4}{9}$ ________

4. $\frac{2}{5} + \frac{2}{5}$ ________

5. $\frac{3}{10} + \frac{5}{10}$ ________

6. $\frac{3}{6} + \frac{1}{6}$ ________

7. $\frac{3}{12} + \frac{6}{12}$ ________

8. $\frac{4}{10} + \frac{1}{10}$ ________

9. $\frac{2}{8} + \frac{4}{8}$ ________

10. Of Don's sports cards, $\frac{3}{8}$ are baseball cards and $\frac{2}{8}$ are football cards. What fraction of Don's sports cards are either baseball or football cards? ________

11. **Journal** Rosa walks $\frac{3}{10}$ mile to Karen's house. Together they walk $\frac{2}{10}$ mile to school. How far did Rosa walk in all? Write your answer in simplest form. Explain the steps needed to write a sum in simplest form.

____

____

12. Kitty invited $\frac{2}{9}$ of the girls and $\frac{1}{9}$ of the boys in her class to her birthday party. What fraction of the class did she invite? Write your answer in simplest form.

____

13. What is $\frac{4}{12} + \frac{6}{12}$?

- ○ $\frac{2}{3}$
- ○ $\frac{3}{4}$
- ○ $\frac{4}{5}$
- ○ $\frac{5}{6}$

14. **Geometry** Jon drew a rectangle divided into sixths. He colored $\frac{2}{6}$ red and $\frac{1}{6}$ blue. What fraction in simplest form does Jon still need to color?

____

Name ______________________________

Reteaching

13-3

Using Models to Subtract Fractions

You can use fraction strips to subtract fractions.

Subtract $\frac{7}{8} - \frac{3}{8}$.

Step 1

Use seven $\frac{1}{8}$ fraction strips. Cross out 3 of the fraction strips.

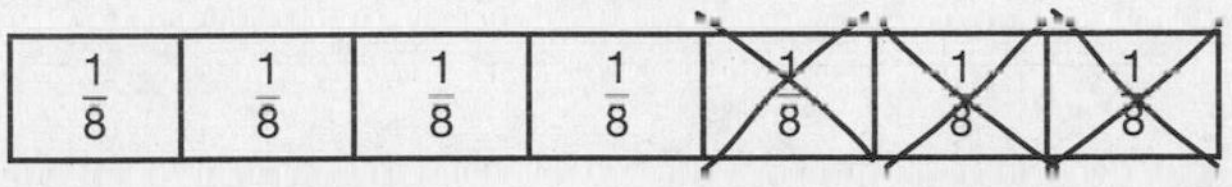

How many $\frac{1}{8}$ fraction strips are left?

____

Step 2

Write the sum in simplest form.

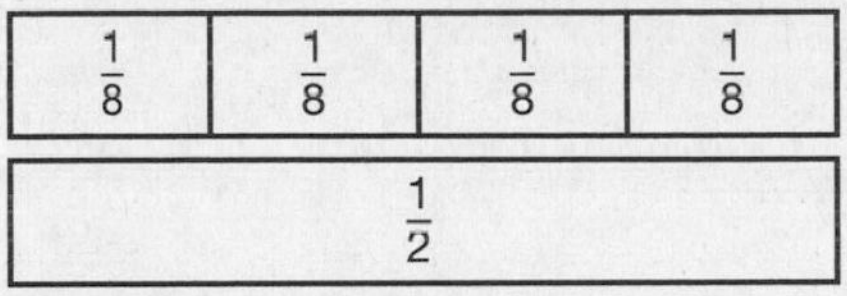

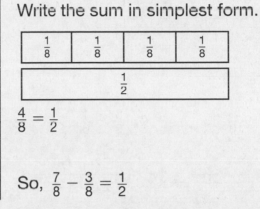

$\frac{4}{8} = \frac{1}{2}$

So, $\frac{7}{8} - \frac{3}{8} = \frac{1}{2}$

Subtract. Write the difference in simplest form. You may use fraction strips or draw a picture to help.

1. $\frac{5}{6} - \frac{3}{6}$

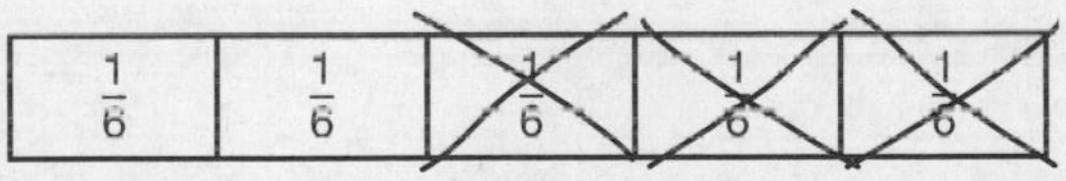

____

2. $\frac{7}{10} - \frac{1}{10}$

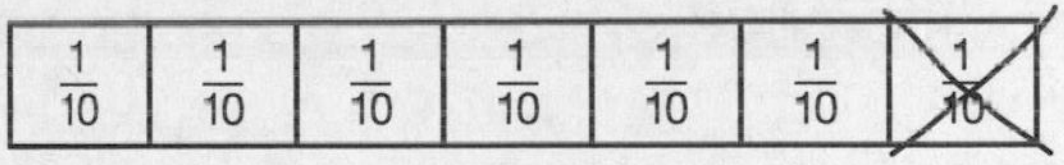

____

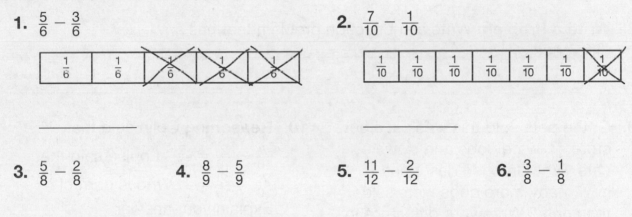

3. $\frac{5}{8} - \frac{2}{8}$ __________

4. $\frac{8}{9} - \frac{5}{9}$ __________

5. $\frac{11}{12} - \frac{2}{12}$ __________

6. $\frac{3}{8} - \frac{1}{8}$ __________

7. Reasoning Judy left $\frac{4}{5}$ of a pot of stew for Dan. Dan ate $\frac{2}{5}$ of what she left. What fraction of the pot of stew was left after Dan ate?

____

Name ______________________

Using Models to Subtract Fractions

Subtract. Write the difference in simplest form. You may draw a picture to help.

1. $\frac{7}{12} - \frac{5}{12}$

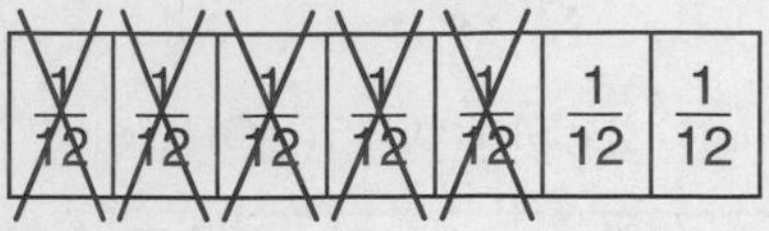

______

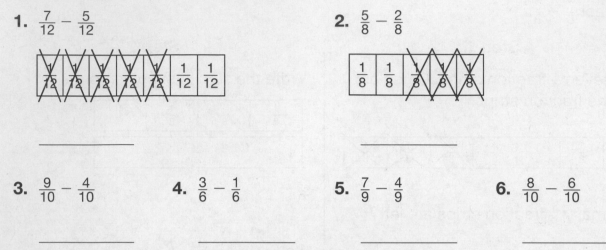

2. $\frac{5}{8} - \frac{2}{8}$

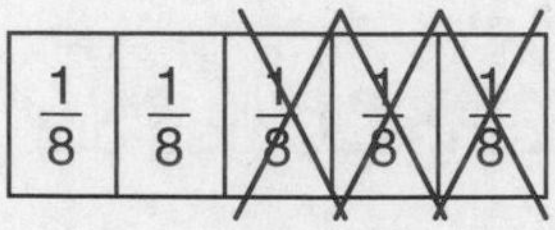

______

3. $\frac{9}{10} - \frac{4}{10}$ ______

4. $\frac{3}{6} - \frac{1}{6}$ ______

5. $\frac{7}{9} - \frac{4}{9}$ ______

6. $\frac{8}{10} - \frac{6}{10}$ ______

7. Patricia is responsible for washing $\frac{6}{8}$ of the desks in her classroom. She has already washed $\frac{4}{8}$ of the desks. What fraction of the desks does she still have to wash? Write your difference in simplest form. ______

8. Write a Problem Write a subtraction problem that has a difference of $\frac{1}{6}$.

____

9. Of the pets sold this week at a pet store, $\frac{5}{10}$ were dogs and $\frac{3}{10}$ were cats. What fraction describes how many more dogs were sold than cats? Write your difference in simplest form.

______

10. Reasoning Colin said that $\frac{7}{10} - \frac{2}{10} = \frac{5}{10}$. Louisa said that $\frac{7}{10} - \frac{2}{10} = \frac{1}{2}$. Who is correct? Explain your answer.

____

____

11. Of the license plates that Sue saw, $\frac{5}{8}$ were from California and $\frac{1}{8}$ were from Oregon. In simplest form, what fraction of the plates were from other states?

______

12. What is $\frac{8}{9} - \frac{4}{9}$?

- ○ $\frac{2}{3}$
- ○ $\frac{5}{9}$
- ○ $\frac{4}{9}$
- ○ $\frac{1}{3}$

Name ______________________________

Subtracting Fractions

When you subtract fractions with like denominators, subtract the numerators. The denominator remains the same.

Subtract $\frac{9}{10} - \frac{3}{10}$.

Subtract with fraction strips.

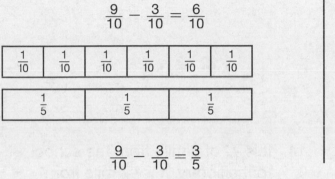

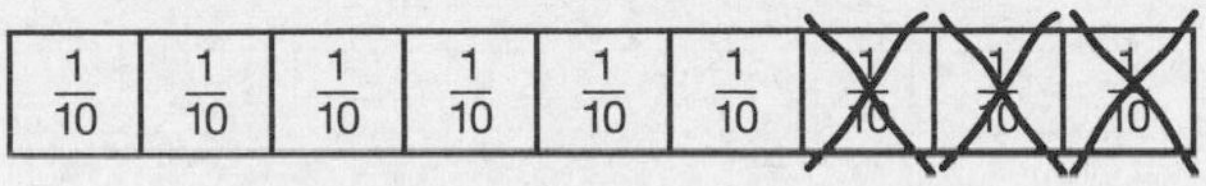

Count the number of fraction strips.

$$\frac{9}{10} - \frac{3}{10} = \frac{6}{10}$$

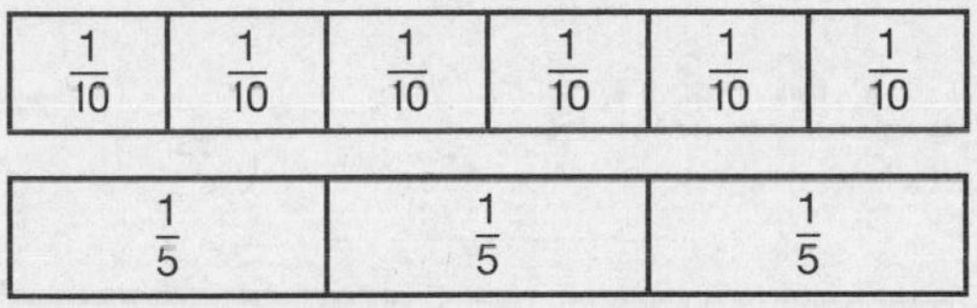

$$\frac{9}{10} - \frac{3}{10} = \frac{3}{5}$$

Subtract the numerators.

$$\frac{9}{10} - \frac{3}{10} = \frac{9 - 3}{10} = \frac{6}{10}$$

Write the sum in simplest form.

$$\frac{6}{10} \div \frac{2}{2} = \frac{3}{5}$$

$$\frac{9}{10} - \frac{3}{10} = \frac{3}{5}$$

Subtract. Write the difference in simplest form.

1. $\frac{3}{5} - \frac{1}{5}$ ________

2. $\frac{7}{8} - \frac{3}{8}$ ________

3. $1 - \frac{1}{4}$ ________

4. $\frac{7}{10} - \frac{5}{10}$ ________

5. $\frac{4}{9} - \frac{1}{9}$ ________

6. $\frac{9}{12} - \frac{4}{12}$ ________

7. $1 - \frac{2}{10}$ ________

8. $\frac{11}{12} - \frac{9}{12}$ ________

9. $\frac{7}{9} - \frac{1}{9}$ ________

10. Number Sense How can you check that Example 6 is correct?

____

____

Name ___________________________

Practice
13-4

Subtracting Fractions

Subtract. Write the difference in simplest form.

1. $\frac{4}{5} - \frac{2}{5}$ ________

2. $\frac{7}{8} - \frac{3}{8}$ ________

3. $\frac{6}{10} - \frac{3}{10}$ ________

4. $\frac{7}{9} - \frac{2}{9}$ ________

5. $1 - \frac{7}{12}$ ________

6. $\frac{4}{6} - \frac{1}{6}$ ________

7. $\frac{8}{10} - \frac{6}{10}$ ________

8. $\frac{5}{8} - \frac{3}{8}$ ________

9. $\frac{8}{12} - \frac{5}{12}$ ________

10. $1 - \frac{3}{6}$ ________

11. $\frac{5}{7} - \frac{2}{7}$ ________

12. $\frac{8}{9} - \frac{5}{9}$ ________

13. A fence has 8 posts. Five posts are blue. Three posts are red. What number sentence shows how to find how much more of the fence posts are blue than red?

____

____

14. It is $\frac{7}{10}$ of a mile from the school to the library. It is $\frac{3}{10}$ mile from the school to the bookstore. In simplest form, how much closer to the school is the bookstore than the library?

____

15. **Writing to Explain** Jason's family bought a watermelon. They ate $\frac{1}{4}$ on Friday and $\frac{1}{4}$ on Saturday. In simplest form, what fraction of the watermelon remained? Explain how you found your answer.

____

16. There is $\frac{6}{8}$ of a pie remaining when Curtis eats $\frac{2}{8}$ of the pie. In simplest form, what fraction of the pie is left?

____

17. What is $\frac{10}{12} - \frac{1}{12}$?

○ $\frac{1}{2}$

○ $\frac{2}{3}$

○ $\frac{3}{4}$

○ $\frac{5}{6}$

Name ______________________________

Problem Solving: Draw a Picture and Write a Number Sentence

Fred read $\frac{2}{5}$ of a book Saturday and $\frac{1}{5}$ Sunday. How much of the book did he read all together? How much more of the book did he read Saturday than Sunday?

Let's answer the first question.

There will be 5 parts, so draw a figure with 5 equal parts. Shade 2 parts one way and 1 part another way. Count how many parts are shaded in all.

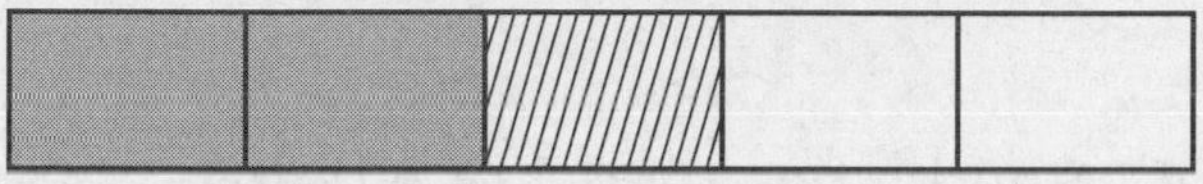

$\frac{2}{5} + \frac{1}{5} = \frac{3}{5}$

So Fred read $\frac{3}{5}$ of the book all together.

Let's answer the second question.

Make a drawing to show what you are comparing.

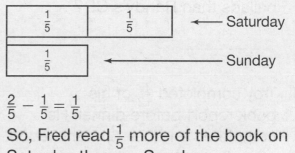

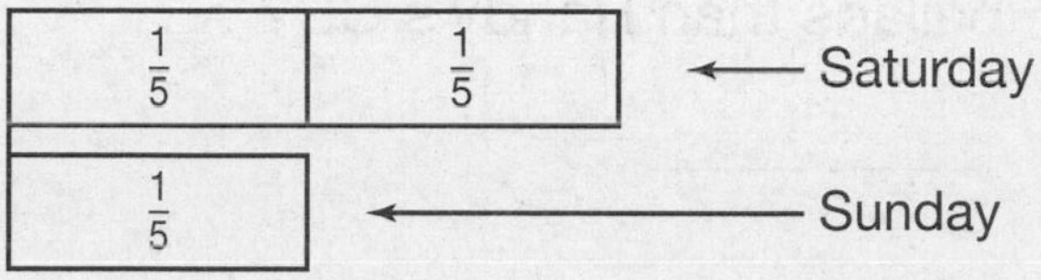

$\frac{2}{5} - \frac{1}{5} = \frac{1}{5}$

So, Fred read $\frac{1}{5}$ more of the book on Saturday than on Sunday.

Solve. Draw a picture and write a number sentence.

1. Of Carlos's stamp collection, $\frac{5}{8}$ are from the United States and $\frac{2}{8}$ are from European countries. In simplest form, what fraction describes how many more of Carlos's stamps are from the United States than Europe?

   ____

2. Third-grade students make up $\frac{4}{10}$ of the swim team. Fourth-grade students make up $\frac{4}{10}$ of the team. In simplest form, what fraction of the team is from the third and fourth grades?

   ____

Name ______________________

Practice
13-5

Problem Solving: Draw a Picture and Write a Number Sentence

Solve. Draw a picture and write a number sentence.

1. Candi and Randy each have a CD with the same number of songs. On Candi's CD, $\frac{5}{8}$ of the songs are ballads. On Randy's CD, $\frac{2}{8}$ of the songs are ballads. How much more of Candi's CD contains ballads than Randy's CD?

____

2. Jaime is painting his backyard fence. He paints $\frac{4}{10}$ of the slats red. Then he paints $\frac{2}{10}$ of the slats blue. In simplest form, what fraction of the fence did Jaime paint in all?

____

3. Troy completed $\frac{5}{12}$ of his book report before dinner. He completed another $\frac{3}{12}$ of the report after dinner. In simplest form, how much of the report did he finish in all?

____

4. Sandra has read $\frac{3}{4}$ of a comic book. Tricia has read $\frac{1}{4}$ of the same comic book. How much more of the comic book has Sandra read than Tricia?

____

5. Write a Problem Write a real-world problem with fractions that you can solve by drawing a picture and writing a number sentence.

____

____

____

____

____

6. Reasoning When you add or subtract fractions with the same denominator, what happens to the denominator in your answer?

____

____

____

Name ____________________________

Reteaching **14-1**

Using Mental Math to Multiply

You can use multiplication patterns to help multiply multiples of 10, 100, and 1,000.

When one of the factors you are multiplying has zeros on the end, you can multiply the nonzero digits, and then insert the extra zeros.

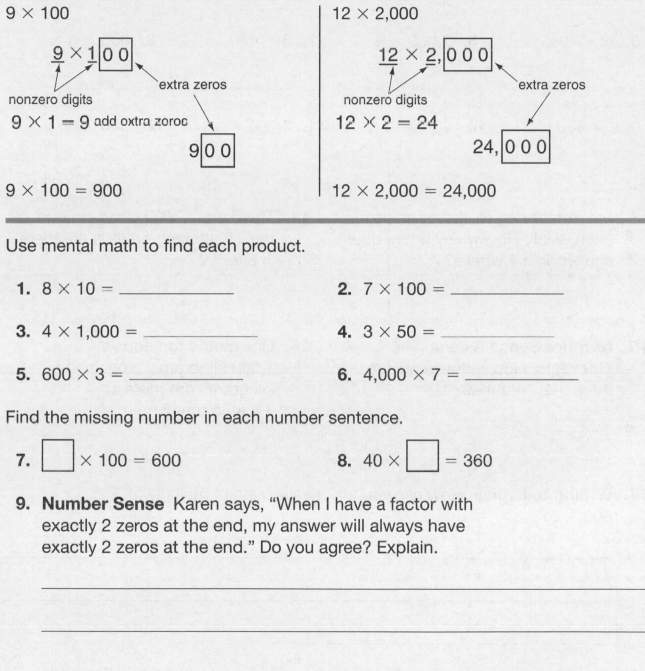

9 × 100

9 × 1[0 0]

nonzero digits: 9, 1 — extra zeros: 0 0

9 × 1 = 9 add extra zeros

9[0 0]

9 × 100 = 900

12 × 2,000

12 × 2,[0 0 0]

nonzero digits: 12, 2 — extra zeros: 0 0 0

12 × 2 = 24

24,[0 0 0]

12 × 2,000 = 24,000

Use mental math to find each product.

1. 8 × 10 = ____________

2. 7 × 100 = ____________

3. 4 × 1,000 = ____________

4. 3 × 50 = ____________

5. 600 × 3 = ____________

6. 4,000 × 7 = ____________

Find the missing number in each number sentence.

7. □ × 100 = 600

8. 40 × □ = 360

9. **Number Sense** Karen says, "When I have a factor with exactly 2 zeros at the end, my answer will always have exactly 2 zeros at the end." Do you agree? Explain.

____

____

____

____

Name ______________________

Practice 14-1

Using Mental Math to Multiply

Find each product.

1. 3×10 ______

2. 6×100 ______

3. $9 \times 1{,}000$ ______

4. 80×3 ______

5. 4×700 ______

6. $2{,}000 \times 5$ ______

7. 6×400 ______

8. 800×8 ______

9. 6×900 ______

10. 90×7 ______

11. $3{,}000 \times 4$ ______

12. 500×4 ______

13. Ms. Armstrong works 40 hours each week. How many hours does she work in 4 weeks?

______

14. There are 2,000 pounds in one ton. How many pounds are there in 6 tons?

______

15. **Number Sense** A century is 100 years. How many years are there in 8 centuries?

______

16. One metric ton equals 1,000 kilograms. How many kilograms are there in 7 metric tons?

______

17. **Writing to Explain** How can you use mental math to multiply 800×5?

____

____

____

18. Each time you pass "Start" on a board game you receive 300 points. How many points will you receive if you pass "Start" 6 times?

○ 180 ○ 1,800 ○ 18,000 ○ 180,000

Name ______________________

Estimating Products

You can use rounding to estimate products. Remember, look at the digit to the right of the place that you are rounding. If the digit is 5 or more, round up. If the digit is less than 5, round down.

Estimate 6×22.

Round 22 to the nearest ten.
Look at the digit in the ones place.
$2 < 5$, so 22 rounds to 20.

$6 \times 20 = 120$
So, 6×22 is about 120.

Estimate 8×378

Round 378 to the nearest hundred.
Look at the digit in the tens place.
$7 > 5$, so 378 rounds to 400.

$8 \times 400 = 3{,}200$
So, 8×378 is about 3,200.

Estimate each product.

1. 8×91 ______ **2.** 4×69 ______ **3.** 3×53 ______ **4.** 2×23 ______ **5.** 7×67 ______

6. 9×632 ______ **7.** 8×718 ______ **8.** 5×486 ______ **9.** 8×212 ______ **10.** 9×591 ______

11. $6 \times 3{,}172$ ______ **12.** $7 \times 8{,}683$ ______ **13.** $8 \times 4{,}927$ ______ **14.** $5 \times 4{,}123$ ______ **15.** $6 \times 6{,}921$ ______

16. **Number Sense** Is the product of $4 \times 8{,}827$ less than 36,000? How do you know?

____

____

____

Name ____________________

Practice
14-2

Estimating Products

Estimate each product.

1. 7×22 ______ **2.** 6×47 ______ **3.** 5×578 ______ **4.** 9×232 ______ **5.** 3×777 ______

6. 6×731 ______ **7.** $3 \times 2{,}709$ ______ **8.** $7 \times 9{,}125$ ______ **9.** $8 \times 3{,}126$ ______ **10.** $4 \times 8{,}872$ ______

11. A basketball player scores 32 points each game. About how many points will he score in 6 games?

______

12. Reasoning Marcia said that if she estimates 73×7, the product will be less than the exact answer. Is she correct? Explain.

______
______
______
______

13. There are 365 days in a year. About how many days has Jared lived if he has reached his 8th birthday?

______

14. An arena seats 7,893 people. The circus is in town and all of the tickets have been sold. If the circus has 4 performances, about how many tickets were sold?

______

15. Explain It Each video game at an arcade requires 375 tokens. Tom has 2,000 tokens. He said he can play 6 games. Is he correct? Explain.

______
______
______
______

16. Which is the best estimate for $6 \times 8{,}182$?

○ 48,000 ○ 54,000
○ 60,000 ○ 80,000

Name ______________________

Reteaching

14-3

Multiplication and Arrays

You can draw a picture of an array to show multiplication.

Multiply 3×17.

What You Show

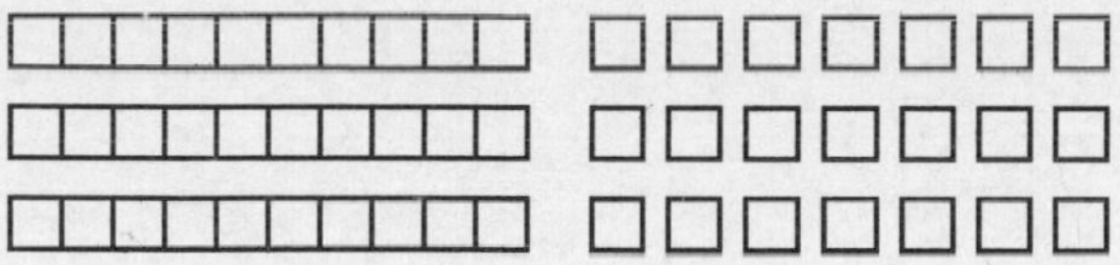

What You Think

3 rows of 1 ten = 3 tens

3 rows of 7 ones = 21 ones

$30 + 21 = 51$

To find the product, count the tens and the ones.
Then add them together.

There are 3 tens and 21 ones. Add $30 + 21 = 51$.

So, $3 \times 17 = 51$.

Use place-value blocks or draw an array to find each product.

1. 4×14 ______ **2.** 2×37 ______ **3.** 5×21 ______ **4.** 3×43 ______ **5.** 6×18 ______

6. 3×46 ______ **7.** 7×13 ______ **8.** 2×19 ______ **9.** 9×14 ______ **10.** 3×34 ______

11. Strategy Practice Explain how you can multiply 3×24 by using arrays. Then give the product.

____

____

____

Name ________________________

Multiplication and Arrays

Find each product. You may use place-value blocks or draw a picture to help.

1. 3 × 17

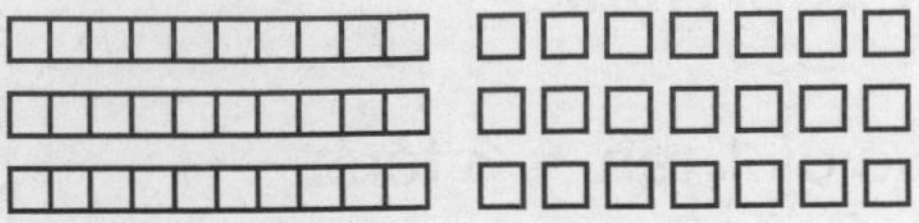

______

2. 2 × 22

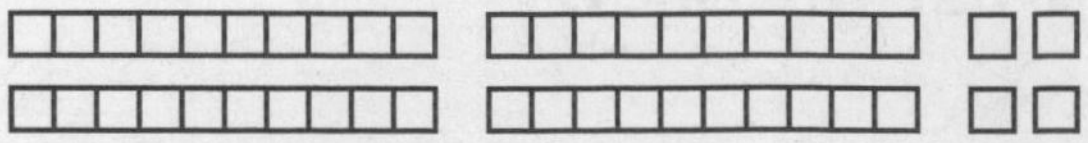

______

3. 5 × 34 ______ **4.** 4 × 13 ______ **5.** 3 × 57 ______ **6.** 2 × 34 ______ **7.** 6 × 22 ______

8. 3 × 43 ______ **9.** 5 × 26 ______ **10.** 6 × 18 ______ **11.** 4 × 24 ______ **12.** 5 × 29 ______

In **13–15**, use the table at the right.

Days Worked in April

Employee	Days Worked
Bob	19
Josh	25
Marvin	13

13. Bob works 7 hours each day. How many hours did he work in April all together?

______

14. Josh works 8 hours each day. How many hours did he work in April all together?

______

15. Marvin works 9 hours each day. How many more hours did Bob work than Marvin in April?

______

16. Writing to Explain How can you use an array to find 4 × 13?

____

____

17. What is the product of 27 × 4?

○ 36 ○ 88 ○ 108 ○ 127

Name ____________________

Breaking Apart to Multiply

You can make multiplication simpler by breaking numbers apart by place value.

Find 3×235.

Use place-value models.

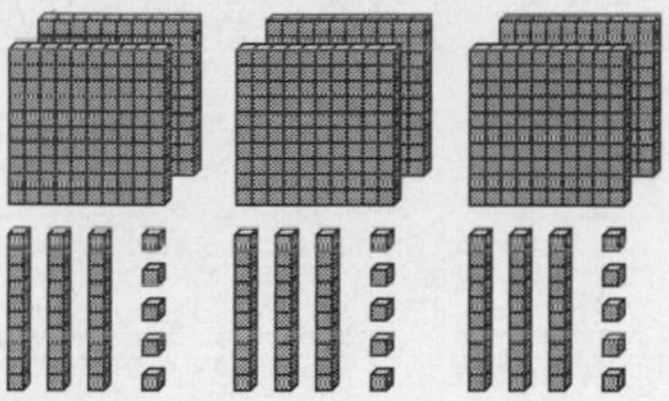

$235 + 235 + 235 = 705.$

Write it.
Multiply the hundreds: $3 \times 200 = 600$
Multiply the tens: $3 \times 30 = 90$
Multiply the ones: $3 \times 5 = 15$
Add the products: $600 + 90 + 15 = 705$

Complete.

1. 5×178

5×1 hundred = ☐ hundreds or 500

5×7 tens = ☐ tens or 350

5×8 ones = 40 ones or ☐

☐ + ☐ + ☐ = ☐

2. $4 \times 2{,}256$

$4 \times 4{,}000$ = ☐

4×200 = ☐

4×50 = ☐

4×6 = ☐

☐ + ☐ + ☐ + ☐ = ☐

Find each product. You may use place-value blocks or drawings to help.

3. 6×21 ______ **4.** 5×435 ______ **5.** 3×616 ______ **6.** $2 \times 3{,}122$ ______ **7.** $3 \times 2{,}543$ ______

8. Number Sense Tim said, "To find 6×33, I can add $18 + 18$." Do you agree with him? Why or why not?

____

____

____

Name ____________________

Practice 14-4

Breaking Apart to Multiply

Find each product. You may use place-value blocks or drawings to help

1. 4 × 43 ______ **2.** 5 × 18 ______ **3.** 5 × 13 ______ **4.** 2 × 88 ______ **5.** 4 × 34 ______

6. 3 × 492 ______ **7.** 6 × 426 ______ **8.** 4 × 569 ______ **9.** 4 × 719 ______ **10.** 5 × 264 ______

11. 2 × 5,429 ______ **12.** 4 × 3,527 ______ **13.** 3 × 2,293 ______ **14.** 5 × 5,257 ______ **15.** 3 × 3,242 ______

16. Mr. Roberts commutes 47 miles each day to and from work. He works 5 days each week. How many miles does he commute each week?

____

17. **Explain It** How can you multiply 42 × 8 by breaking apart numbers?

____

____

18. A truck driver drives 1,352 miles each week. How many miles does he drive in 8 weeks?

____

19. A Ferris wheel can seat 248 people at one time. The Ferris wheel is run 4 times each hour. How many people can ride the Ferris wheel each hour?

____

20. **Number Sense** Johnny has 275 baseball cards in each of 5 boxes. Mariano has 325 baseball cards in each of 4 boxes. Who has more baseball cards? How many more? Explain.

____

____

____

21. Which is equal to 5 × 25?

- ○ 25 + 10
- ○ 100 + 5
- ○ 115
- ○ 100 + 25

Name ______________________

Using an Expanded Algorithm

You can multiply 2-digit numbers by finding partial products.

Find 3×27.
First multiply the ones. Next, multiply the tens.
Then, add the partial products.

What You Show

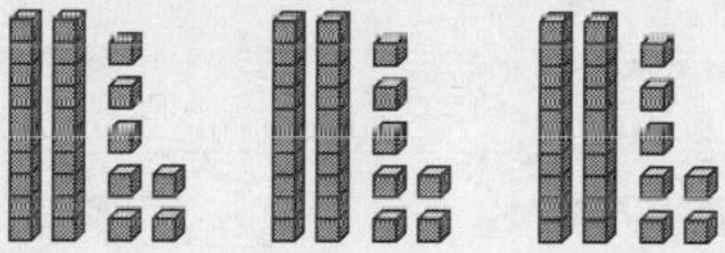

What You Write

$$\begin{array}{r} 27 \\ \times\ 3 \\ \hline 21 \\ +60 \\ \hline 81 \end{array}$$

21 → 3×7
+60 → 3×20

So, $3 \times 27 = 81$.

For **1** and **2** complete. For **3–5**, find the product.
Use place-value blocks or drawings to help.

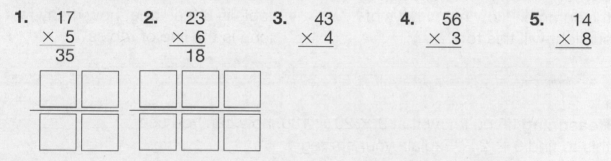

1. $\begin{array}{r} 17 \\ \times\ 5 \\ \hline 35 \end{array}$

2. $\begin{array}{r} 23 \\ \times\ 6 \\ \hline 18 \end{array}$

3. $\begin{array}{r} 43 \\ \times\ 4 \\ \hline \end{array}$

4. $\begin{array}{r} 56 \\ \times\ 3 \\ \hline \end{array}$

5. $\begin{array}{r} 14 \\ \times\ 8 \\ \hline \end{array}$

6. Number Sense Mindy's backyard is 38 yards wide.
There are 3 feet in a yard. How many feet are in 38 yards?

____

Name ______________________________

Using an Expanded Algorithm

In **1** and **2** complete. In **3–5**, find each product. You may use place-value blocks or drawings to help.

1. $\begin{array}{r} 27 \\ \times\ 3 \\ \hline 21 \end{array}$

2. $\begin{array}{r} 43 \\ \times\ 5 \\ \hline 15 \end{array}$

3. $\begin{array}{r} 19 \\ \times\ 4 \\ \hline \end{array}$

4. $\begin{array}{r} 36 \\ \times\ 5 \\ \hline \end{array}$

5. 6×45 ______

Find each product. You may use place-value blocks or drawings to help.

6. $\begin{array}{r} 96 \\ \times\ 3 \\ \hline \end{array}$

7. $\begin{array}{r} 27 \\ \times\ 5 \\ \hline \end{array}$

8. $\begin{array}{r} 57 \\ \times\ 4 \\ \hline \end{array}$

9. $\begin{array}{r} 44 \\ \times\ 3 \\ \hline \end{array}$

10. 6×27 ______

11. An area in Norway gets sunlight all day for 14 weeks straight during the summer. How many days of sunlight will this total?

______

12. There are 19 tables end-to-end in a line at a flea market. If each table is 6 feet long, how many feet long is the line of tables?

______

13. **Reasoning** If you know that $9 \times 20 = 180$, how can you use this to find 9×24? Explain your strategy.

____

____

____

____

14. A pound is equal to 16 ounces. How many ounces are there in 6 pounds?

○ 66 ○ 86 ○ 96 ○ 106

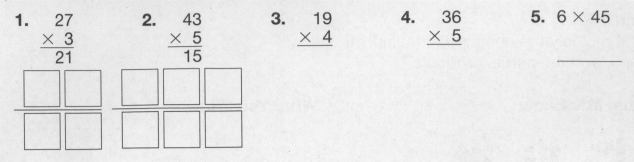

Name ___________________________

Reteaching
14-6

Multiplying 2-Digit by 1-Digit Numbers

You can multiply a 2-digit number by a 1-digit number without finding partial products.

Find 6×48.
Estimate $6 \times 50 = 300$.

Step 1

Multiply the ones.
Regroup if needed.

$6 \times 8 = 48$ ones
Regroup 48 ones as 4 tens and 8 ones.

$$\begin{array}{r} {}^{4} \\ 48 \\ \times\ 6 \\ \hline 8 \end{array}$$

Step 2

Multiply the tens.
Add the regrouped tens.

$6 \times 4 = 24$ tens
24 tens + 4 tens = 28 tens

$$\begin{array}{r} {}^{4} \\ 48 \\ \times\ 6 \\ \hline 288 \end{array}$$

Is the answer reasonable?
Yes. 288 is close to the estimate of 300.
So, $6 \times 48 = 288$.

For **1** and **2** complete. For **3–10**, find the product.
Use place-value blocks or drawings to help.

1. $\begin{array}{r} \square \\ 14 \\ \times\ 7 \\ \hline \square 8 \end{array}$

2.

3. $\begin{array}{r} 36 \\ \times\ 4 \\ \hline \end{array}$

4. $\begin{array}{r} 73 \\ \times\ 6 \\ \hline \end{array}$

5. $\begin{array}{r} 47 \\ \times\ 5 \\ \hline \end{array}$

6. $\begin{array}{r} 36 \\ \times\ 7 \\ \hline \end{array}$

7. $\begin{array}{r} 54 \\ \times\ 3 \\ \hline \end{array}$

8. $\begin{array}{r} 28 \\ \times\ 7 \\ \hline \end{array}$

9. $\begin{array}{r} 64 \\ \times\ 8 \\ \hline \end{array}$

10. $\begin{array}{r} 86 \\ \times\ 2 \\ \hline \end{array}$

11. Reasonableness Rick multiplied 53×7 and got a product of 351. Is Rick correct? Explain why or why not.

____

____

____

Name ____________________

Practice 14-6

Multiplying 2-Digit by 1-Digit Numbers

Estimate and then find each product. You may use drawings to help.

1. 48 × 4

2. 52 × 7

3. 36 × 3

4. 67 × 5

5. 4 × 33

Find each product.

6. 53 × 4

7. 61 × 3

8. 74 × 4

9. 96 × 2

10. 5 × 57

11. 3 × 48

12. 63 × 4

13. 8 × 27

14. 39 × 5

15. Bruce reads 35 pages of a book each day. It will take him 9 days to finish the book. How many pages is the book?

16. Estimation Jose drinks 64 fluid ounces of water each day. About how much water does he drink each week?

17. Reasonableness Celeste multiplied 44 × 5 = 202. Is her product reasonable? Explain why or why not?

18. Each bus in the Turtle System can seat 48 passengers. How many passengers can be seated on 6 Turtle System buses?

○ 248 ○ 252 ○ 268 ○ 288

Name ______________________

Multiply 3- and 4-Digit Numbers

Three- and four-digit factors are multiplied the same way as a two-digit factor is. Multiply from right to left.

Find 523 × 7.

Step 1	Step 2	Step 3
Multiply the ones. Write the 1. Regroup the 2 tens.	Multiply the tens. Add the regrouped tens. Write the 6. Regroup the 1 hundred.	Multiply the hundreds. Add the regroup hundreds.
(2) 523 × 7 = 1	(1 2) 523 × 7 = 61	(1 2) 523 × 7 = 3,661

So, 523 × 7 = 3,661.

Find each product.

1. 167 × 4 = 8
2. 624 × 6 = 4
3. 1,293 × 3 = 9
4. 2,158 × 4 = 2
5. 752 × 8
6. 597 × 5
7. 4,376 × 7
8. 8,649 × 5

9. **Number Sense** The Tonga micro-plate near Samoa moves at a rate of 240 millimeters each year. At that rate, how many millimeters will the plate have moved in 5 years?

____

Name ______________________

Practice 14-7

Multiplying 3- and 4-Digit Numbers

Find each product.

1. $\begin{array}{r} 246 \\ \times\ 7 \\ \hline 2 \end{array}$

2. $\begin{array}{r} 3{,}207 \\ \times\ 4 \\ \hline 8 \end{array}$

3. $\begin{array}{r} 735 \\ \times\ 8 \\ \hline \end{array}$

4. $\begin{array}{r} 1{,}758 \\ \times\ 6 \\ \hline \end{array}$

5. $\begin{array}{r} 4{,}362 \\ \times\ 5 \\ \hline \end{array}$

6. $\begin{array}{r} 593 \\ \times\ 9 \\ \hline \end{array}$

7. $\begin{array}{r} 6{,}327 \\ \times\ 7 \\ \hline \end{array}$

8. $\begin{array}{r} 4{,}362 \\ \times\ 5 \\ \hline \end{array}$

9. 8×924 ______

10. $6 \times 3{,}264$ ______

11. There are 3 outs in an inning for each team. A pitcher pitched 189 innings this season. How many outs did the pitcher record?

______

12. The distance between Los Angeles and San Francisco is 379 miles. Ms. Lincoln made two round trips between the two cities last week. How many miles did she drive in all?

______

13. **Reasoning** If you know that $7 \times 4{,}000 = 28{,}000$, how can you find the product of $7 \times 4{,}056$? What is the product?

______

______

______

14. A race is 3,520 yards. There are 3 feet in a yard. How many feet long is the race?

______

15. **Number Sense** What is the greatest product you can make by multiplying a 3-digit number by a 1-digit number? What were your factors?

______

______

16. What is 738×6?

- ○ 4,288
- ○ 4,328
- ○ 4,388
- ○ 4,428

Name ______________________________

Reteaching
14-8

Problem Solving: Draw a Picture and Write a Number Sentence

Mr. Petty commutes 28 miles to and from work 4 days each week. How many miles does he commute to work each week?

You can use a diagram to show what you know.

__________ miles in all

28	28	28	28

Multiply.

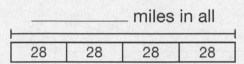

$$\begin{array}{r} 28 \\ \times\ 4 \\ \hline \end{array}$$

Mr. Petty commutes 112 miles each week.

Estimate to check.

28 rounds to 30.

$30 \times 4 = 120$

Since 112 is close to 120, the answer is reasonable.

1. Joel rode his bicycle 14 miles each of the 6 days he cycled this week. How many miles did he cycle all together?

__________ miles in all

14	14	14	14	14	14

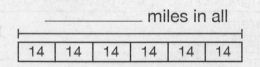

2. There are 24 hours in each day. There are 7 days in one week. How many hours are there in one week?

__________ hours in all

24	24	24	24	24	24	24

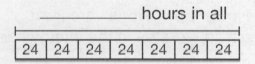

3. Ms. Till works 8 hours each day that she works. In February she worked 19 days. How many hours did she work in February?

__________ hours in all

19	19	19	19	19	19	19	19

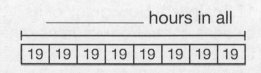

4. **Estimation** It is suggested that you drink 8 cups of water each day. About how many cups of water will you drink in one month?

____

Tip: A month can have as few as 28 days or as many as 31 days.

Name ____________________

Practice **14-8**

Problem Solving: Draw a Picture and Write a Number Sentence

1. At dress rehearsal Wednesday, there were 66 people in the audience. On opening night Thursday, there were 3 times as many people. How many people were in the audience for opening night?

Dress rehearsal	66		
Opening night	66	66	66

__________ in all

2. At Heather and Bob's wedding, there were 32 tables. Each table seats 8 people. All of the tables were full. How many people attended the wedding?

__________ people in all

32	32	32	32	32	32	32	32

The chart shows the number of calories in fats, proteins, and carbohydrates. Use the chart for **3–5**.

Nutritional Information

Ingredients	Calories Per Gram
Protein	4
Carbohydrate	4
Fat	9

3. The energy bar that Kyle is eating has 37 grams of carbohydrates. How many calories are from carbohydrates in the energy bar?

__________ calories in all

37	37	37	37

4. A serving of chicken has 27 grams of protein and 3 grams of fat. How many calories are in a serving of chicken?

____

5. A banana has 27 grams of carbohydrates. It has a total of 121 calories. How many of its calories come from sources other than carbohydrates?

____

6. **Write a Problem** Write a problem that can be solved by drawing a picture. Draw the picture and solve the problem.

Name ______________________________

Mental Math

You can use a pattern to divide multiples of 10, 100, and 1,000.

Find 180 ÷ 2.

Use a basic fact and then follow the pattern.

18 ÷ 2 = 9

180 ÷ 2 = 90

The dividend was 10 times greater, so the quotient was 10 times greater.

Find 3,600 ÷ 4.

Use a basic fact and then follow the pattern.

36 ÷ 4 = 9

360 ÷ 4 = 90

3,600 ÷ 4 = 900

The dividend was 100 times greater, so the quotient was 100 times greater.

Find 6,000 ÷ 2.

Use a basic fact and then follow the pattern.

6 ÷ 2 = 3

60 ÷ 2 = 30

600 ÷ 2 = 300

6,000 ÷ 2 = 3,000

The dividend was 1,000 times greater, so the quotient was 1,000 times greater.

You can find the quotient by using a basic fact and then inserting the same number of 0s that are in the dividend.

Use patterns and mental math to find each quotient.

1. 16 ÷ 8 __________

160 ÷ 8 __________

1,600 ÷ 8 __________

2. 54 ÷ 6 __________

540 ÷ 6 __________

5,400 ÷ 6 __________

3. 35 ÷ 5 __________

350 ÷ 5 __________

3,500 ÷ 5 __________

4. Reasonableness Andy said that 2,000 ÷ 4 = 5,000 because 20 ÷ 4 = 5 and the dividend has 3 zeros. Is Andy correct? Explain why or why not.

____

____

____

Name ______________________

Practice 15-1

Mental Math

Use patterns to find each quotient.

1. 24 ÷ 4 ________

240 ÷ 4 ________

2,400 ÷ 4 ________

2. 42 ÷ 6 ________

420 ÷ 6 ________

4,200 ÷ 6 ________

3. 12 ÷ 3 ________

120 ÷ 3 ________

1,200 ÷ 3 ________

4. 25 ÷ 5 ________

250 ÷ 5 ________

2,500 ÷ 5 ________

5. 63 ÷ 7 ________

630 ÷ 7 ________

6,300 ÷ 7 ________

6. 64 ÷ 8 ________

640 ÷ 8 ________

6,400 ÷ 8 ________

Use mental math to find each quotient.

7. 240 ÷ 3 ________

8. 5,600 ÷ 8 ________

9. 1,000 ÷ 5 ________

10. 490 ÷ 7 ________

11. 1,500 ÷ 3 ________

12. **Number Sense** How many $5 bills are there in $2,000?

____

13. There were 80 people at a banquet. There were 4 tables that had the same number of people. How many people were at each table?

____

14. A race is 1,600 yards long. The runners have to run 4 laps around the track. How many yards is each lap?

____

15. On a cross-country trip, the Smiths drove 2,700 miles in 9 days. They drove the same number of miles each day. How many miles did they drive each day?

○ 3 ○ 30

○ 300 ○ 3,000

16. **Explain It** How can you use a pattern to find 2,100 ÷ 3? What is the quotient?

____

____

Name ______________________________

Estimating Quotients

To estimate quotients, you can use a number that is close to the dividend.

Pedro has 357 CDs on 5 shelves. Each shelf has about the same number of CDs. About how many CDs are on each shelf?

Use a number that is close to 357 and is easy to divide by 5.

You know that $35 \div 5 = 7$ and $350 \div 5 = 70$.

So, $357 \div 5$ is about 70, so Pedro has about 70 CDs on each shelf.

Estimate each quotient.

1. $78 \div 4$ ________ **2.** $306 \div 8$ ________ **3.** $437 \div 5$ ________ **4.** $348 \div 6$ ________ **5.** $2{,}957 \div 9$ ________

6. $732 \div 9$ ________ **7.** $4{,}729 \div 7$ ________ **8.** $524 \div 6$ ________ **9.** $393 \div 4$ ________ **10.** $2{,}035 \div 4$ ________

11. The Klein family drove 422 miles in 8 hours. Which number would you use to estimate the number of miles the Klein family drove each hour? About how many miles did they drive each hour?

____

12. **Explain It** Mrs. O'Neill has 6 monthly payments left on her car. She still owes $1,932. About how much money does she have to pay each month? Explain how you found your answer.

____

____

Name ______________________

Practice

15-2

Estimating Quotients

Estimate each quotient.

1. 78 ÷ 8 ________

2. 221 ÷ 3 ________

3. 620 ÷ 9 ________

4. 225 ÷ 6 ________

5. 5,341 ÷ 8 ________

6. 537 ÷ 6 ________

7. 2,512 ÷ 4 ________

8. 348 ÷ 7 ________

9. 427 ÷ 7 ________

10. 1,925 ÷ 6 ________

11. 812 ÷ 9 ________

12. 1,253 ÷ 4 ________

13. 3,173 ÷ 8 ________

14. 2,833 ÷ 6 ________

15. 4,173 ÷ 5 ________

16. There are 365 days in a year. Elroy has piano practice once every 5 days. About how many times does Elroy have piano practice in a year?

____

17. A restaurant offers a buffet dinner for $9. The restaurant earned $5,517 in buffet dinner receipts last week. About how many dinners were served?

____

18. Number Sense Will the estimate of 537 ÷ 8 be less than or greater than the actual quotient? Explain your answer.

____

____

____

19. There are 225 students that signed up to play in a basketball league. Each team will have 8 players. About how many teams will there be?

- ○ 2
- ○ 3
- ○ 20
- ○ 30

Name ______________________________

Connecting Models and Symbols

Find 45 ÷ 3.

Step 1

Use place-value blocks to show 45. Draw 3 circles to show how many equal groups you will make.

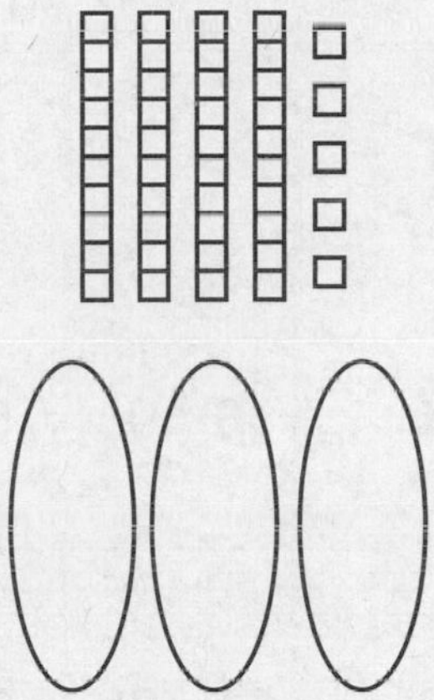

Step 2

Divide the tens. Put an equal number of tens in each circle. There will be 1 ten left over.

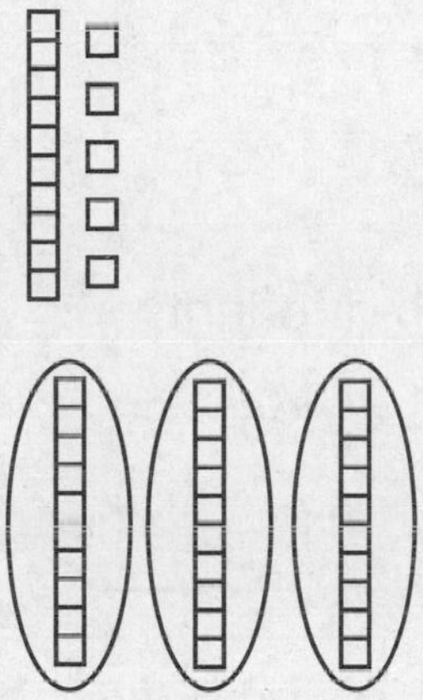

Step 3

Regroup the leftover ten as ones. Combine them with the ones that were already there. Place an equal number of ones in each circle.

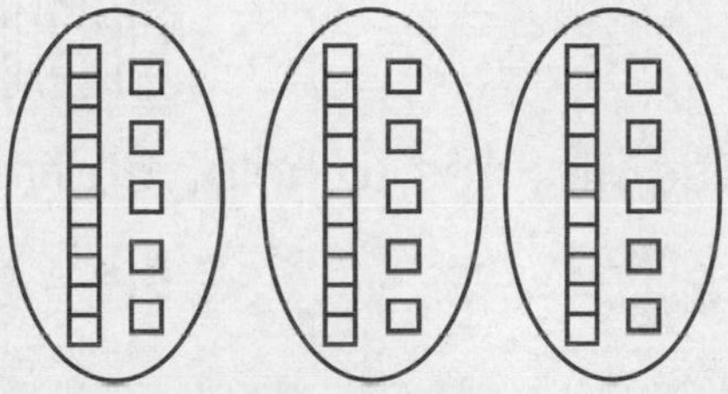

There are 1 ten and 5 ones in each group or 15.
So, 45 ÷ 3 = 15

Complete. Find the quotient.

1. 52 ÷ 4

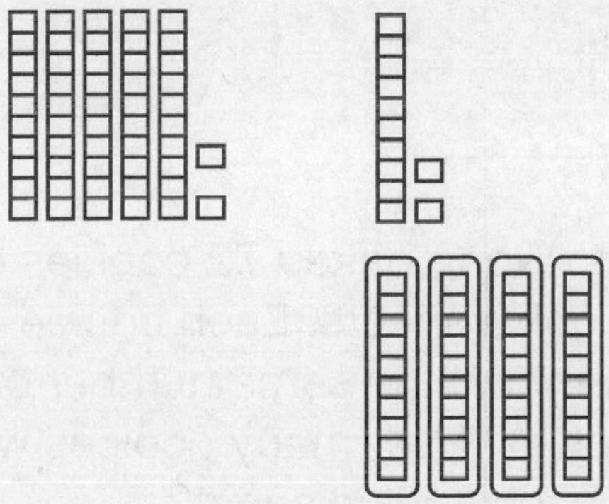

$4\overline{)52}$ ____

$4\overline{)52}$, − 40, ____

$4\overline{)52}$, − 40, ____, − ____, 0

Use pictures to help you find each quotient.

2. 64 ÷ 4 ________

3. 54 ÷ 2 ________

4. 65 ÷ 5 ________

5. 84 ÷ 4 ________

6. 75 ÷ 3 ________

Name ______________________________

Practice
15-3

Connecting Models and Symbols

Use pictures or place-value blocks to help you find each quotient.

1. 42 ÷ 3 →

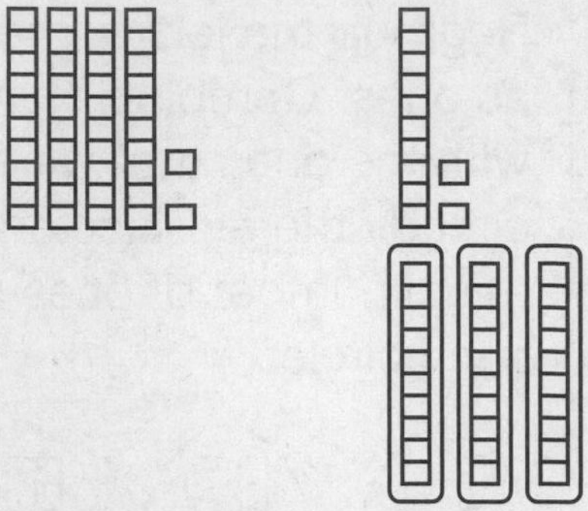

3)42	3)42	3)42
	− 30	− 30
____	____	____
		− ___
		0

Use pictures to help you find each quotient.

2. 54 ÷ 3 ______ **3.** 76 ÷ 2 ______ **4.** 95 ÷ 5 ______ **5.** 68 ÷ 4 ______ **6.** 90 ÷ 6 ______

7. 52 ÷ 2 ______ **8.** 78 ÷ 6 ______ **9.** 98 ÷ 7 ______ **10.** 48 ÷ 3 ______ **11.** 38 ÷ 2 ______

12. Trisha collected 4 times as many bugs as Shirley. If Trisha collected 60 bugs, how many did Shirley collect?

______

13. Max bought 6 CDs for $96. All of the CDs cost the same amount. How much money did each CD cost?

______

14. Estimation Will the quotient of 63 ÷ 3 be greater than or less than 20? Explain.

____

____

____

15. Mrs. Wong baked 72 cookies on 4 cookie sheets. Each cookie sheet had the same number of cookies. How many cookies were on each cookie sheet?

○ 14 ○ 16
○ 17 ○ 18

Name ______________________

Dividing 2-Digit Numbers

Find 51 ÷ 3.

	What You Think	What You Write
Step 1	Divide the tens. 5 tens ÷ 3 = 1 ten with 2 tens left over.	1 ⟵ 1 ten in each group 3⟌51 − 3 ⟵ (3 × 1) tens used 2 ⟵ 2 tens left over
Step 2	Regroup the tens as ones. 2 tens = 20 ones. Combine with the 1 one already there.	1 3⟌51 − 3↓ 21 Bring down the 1 one. 21 ones in all
Step 3	Divide the ones.	17 ⟵ 17 ones in each group 3⟌51 − 3 21 − 21 ⟵ (7 × 3) ones used 0 ⟵ 0 ones left over

Complete. Check your answer.

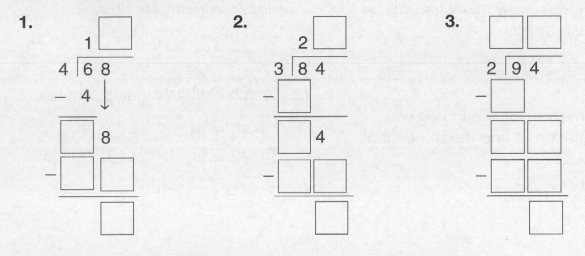

1.

1 ☐
4⟌6 8
− 4 ↓
☐ 8
− ☐ ☐
☐

2.

2 ☐
3⟌8 4
− ☐
☐ 4
− ☐ ☐
☐

3.

☐ ☐
2⟌9 4
− ☐
☐ ☐
− ☐ ☐
☐

Divide. Check your answers.

4. 72 ÷ 2 = ________ **5.** 63 ÷ 3 = ________ **6.** 96 ÷ 4 = ________

7. Number Sense How can you use multiplication to check if a quotient is correct?

____

____

Name ______________________

Practice
15-4

Dividing 2-Digit Numbers

Complete. Find each quotient. Check your answers.

1. $\begin{array}{r} 3 \\ 3\overline{)96} \\ -\ 90 \\ \hline 6 \\ - \\ \hline 0 \end{array}$

2. $\begin{array}{r} 5\overline{)75} \\ - \\ \hline \_5 \\ - \\ \hline \_\_ \end{array}$

3. $\begin{array}{r} 1 \\ 4\overline{)68} \\ -\ 40 \\ \hline \_8 \\ - \\ \hline 0 \end{array}$

4. $\begin{array}{r} 2\overline{)98} \\ - \\ \hline \_8 \\ - \\ \hline \_\_ \end{array}$

5. $\begin{array}{r} 6\overline{)78} \\ -\ 60 \\ \hline \_8 \\ - \\ \hline 0 \end{array}$

6. $\begin{array}{r} 3\overline{)69} \\ - \\ \hline 9 \\ - \\ \hline \_\_ \end{array}$

7. $\begin{array}{r} 1 \\ 5\overline{)65} \\ - \\ \hline \_5 \\ - \\ \hline 0 \end{array}$

8. $\begin{array}{r} 4\overline{)56} \\ - \\ \hline \_6 \\ - \\ \hline \_\_ \end{array}$

9. Jennifer has 57 fish. She wants to put them in 3 fish tanks. If she puts the same number of fish in each tank, how many fish will be in each tank?

____

10. There are 84 chairs in a restaurant. Each table in the restaurant has 6 chairs around it. How many tables does the restaurant have?

____

11. Estimation How can you use estimation to find the quotient of 57 ÷ 3?

____

____

____

____

12. Which has the greatest quotient?

- ○ 75 ÷ 3
- ○ 76 ÷ 4
- ○ 72 ÷ 2
- ○ 75 ÷ 5

Name ______________________

Reteaching
15-5

Dividing 3- and 4-Digit Numbers

Dividing 3- and 4-digit numbers is like dividing 2-digit numbers.

Find 837 ÷ 3.

Step 1	Step 2	Step 3
Divide the hundreds.	Divide the tens.	Divide the ones.
2 3)837 600 237	27 3)837 − 600 237 − 210 27	279 3)837 − 600 237 − 210 27 − 27 0

So, 837 ÷ 3 = 279.

Complete. Find each quotient.

1. 7
6)456
− 420

− ____

2. 2
4)948
− 800

− 120

− ____
0

3. 9
5) 4,740
−4,500

− ____

− ____
0

4. 1,
7)7,868
−7,000

− 700

− ____

− ____
0

5. **Number Sense** When dividing a 3-digit number, how do you know where the first digit will be in the quotient?

____

____

____

Name ______________________________

Practice
15-5

Dividing 3- and 4-Digit Numbers

Complete. Find each quotient. Check your answers.

1.
9
5)495
− 450
____
− ____

2.
1
3)465
− 300
____
− 150
____
− ____
0

3.
4
4)1,764
−1,600
____
− ____
− ____
0

4.
1,
6)6,954
−6,000
____
− 600
____
− ____
54
− ____
0

5. Rick traveled 645 miles by train in 5 hours. How many miles did the train travel each hour?

____

6. A mile is 5,280 feet long. A yard is 3 feet long. How many yards are there in a mile?

____

7. The Floyds have 584 feet of fencing on their property. Each piece of fence is 8 feet long. How many pieces of fence do the Floyds have?

____

8. **Journal** How do you know which place to use for the first number in a quotient?

____

____

____

____

9. **Number Sense** How can you use multiplication to check a quotient?

____

____

____

____

____

10. How many groups of 7 can be made from 532?

- ○ 66
- ○ 72
- ○ 74
- ○ 76

Name ______________________

Zero in the Quotient

If 0 is one of the numbers in a quotient, make sure you write it before you continue to divide.

Find 828 ÷ 4.

Step 1	Step 2	Step 3
Divide the hundreds.	There are not enough tens to divide. Write a 0 in the quotient to show 0 tens.	Divide the ones.
$$\begin{array}{r} 2 \\ 4\overline{)828} \\ -\ 800 \\ 28 \end{array}$$	$$\begin{array}{r} 20 \\ 4\overline{)828} \\ -\ 800 \\ 28 \end{array}$$	$$\begin{array}{r} 207 \\ 4\overline{)828} \\ -\ 800 \\ 28 \\ -\ 28 \\ 0 \end{array}$$

So, 828 ÷ 4 = 207.

Divide. Check your answer.

1. $5\overline{)535}$ **2.** $3\overline{)624}$ **3.** $2\overline{)812}$ **4.** $4\overline{)8{,}204}$

5. $6\overline{)630}$ **6.** $5\overline{)6{,}040}$ **7.** $3\overline{)9{,}309}$ **8.** $2\overline{)4{,}104}$

9. Reasonableness The town Mo lives in has a population of 2,724 people. The town has an area of 3 square miles. Mo said that 98 people live in each square mile. Is Mo's answer reasonable? Explain why or why not.

____

____

____

Name ________________________

Practice 15-6

Zero in the Quotient

Divide. Check your answer.

1. $6\overline{)648}$	**2.** $4\overline{)828}$	**3.** $5\overline{)540}$	**4.** $3\overline{)6{,}096}$
5. $4\overline{)828}$	**6.** $2\overline{)6{,}162}$	**7.** $4\overline{)8{,}276}$	**8.** $9\overline{)9{,}630}$
9. $3\overline{)912}$	**10.** $5\overline{)8{,}525}$	**11.** $6\overline{)7{,}254}$	**12.** $2\overline{)410}$

13. Mr. Stevens earned $6,342 in the last 6 weeks. He earned the same amount of money each week. How much money did he earn each week?

____

14. Maggie is starting a book that is 420 pages long. She plans to complete the book in 4 days. She will read the same number of pages each day. How many pages does she need to read today?

____

15. A basketball team scored 872 points in its first 8 games. It scored the same points in each game. How many points has it scored in each game?

____

16. Geometry The sum of the angle measures of a pentagon is 540°.

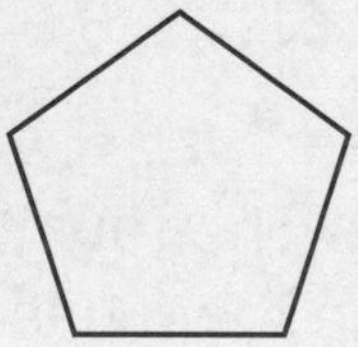

If each of the 5 angles has the same measure, what is the measure of each angle?

- ○ 18°
- ○ 108°
- ○ 112°
- ○ 180°

17. Reasonableness Lorraine divided 3,270 ÷ 3 = 190. Is Lorraine's quotient reasonable? Explain why or why not.

____

____

____

____

____

Name ______________________

Reteaching
15-7

Dividing with Remainders

Jim has 21 sports cards. Each plastic sleeve holds 6 cards. How many sleeves will be filled? Will there be any cards left over?

Find 21 ÷ 6.

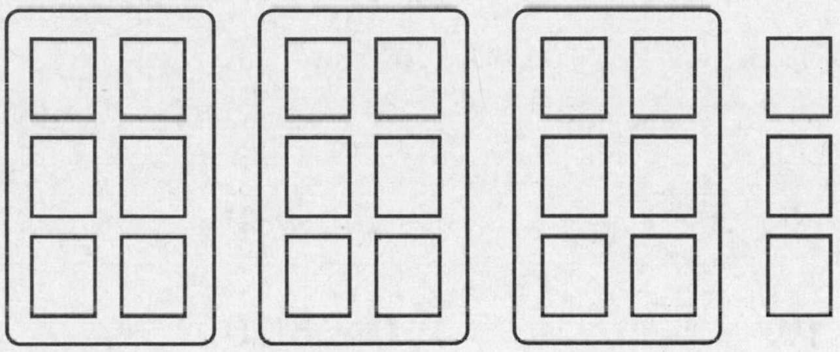

$$\begin{array}{r} 3\ \text{R3} \\ 6\overline{)21} \\ -\,18 \\ \hline 3 \end{array}$$

So, 3 sleeves are filled and there are 3 cards left over.

Divide. Check your answer.

1. $4\overline{)23}$ **2.** $7\overline{)32}$ **3.** $5\overline{)33}$

Use counters or draw a picture to find each quotient and remainder.

4. $8\overline{)45}$ **5.** $4\overline{)18}$ **6.** $9\overline{)51}$ **7.** $5\overline{)33}$

8. $6\overline{)27}$ **9.** $3\overline{)25}$ **10.** $8\overline{)57}$ **11.** $6\overline{)40}$

12. Reasoning Why must a remainder be less than the divisor?

____

____

Name ____________________

Practice 15-7

Dividing with Remainders

Complete. Check your answers.

1. $5\overline{)36}$ $-$

2. $2\overline{)36}$ $-$

3. $8\overline{)52}$ $-$

Find each quotient. Check your answers.

4. $6\overline{)45}$

5. $8\overline{)37}$

6. $3\overline{)20}$

7. $9\overline{)80}$

8. $7\overline{)38}$

9. $5\overline{)42}$

10. $7\overline{)62}$

11. $8\overline{)20}$

12. **Number Sense** Regina is going to divide a number by 8. What is the greatest remainder that she can have?

____

13. There are 43 girls trying out for cheerleading. Each cheerleading squad will have exactly 8 girls. How many girls will not make a cheerleading squad?

____

14. **Reasoning** Each costume that Ms. Wren is making uses 3 yards of yarn. She has 26 yards of yarn. How many complete costumes can Ms. Wren make?

____

15. The chorus has 21 students. For a concert, they are being driven in cars that can each hold 4 students. How many cars are needed?

○ 4 ○ 5
○ 6 ○ 7

Name ______________________

Problem Solving: Multiple-Step Problems

When solving a multiple-step problem, you may need to find the answer to a hidden question. A hidden question is a question that is not asked, but whose answer is needed to solve the problem.

A politician served 30 years in elected office in Washington, D.C. A term in the Senate is 6 years and a term in the House of Representatives is 2 years. She served 3 terms in the Senate. How many terms did she serve in the House of Representatives?

What do you know?

- She served 3 terms in the Senate.
- A term in the Senate is 6 years.
- A term in the House is 2 years.
- She served 30 years all together.

What do I need to find out?

- How many years did she serve in the Senate? (This is the hidden question).
- How many years did she serve in the House?
- How many terms did she serve in the House?

Find the number of years she served in the Senate:
$3 \text{ terms} \times 6 \text{ years} = 18 \text{ years}.$

Find the number of years she served in the House:
$30 \text{ years} - 18 \text{ years} = 12 \text{ years}.$

Find the number of terms she served in the House:
$12 \text{ years} \div 2 = 6.$

The politician served 6 terms in the House of Representatives.

Solve.

1. There are 8 players on a basketball team. All but 2 players scored 6 points each. The other two players scored the same number of points. The team scored 72 points. How many points did the other two players each score?

____

HINT: Hidden Question—How many points were scored all together by the players who scored 6 points each?

Name ______________________________

Problem Solving: Multiple-Step Problems

Solve. Answer the hidden question first.

1. Marcus counted a total of 40 wheels from bicycles and tricycles while sitting on a park bench. Marcus counted 11 bicycles. How many tricycles did Marcus count?

   ____

HINT: Hidden Question—How many wheels did the bicycles have?

2. Julie bought 15 baseballs and some softballs. The total cost of the balls is $90. Each ball costs $5. How many softballs did Julie buy?

   ____

HINT: How much money did Julie spend on baseballs?

3. Bert bought 4 books for $7 each and a magazine for $5. He paid with a $50 bill. How much money did Bert receive back from the cashier?

   ____

HINT: Hidden Question—How much money did Bert spend?

4. A community group bought 12 student tickets and 3 adult tickets to the movies. The total cost of the tickets was $96. Student tickets cost $6. How much money does an adult ticket cost?

   ____

HINT: How much money did the group spend on student tickets?

5. There are 48 students in the band. The boys and girls are in separate rows. There are 6 students in each row. There are 3 rows of boys. How many rows of girls are there?

   ____

HINT: Hidden Question—How many boys are there?

6. **Write a Problem** Write a real-world problem that can be solved by finding and answering a hidden question.

   ____

   ____

   ____

Name ____________________

Reteaching
16-1

Understanding Measurement

To use a ruler, line up the object with the 0 mark.

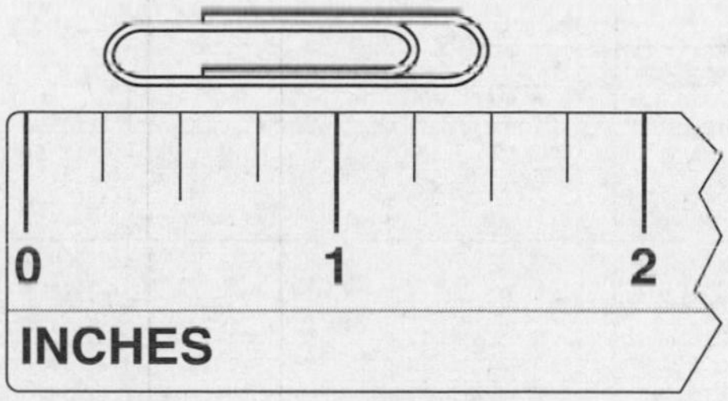

Wrong way. The paper clip is not lined up with the zero

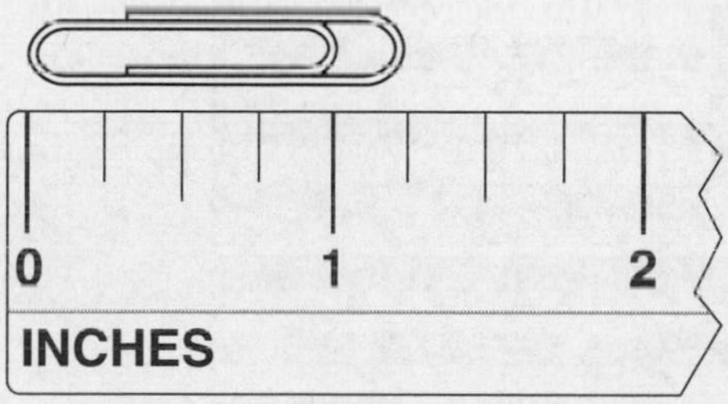

Right way. By lining the paper clip up with the zero, you can see that it is $1\frac{1}{4}$ inches long, which is 1 inch long to the nearest inch.

Estimate each length. Then measure it to the nearest inch.

1.

____

2.

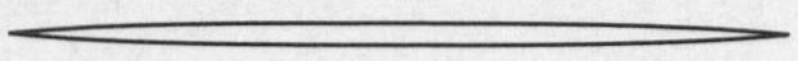

____

3.

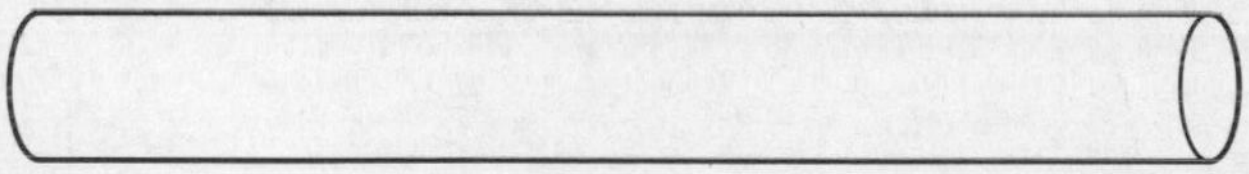

____

4.

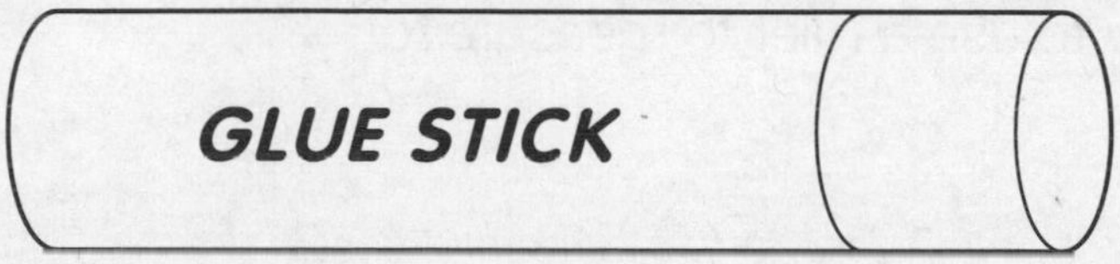

____

5. **Number Sense** Estimate the length of one of your index fingers. Then measure. Record the measurement to the nearest inch.

____

Name ____________________

Practice
16-1

Understanding Measurement

Estimate each length. Then measure to the nearest inch.

1. 

____

2. 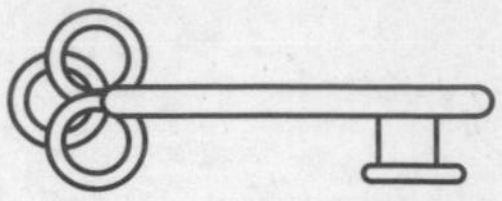

____

3. 

____

4. 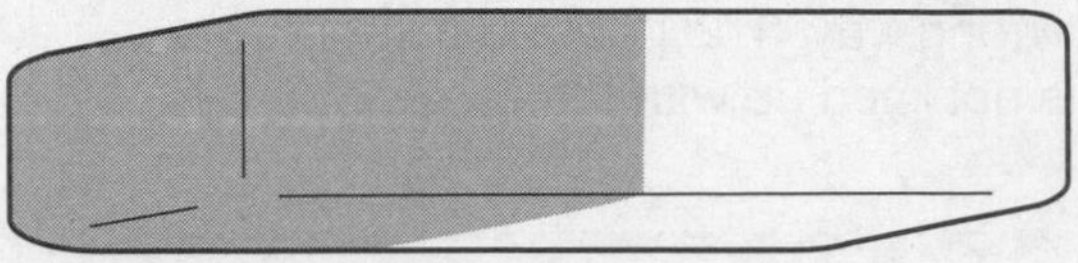

____

5. **Reasoning** To measure the length of a closet, Aaron used his foot and measured 6-foot lengths. His father measured 4-foot lengths. Could they be measuring the same closet? Explain.

____

____

6. Draw a line segment that is 2 inches long.

7. **Writing to Explain** Describe how to use a ruler to measure to the nearest inch.

____

____

8. Which paper clip is 1 inch long?

○ 

○ 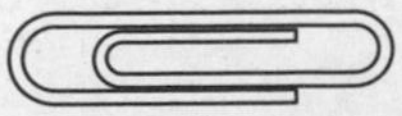

○ 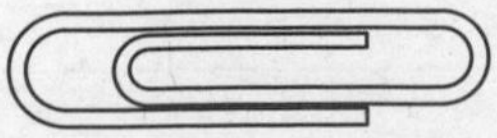

○ 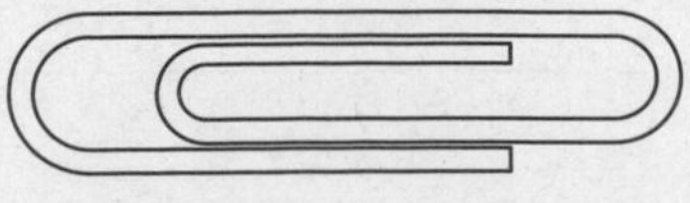

Name ______________________________

Reteaching
16-2

Fractions of an Inch

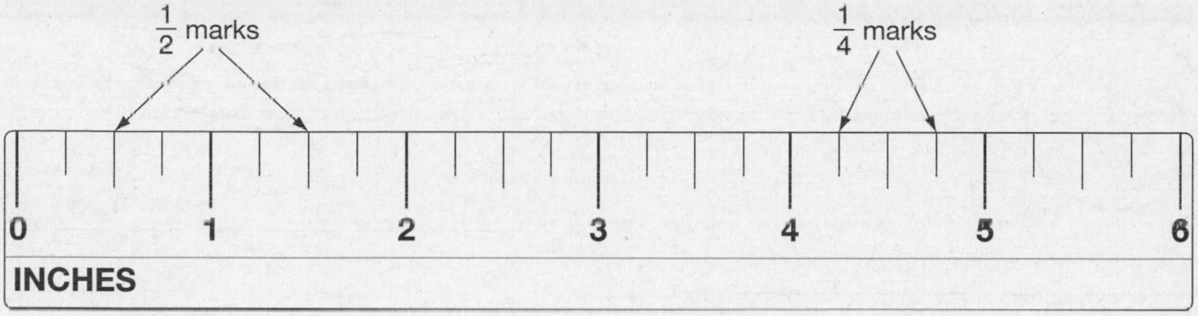

How long is the peanut to the nearest $\frac{1}{2}$ inch?

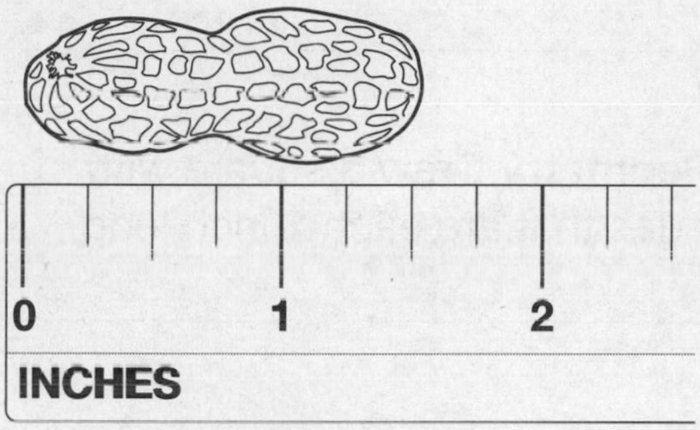

The peanut is $1\frac{1}{2}$ in. to the nearest $\frac{1}{2}$ inch.

How long is the chalk to the nearest $\frac{1}{4}$ inch?

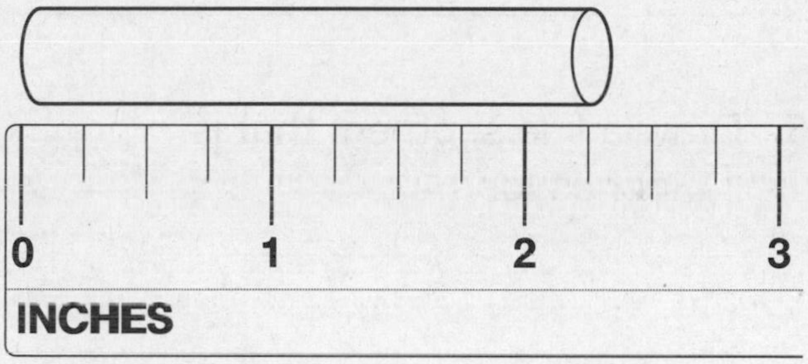

The chalk is $2\frac{1}{4}$ in. to the nearest $\frac{1}{4}$ inch.

Measure the length of each object to the nearest $\frac{1}{2}$ and $\frac{1}{4}$ inch.

1. 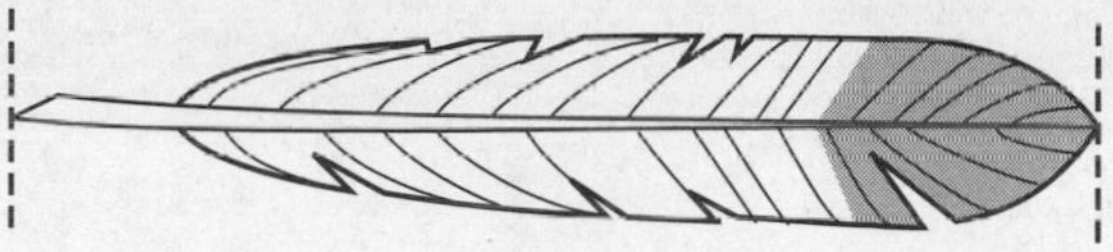

____

2. 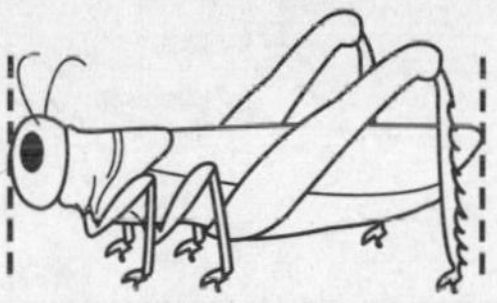

____

3. 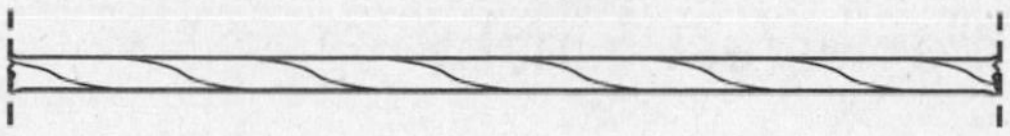

____

4. 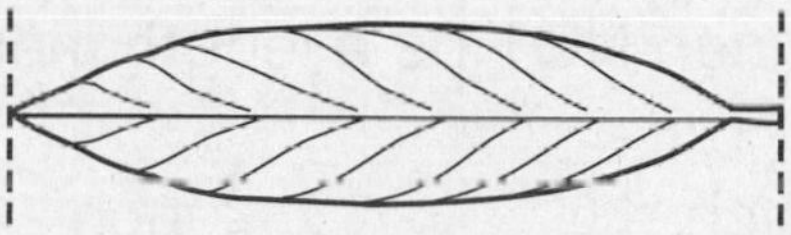

____

Name ____________________

Practice
16-2

Fractions of an Inch

Measure the length of each object to the nearest $\frac{1}{2}$ inch and $\frac{1}{4}$ inch.

1.

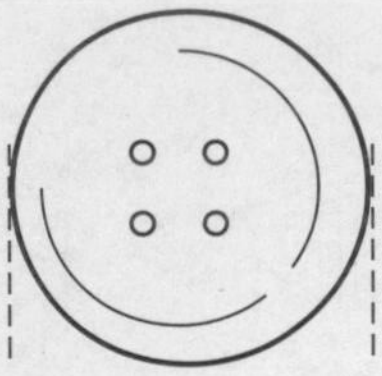

____

2.

____

3.

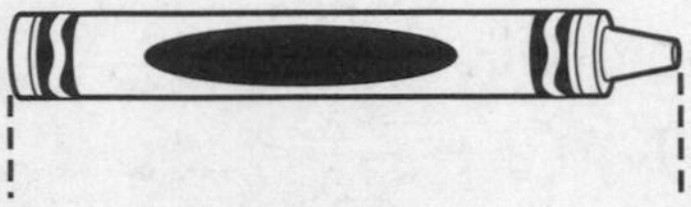

____

4.

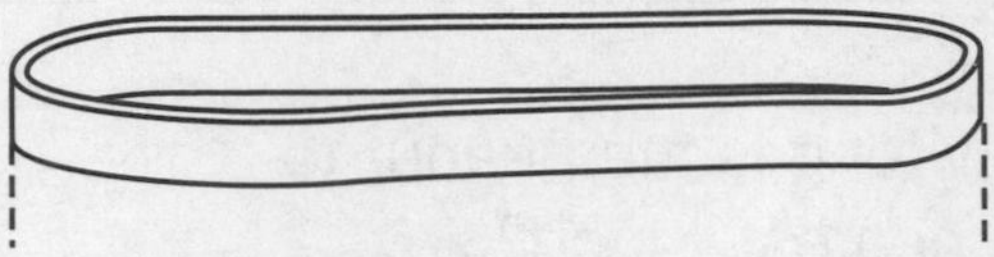

____

5. Draw a line segment that is $1\frac{1}{2}$ inches long.

6. **Geometry** Draw a square with sides that are each 1 inch long.

7. **Reasoning** Eric and Madison both measured the same trading card. Eric says the card is about 3 inches long. Madison says it is about $2\frac{3}{4}$ inches long. Their teacher says they are both correct. How is that possible?

____

____

____

8. Which can NOT be a length measured to the nearest $\frac{1}{4}$ inch?

○ $\frac{1}{4}$ inch ○ $\frac{3}{8}$ inch ○ $\frac{1}{2}$ inch ○ $\frac{3}{4}$ inch

Name ______________________

Reteaching
16-3

Using Inches, Feet, Yards, and Miles

The customary units of length include inches (in.), feet (ft), yards (yd), and miles (mi).

An inch is the length of this line segment. __________

A foot is about the length of the long side of this book.

A yard is about the width of a doorway.

A mile is the distance that people can walk in about 15 minutes.

Choose the better estimate.

1. The width of a book
8 inches or 8 feet

____

2. The length of a pair of scissors
6 inches or 6 feet

____

3. The depth of a diving pool
12 inches or 12 feet

____

4. The height of a third-grade student
4 feet or 4 yards

____

5. The length across a town
5 yards or 5 miles

____

6. The length of a sprint
100 yards or 100 miles

____

7. **Explain It** Would you measure the length of a stapler in inches or in feet? Explain your answer.

____

____

Name ______________________

Practice
16-3

Using Inches, Feet, Yards, and Miles

Choose the better estimate.

1. The depth of a swimming pool
10 feet or 10 miles

____

2. The length of your desk
2 inches or 2 feet

____

3. The height of a telephone pole
20 feet or 20 miles

____

4. The height of a tall person
6 feet or 6 yards

____

5. The length of a pencil
5 inches or 5 feet

____

6. The width of a door
1 inch or 1 yard

____

7. The length between bases on a baseball field
90 feet or 90 yards

____

8. The distance between San Francisco and Los Angeles
400 yards or 400 miles

____

9. What item in your home is about 6 feet long?

____

10. Reasonableness Would you measure the length between two states in feet or miles?

____

____

____

11. Which measurement best describes the length of a computer?

○ 2 inches ○ 2 feet
○ 2 yards ○ 2 miles

12. Which units would be best to to measure the length of your pinky?

○ inches ○ feet
○ yards ○ miles

Name ______________________________

Reteaching
16-4

Customary Units of Capacity

Capacity is the amount of liquid a container can hold. The containers show the different units of customary capacity.

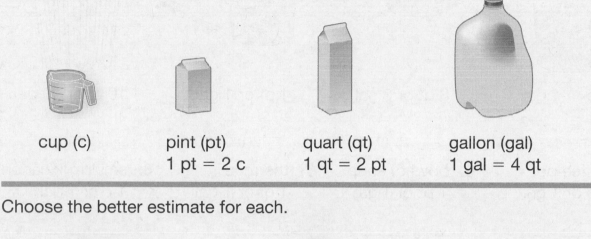

cup (c)

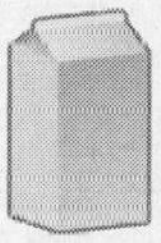

pint (pt)
1 pt = 2 c

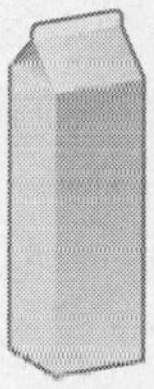

quart (qt)
1 qt = 2 pt

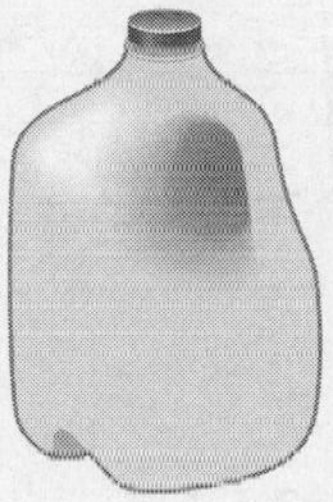

gallon (gal)
1 gal = 4 qt

Choose the better estimate for each.

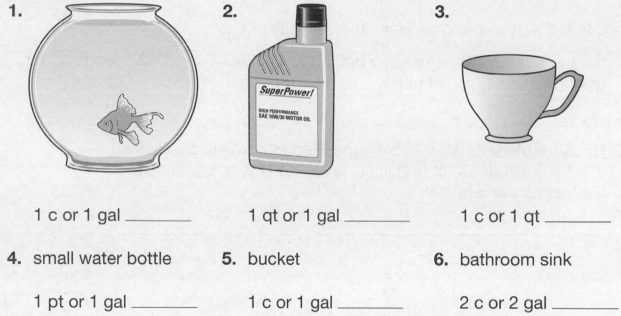

1.

1 c or 1 gal ________

2.

1 qt or 1 gal ________

3.

1 c or 1 qt ________

4. small water bottle

1 pt or 1 gal ________

5. bucket

1 c or 1 gal ________

6. bathroom sink

2 c or 2 gal ________

7. **Reasoning** Suppose you want to fill a pot with 1 gallon of water. You can use a measuring cup the size of a cup or a quart. Which would be best to use? Explain your reasoning.

____

____

____

Name ______________________

Practice 16-4

Customary Units of Capacity

Choose the better estimate for each.

1. 

1 c or 1 gal

____

2. 

3 qt or 3 gal

____

3. 

1 pt or 1 gal

____

4. 

10 qt or 10 gal

____

5. coffee pot
1 c or 1 gal
____

6. bowl of soup
1 pt or 1 gal
____

7. thermos
1 qt or 1 gal
____

8. small milk carton
1 c or 1 gal
____

Choose the better unit to measure the capacity of each.

9. hot tub
qt or gal
____

10. shampoo bottle
pt or gal
____

11. bucket
c or gal
____

12. sports cooler
qt or gal
____

13. **Reasonableness** John has 4 cups filled with fruit juice. He said that he has a gallon of fruit juice. Is his statement reasonable? Explain why or why not.

____

____

____

14. **Estimate** Which measurement best describes the capacity of a kitchen sink?

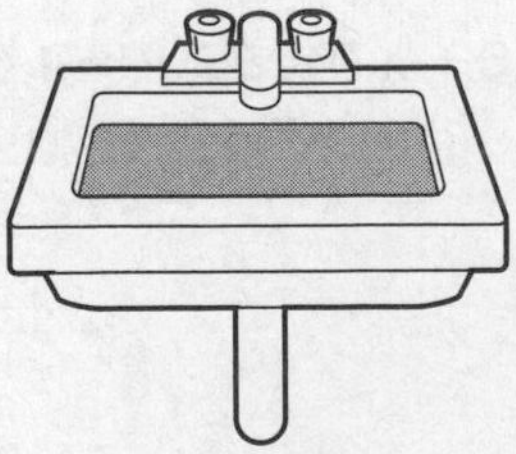

○ 5 quarts ○ 5 pints ○ 5 cups ○ 5 gallons

Name ______________________________

Units of Weight

Weight is the measure of how heavy an object is.
The units of weight are listed below.

1 pound (lb) = 16 ounces (oz)
1 ton (T) = 2,000 pounds

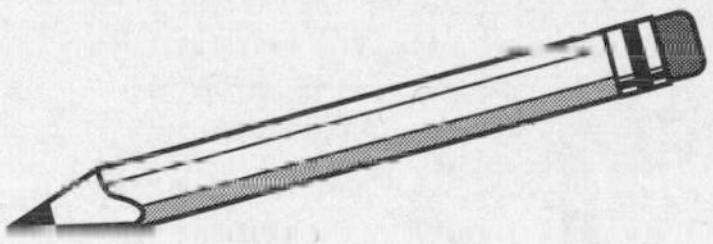

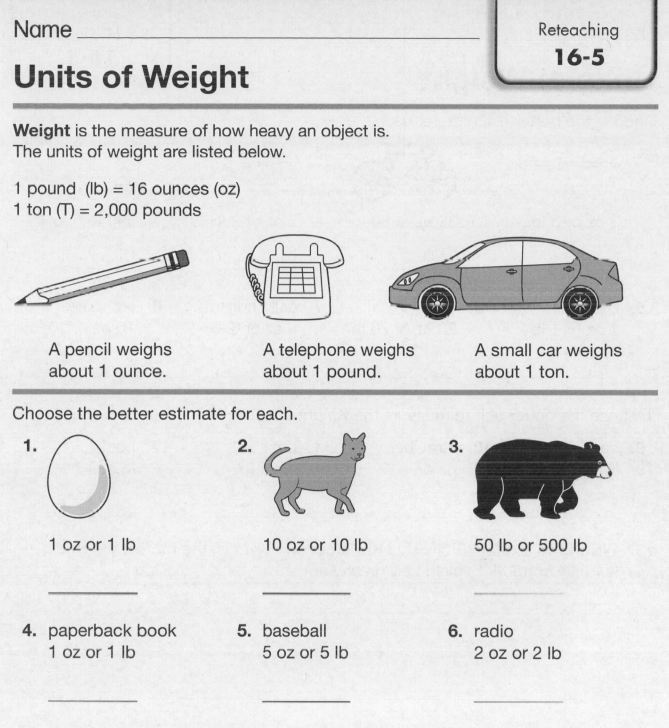

A pencil weighs about 1 ounce.

A telephone weighs about 1 pound.

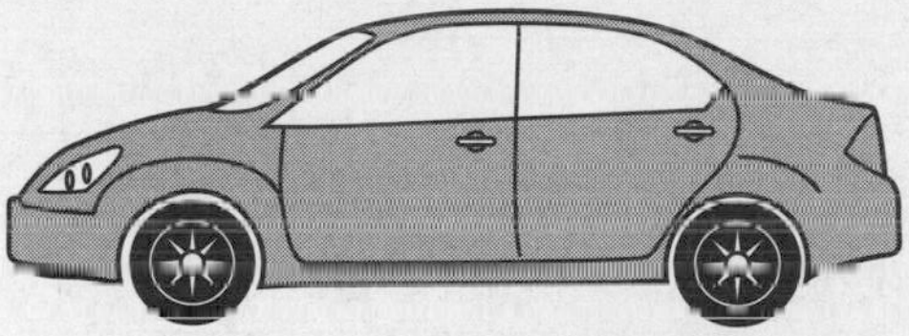

A small car weighs about 1 ton.

Choose the better estimate for each.

1. 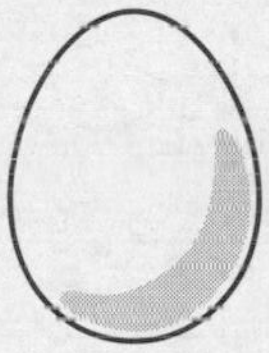

1 oz or 1 lb

____

2. 

10 oz or 10 lb

____

3. 

50 lb or 500 lb

____

4. paperback book
1 oz or 1 lb

____

5. baseball
5 oz or 5 lb

____

6. radio
2 oz or 2 lb

____

7. **Number Sense** Mrs. Robertson wants to buy as big a package of chopped meat as possible. There is a 20-ounce package and a 1-pound package. She only wants to buy one package. Which should she buy?

____

____

____

Name ______________________________

Practice
16-5

Units of Weight

Choose the better estimate for each.

1. 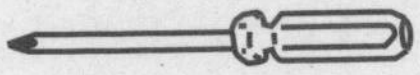

3 oz or 3 lb

____

2. 

30 oz or 30 lb

____

3. 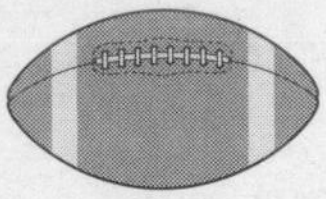

2 oz or 2 lb

____

4. 

500 lb or 5 T

____

5. DVD
1 oz or 1 lb

____

6. chair
20 oz or 20 lb

____

7. cell phone
6 oz or 6 lb

____

8. computer
10 oz or 10 lb

____

Choose the better unit to measure the weight of each.

9. car
lb or T

____

10. strawberry
oz or lb

____

11. baseball
oz or lb

____

12. book
lb or T

____

13. **Writing to Explain** Emily said the larger an object is, the more it weighs. Is Emily correct? Explain why or why not.

____

____

____

14. **Estimate** Which of the following objects can best be measured in ounces?

○ pencil ○ couch ○ desk ○ doghouse

Name ______________________

Reteaching
16-6

Converting Customary Units

Customary Units

Units of Length	Units of Weight	Units of Capacity
12 inches (in.) – 1 foot (ft) 1 yard (yd) = 3 feet	1 pound (lb) – 16 ounces (oz)	1 quart (qt) = 2 pints (pt) 1 gallon (gal) = 4 quarts

To convert a larger unit to a smaller unit, multiply.
For example, to convert feet to inches, multiply by 12.

To convert a smaller unit to a larger unit, divide.
For example to convert, quarts to gallons, divide by 4.

Complete to change the units.

1. 4 feet = ■■ inches

____

2. 8 quarts = ■ gallons

____

3. How many inches are there in 4 feet 8 inches?

____

4. How many ounces are there in 6 pounds 4 ounces?

____

5. Critical Thinking Michelle is making a recipe that requires 1 gallon of water. All she has is a 1-pint measure. How many times will she need to fill the 1-pint measure? Explain your answer.

____

____

Name ____________________

Practice
16-6

Converting Customary Units

Change the units. Complete.

1. 9 feet = ■ yards

2. 2 pounds = ■■ ounces

3. 2 gallons = ■■ pints

4. 4 feet = ■■ inches

5. How many quarts are in 3 gallons, 2 quarts?

6. How many inches are there in 3 feet 7 inches?

7. **Journal** How can you convert feet to inches?

8. **Reasonableness** John has 4 cups filled with fruit juice. He said that he has a gallon of fruit juice. Is his statement reasonable? Explain why or why not.

9. Abraham Lincoln was 6 feet 4 inches tall. How many inches tall was Lincoln?

10. A baseball diamond has 90 feet between each base. A softball diamond has 60 feet between each base. How many yards longer is the space between the bases on a baseball diamond than a softball diamond?

○ 10 ○ 30 ○ 50 ○ 90

Name ______________________

Units of Time

There are 60 minutes (min) in an hour (h).
There are 24 hours in a day (d).
There are 7 days in a week (wk).

To convert a larger unit to a smaller unit, multiply.

To find the number of hours in 2 days, multiply $24 \times 2 = 48$.
So, there are 48 hours in 2 days.

Complete to change the units.

1. 6 weeks = ■■ days

____

2. 3 days = ■■ hours

____

3. How many days are there in 7 weeks?

____

4. How many minutes are there in 9 hours?

____

5. How many days are there in 3 weeks 4 days?

____

6. How many minutes are there in 4 hours 30 minutes?

____

7. **Explain It** Nikki's school day lasts 7 hours 20 minutes. How many minutes does Nikki's school day last? Explain how you found your answer.

____

____

____

____

Name ______________________

Practice
16-7

Units of Time

Change the units. Complete.

1. 5 hours = ■■■ minutes

____

2. 3 weeks = ■■ days

____

3. 8 weeks = ■■ days

____

4. 6 hours = ■■■ minutes

____

5. How many minutes are in 3 hours, 30 minutes?

____

6. How many days are there in 4 weeks, 3 days?

____

7. Kendra watched two movies. The first lasted 100 minutes. The second lasted 1 hour 55 minutes. Which movie was longer? By how many minutes?

____

____

____

8. **Explain It** How many hours are there in a week? Explain how you found your answer.

____

____

____

____

9. The Wilson family is going on a 5-week vacation through Australia and New Zealand this summer. How many days will the Wilson's be on vacation?

____

10. Lacy slept 8 hours last night. How many minutes did Lacy sleep?

○ 400 ○ 480
○ 640 ○ 800

Name ______________________

Elapsed Time

A children's museum is open from 1:00 P.M. to 6:35 P.M. every day.
How long is the museum open?

Step 1

Start at the starting time.

Step 2

Count the hours.

There are 5 hours.

Step 3

Count the minutes.

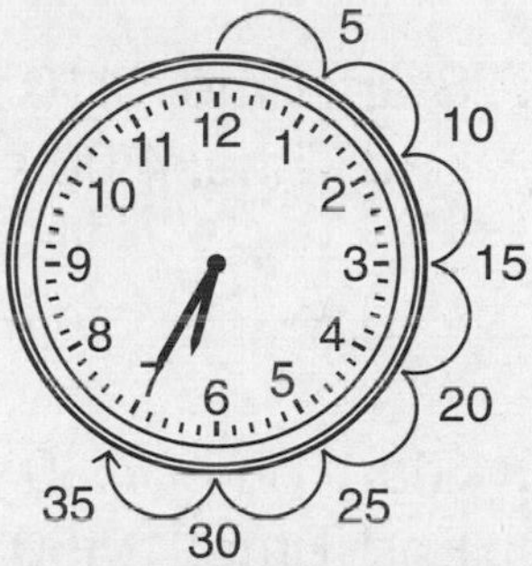

There are 35 minutes.

The museum is open 5 hours 35 minutes.

Find the elapsed time.

1. Start Time: 3:30 P.M.
End Time: 7:00 P.M.

____

2. Start Time: 8:10 A.M.
End Time: 10:55 A.M.

____

3. Start Time: 1:20 P.M.
End Time: 2:00 P.M.

____

4. Start Time: 8:00 A.M.
End Time: 1:15 P.M.

____

5. **Write a Problem** Write the start time and the ending time of an activity that you did during the weekend. Then find the elapsed time. Write your answer in hours and minutes.

____

____

____

Name ______________________________

Elapsed Time

Find the elapsed time.

1. Start Time: 6:00 P.M.
   End Time: 7:15 P.M.
   ____

2. Start Time: 9:30 A.M.
   End Time: 1:45 P.M.
   ____

3. Start Time: 3:10 P.M.
   End Time: 4:00 P.M.
   ____

4. Start Time: 11:30 A.M.
   End Time: 5:30 P.M.
   ____

5. Start Time: 7:30 A.M.
   End Time: 10:50 A.M.
   ____

6. Start Time: 9:00 P.M.
   End Time: 4:30 A.M.
   ____

7. Edie is a 1 year old. She naps from 12:45 P.M. to 2:30 P.M. each day. How long is Edie's nap?
   ____

8. Mr. Wellborn arrives at work at 8:40 A.M. He leaves for work 50 minutes before he arrives. At what times does Mr. Wellborn leave for work?
   ____

9. **Explain It** How long is your school day? Explain how you found your answer.
   ____
   ____
   ____
   ____

10. Gary's father dropped him off at soccer practice at 2:45 P.M. His mother picked him up at 5:00 P.M. How long did soccer practice last?
    - ○ 2 hours 15 minutes
    - ○ 2 hours 25 minutes
    - ○ 3 hours 15 minutes
    - ○ 3 hours 25 minutes

Name ______________________

Problem Solving: Work Backward

Natalie finished listening to music at 4:30 P.M. She listened to a CD that lasted 40 minutes. She spent 15 minutes on a phone call after the CD finished. Then she listened to another CD for 45 minutes. At what time did Natalie start listening to music?

You can work backward to solve problems. Use each piece of information to find the starting time.

Natalie finished listening to music at 4:30 P.M.

She listened to the second CD for 45 minutes.	45 minutes from 4:30 P.M. is 3:45 P.M.	
She spent 15 minutes on the phone.	15 minutes from 3:45 P.M. is 3:30 P.M.	
She listened to the first CD for 40 minutes.	40 minutes from 3:30 P.M. is 2:50 P.M.	

Natalie started listening to music at 2:50 P.M.

Solve the problem by drawing a picture and working backward.

1. Patrice read the temperature at 6 P.M. The temperature was 72°F. The temperature was 8°F less than at 4 P.M. The temperature at 10 A.M. was 5°F greater than the 4 P.M. temperature. What was the temperature at 10 A.M.?

____

Name ______________________________

Practice
16-9

Problem Solving: Work Backward

Solve the problem by drawing a picture and working backward.

1. Will arrived at his mother's office at 3 P.M. It took him 30 minutes to walk from his home to the mall. He was in the mall for 45 minutes. It then took him 15 minutes to walk to his mother's office. At what time did Will leave home?

____

2. At 12 noon, Leslie recorded the temperature as 56°F. The temperature had increased by 8°F from 10 A.M. The temperature at 8 A.M. was 2°F warmer than it was at 10 A.M. What was the temperature at 8 A.M.?

____

3. The test that Keyshawn's class took finished at 10:30 A.M. The first part of the test took 30 minutes. There was a 15-minute break. The second part of the test also took 30 minutes. At what time did the test start?

____

4. The temperature was 16°C when Becky returned home at 6 P.M. The temperature was 4°C warmer at 3 P.M. than it was at 6 P.M. It was 3°C warmer at 12 noon than it was at 3 P.M. What was the temperature at 12 noon?

____

5. Elliot finished studying at 4:45 P.M. He spent 30 minutes reading a social studies chapter. He spent 45 minutes on his math homework. In between reading and math, Elliot took a 20-minute break. At what time did Elliot begin studying?

○ 3:00 P.M. ○ 3:10 P.M. ○ 3:30 P.M. ○ 6:20 P.M.

Name ___________________________

Reteaching
17-1

Using Centimeters and Decimeters

A centimeter (cm) is a unit of measurement that is used to measure small objects. A decimeter (dm) is 10 cm long.

1 dm = 10 cm

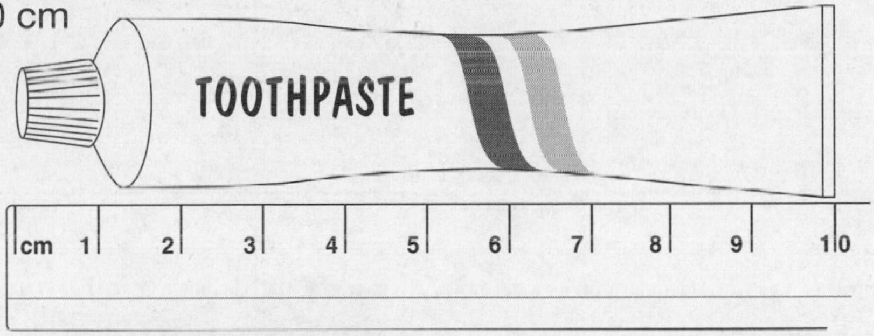

The tube of toothpaste is 10 cm long. We can also say that it is 1 dm long. The cap of the tube is about 1 cm long.

Estimate each length. Then measure to the nearest centimeter.

1. 

____

2. 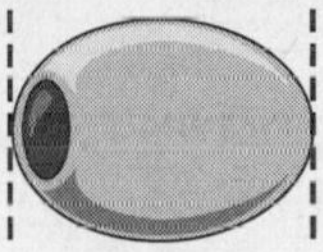

____

3. 

____

4. 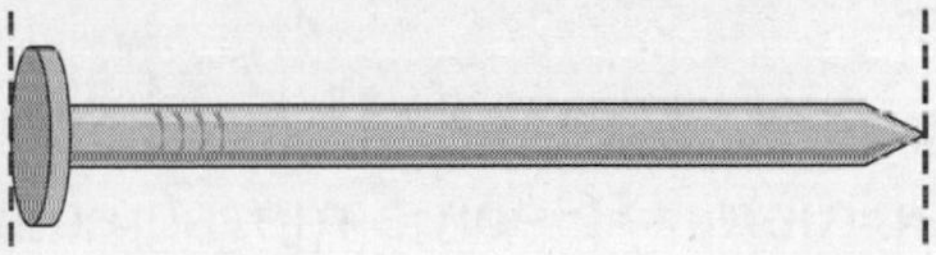

____

5. **Estimation** Estimate the length of your leg in centimeters. Then check your estimate.

____

6. **Reasonableness** Kent says that half of a decimeter is 3 cm. Do you agree? Explain.

____

Name ____________________

Using Centimeters and Decimeters

In **1–4**, estimate each length. Then measure to the nearest centimeter.

1. 

____

2. 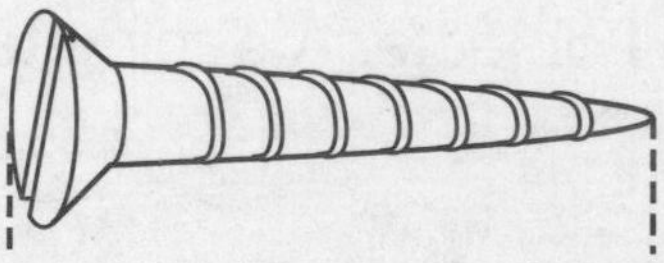

____

3. 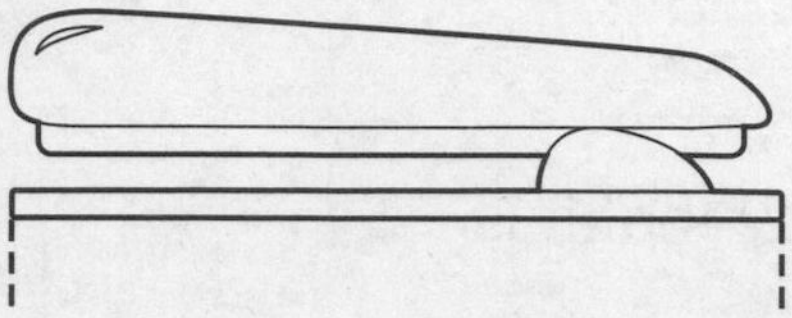

____

4. 

____

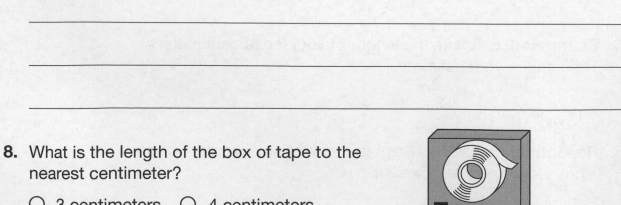

5. Draw a Diagram Draw a line segment that is 6 centimeters long.

6. Estimation Estimate the length of your desk in centimeters. Then measure the length of your desk.

____

7. Reasonableness Marian measured the length of a piece of paper as 7 decimeters. George measured the same length as 70 centimeters. Their teacher said they both are correct. Is that possible?

____

____

____

8. What is the length of the box of tape to the nearest centimeter?

○ 3 centimeters ○ 4 centimeters
○ 5 centimeters ○ 6 centimeters

Name ________________________________

Using Meters and Kilometers

The units of metric length are listed below.

Metric Units of Length		
100 centimeters	=	1 meter (m)
1,000 meters	=	1 kilometer (km)

Meters are used to measure items like large pieces of lumber. They are also used to measure short distances, such as the distance from the house to the garage.

Kilometers are used to measure longer distances, such as the distance between two towns.

In **1–3**, tell if meter or kilometer is the better unit for each measurement.

1. The height of a ceiling

____

2. The length of a football field

____

3. The length of Lake Erie

____

In **4** and **5**, choose the better estimate.

4. The length of a car
5 meters or 5 kilometers

____

5. The length of a racecar track
3 meters or 3 kilometers

____

6. 7 meters = ■ centimeters

____

7. 5 kilometers = ■ meters

____

8. **Writing to Explain** How do you convert 3 meters to centimeters?

____

____

Name ____________________

Practice
17-2

Using Meters and Kilometers

In **1** and **2**, change the units. Complete.

1. How many centimeters are there in 3 meters, 25 centimeters?

____

2. 5 meters = ■ centimeters

____

In **3** and **4**, choose the better estimate.

3. The length of a key
3 centimeters or 3 meters

____

4. The length of bike path
2 meters or 2 kilometers

____

5. Complete the table.

km	1	2	3	4
m	1,000	2,000		

6. **Estimation** Is the length of a pencil greater than or less than 1 meter? Explain.

____

____

____

7. **Reasonableness** Andy lives 6 kilometers from the mall. He said he lives 600 meters away from the mall. Is Andy's statement reasonable? Explain.

____

____

____

8. Which is the best estimate for the length of a calculator?

○ 1 meter ○ 1 centimeter ○ 10 meters ○ 10 centimeters

Name ______________________

Reteaching
17-3

Metric Units of Capacity

Two units of capacity in the metric system are milliliters (mL) and liters (L).

1 liter = 1,000 milliliters

Milliliters are used to measure very small amounts of liquid.

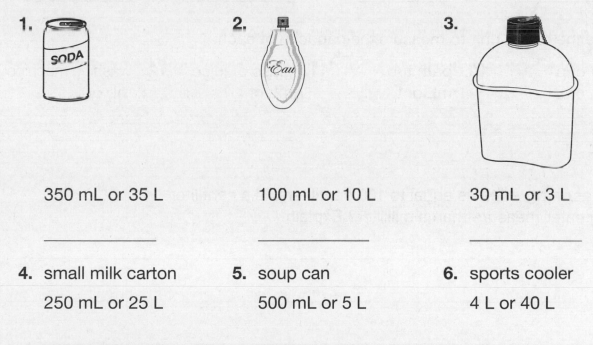

1 teaspoon = 5 milliliters

A liter is slightly larger than a quart. Many beverages are sold in 1-liter and 2-liter bottles.

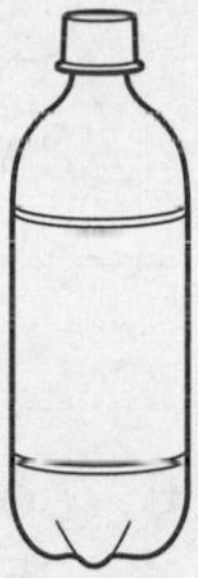

Choose the better estimate for each.

1. 

350 mL or 35 L

______

2. 

100 mL or 10 L

______

3. 

30 mL or 3 L

______

4. small milk carton

250 mL or 25 L

______

5. soup can

500 mL or 5 L

______

6. sports cooler

4 L or 40 L

______

7. **Reasonableness** Which is the better unit to use to measure the capacity of a bathtub: milliliters or liters? Explain your choice.

____

____

____

Name ______________________

Practice
17-3

Metric Units of Capacity

Choose the better estimate for each.

1. 
2 mL or 2 L
______

2. 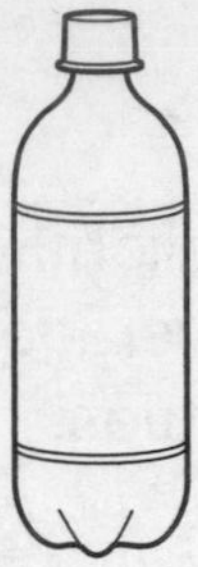
2 mL or 2 L
______

3. 
5 mL or 5 L
______

4. 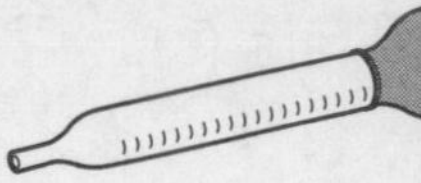
1 mL or 1 L
______

5. kitchen sink
2 L or 20 L
______

6. coffee cup
250 mL or 25 L
______

7. thermos
2 L or 20 L
______

8. pitcher
40 mL or 4 L
______

Choose the better unit to measure the capacity of each.

9. tea cup
mL or L
______

10. bath tub
mL or L
______

11. glass of juice
mL or L
______

12. washing machine
mL or L
______

13. Reasoning A liter is equal to 100 centiliters. Is a centiliter a greater measure than a milliliter? Explain.

____

____

____

14. Estimate Which is the best estimate for the capacity of a large bottle of water?

○ 1 L ○ 400 mL ○ 4 L ○ 40 mL

Name ______________________

Reteaching
17-4

Units of Mass

Mass is the measure of how much matter is in an object. Units of mass include grams (g) and kilograms (kg).

1 kilogram = 1,000 grams

A paper clip has a mass of about 1 gram.

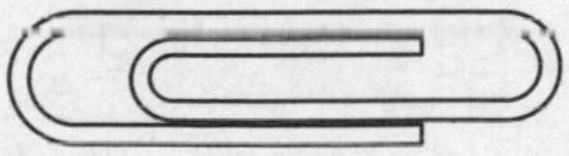

A large baseball bat has a mass of about 1 kilogram.

Choose the better estimate for each.

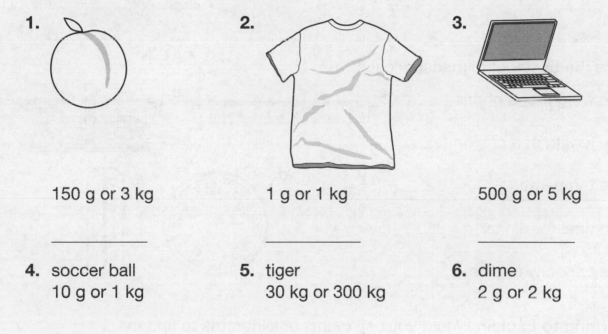

1.

150 g or 3 kg

____

2.

1 g or 1 kg

____

3.

500 g or 5 kg

____

4. soccer ball
10 g or 1 kg

____

5. tiger
30 kg or 300 kg

____

6. dime
2 g or 2 kg

____

7. Number Sense Julie has a box of paper clips that have a mass of 1 gram each. The entire box has a mass of 1 kilogram. How many paper clips are in the box? Explain your answer.

____

____

____

Name ______________________

Practice
17-4

Units of Mass

Choose the better estimate for each.

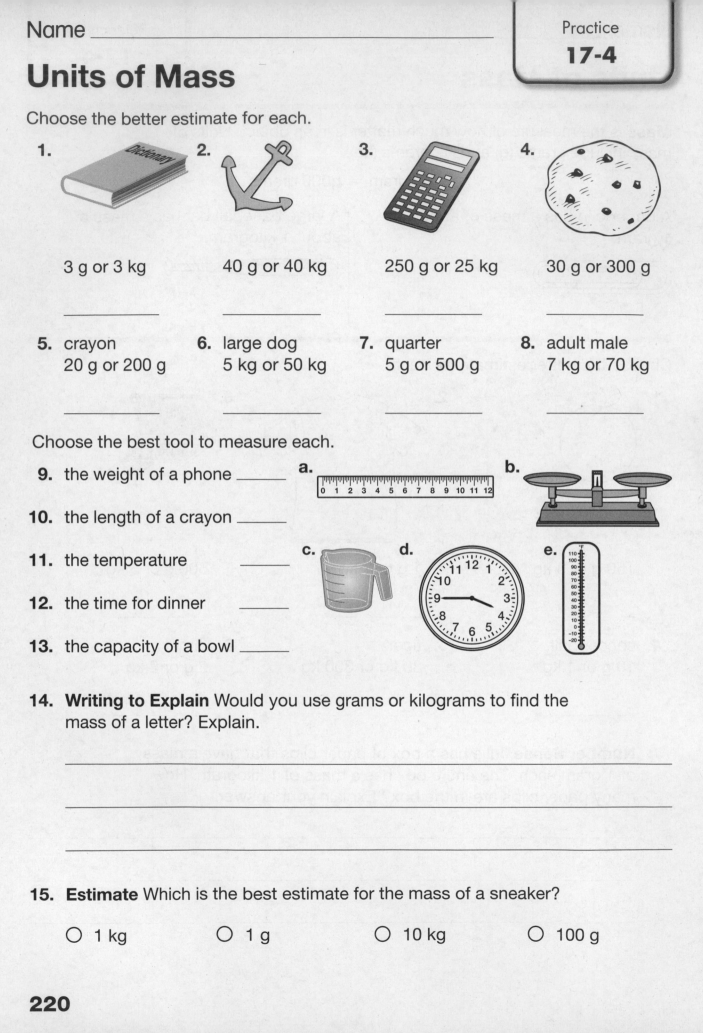

1.

3 g or 3 kg

______

2.

40 g or 40 kg

______

3.

250 g or 25 kg

______

4.
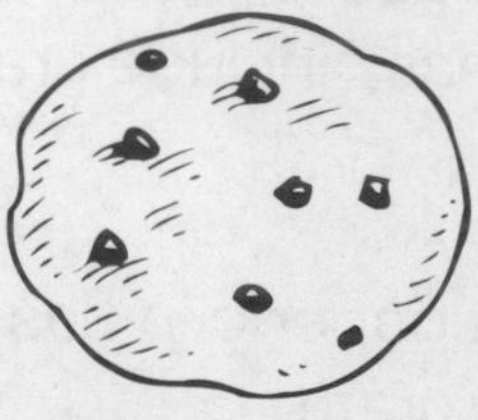

30 g or 300 g

______

5. crayon
20 g or 200 g

______

6. large dog
5 kg or 50 kg

______

7. quarter
5 g or 500 g

______

8. adult male
7 kg or 70 kg

______

Choose the best tool to measure each.

9. the weight of a phone ______

10. the length of a crayon ______

11. the temperature ______

12. the time for dinner ______

13. the capacity of a bowl ______

a.
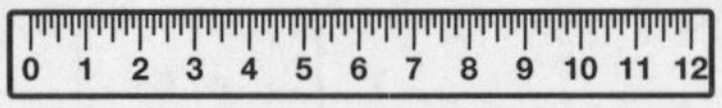

b.
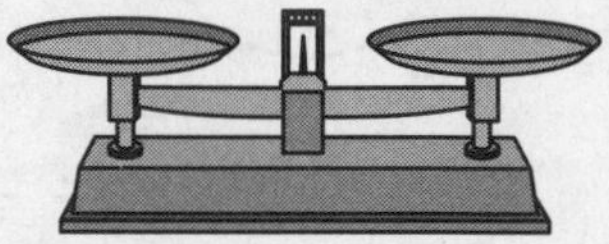

c.

d.

e.
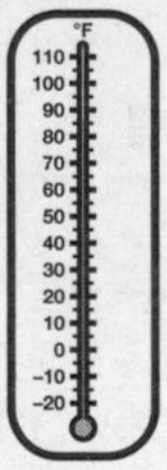

14. Writing to Explain Would you use grams or kilograms to find the mass of a letter? Explain.

____

____

____

15. Estimate Which is the best estimate for the mass of a sneaker?

○ 1 kg ○ 1 g ○ 10 kg ○ 100 g

Name ______________________

Converting Units

Below are the conversions for metric units.

Units of Length	Units of Mass
1 centimeter (cm) = 10 millimeters (mm)	1 kilogram (kg) = 1,000 grams (g)
1 meter (m) = 100 centimeters	**Units of Capacity**
1 kilometer (km) = 1,000 meters	1 liter (L) = 1,000 milliliters (mL)

To convert a larger unit to a smaller unit, multiply. For example, to convert centimeters to millimeters, multiply by 10.

Change the units.

1. 3 liters = ☐ milliliters

2. 4 centimeters = ☐ millimeters

3. 5 kilograms = ☐ grams

4. 7 meters = ☐ centimeters

5. 8 kilometers = ☐ meters

6. 9 meters = ☐ millimeters

7. 5 liters 300 milliliters = ☐ milliliters

8. 6 kilograms 500 grams = ☐ grams

9. **Number Sense** The distance from Beth's home to Susan's home is 3 kilometers 405 meters. How many meters is Beth's home from Susan's home? Explain how you found your answer.

____

____

____

Name ______________________________

Practice
17-5

Converting Units

Change the units.

1. 6 liters = ☐ milliliters
2. 5 meters = ☐ centimeters
3. 4 kilograms = ☐ grams
4. 9 centimeters = ☐ millimeters
5. How many milliliters are there in 3 liters 400 milliliters?
   ____
6. How many centimeters are there in 2 meters 35 centimeters?
   ____
7. Randi is training for a 10-kilometer run. What is the length of the run in meters?
   ____
8. A book has a mass of 2 kilograms. How many grams is the mass of the book?
   ____
9. An eraser is 6 centimeters 5 millimeters long. How many millimeters long is the eraser?
   ____
10. **Reasonableness** Which is a greater length: 80 centimeters or 8 meters? Explain your answer.
    ____
    ____
    ____
11. **Explain It** A park has 3 paths that are each 400 meters long. If you walk each of the paths will you have walked a kilometer? Explain.
    ____
    ____
    ____
12. Which is equal to 4 kilograms 5 grams?
    - ○ 405 grams
    - ○ 4,005 grams
    - ○ 4,050 grams
    - ○ 4,500 grams

Name ______________________________

Reteaching
17-6

Problem Solving: Make a Table and Look for a Pattern

Sharon has started a walking program with her puppy Fido. How many meters will they walk on Day 4? Day 5?

The table shows how many meters Sharon and Fido have walked each day. Look for a pattern.

Day	1	2	3	4	5
Distance Walked (m)	200	400	600		

Each day they walked 200 meters longer than the day before. Use the pattern to find how many meters they will walk on Day 4 and Day 5.

Day 4
600 m + 200 m = 800 m

Day 5
800 m + 200 m = 1,000 m

Complete the table. Write to explain the pattern. Solve.

1. Eddie has a board that is 80 centimeters long. He is cutting the board into pieces that are each 10 centimeters long. What is the length of the board after Eddie has made 3 cuts? 4 cuts?

Number of Cuts	0	1	2	3	4
Length of Board Left	80 cm	70 cm	60 cm		

____

____

____

____

2. Chuck is putting a border in his room. Each piece of border is 2 meters long. What is the length of 4 pieces of border? 5 pieces of border?

Number of Pieces	1	2	3	4	5
Total Length	2 m	4 m	6 m		

____

____

____

____

Name ______________________

Practice
17-6

Problem Solving: Make a Table and Look for a Pattern

Complete the table. Write to explain the pattern.

1. Fred is putting tables together to make one long table. Each table is shaped like a square and is 3 meters long. What is the length of 4 tables? 5 tables?

Number of Tables	1	2	3	4	5
Total Length	3 m	6 m	9 m		

____

____

____

____

2. Sheila is cutting a board that is 72 centimeters long. She is cutting the board into pieces that are each 9 centimeters long. What is the length of the board after Sheila has made 3 cuts? 4 cuts?

Number of Pieces	0	1	2	3	4
Length of Board Left	72 cm	63 cm	54 cm		

____

____

____

____

3. Cindy is linking toy train cars together. What is the total length of the train with 4 cars? 5 cars?

Number of Train Cars	1	2	3	4	5
Total Length	20 cm	40 cm	60 cm		

____

____

____

____

4. Dennis is stacking boxes on top of each other. Each box is 8 centimeters high. What is the height of 4 boxes? 5 boxes?

Number of Boxes	1	2	3	4	5
Total Height	8 cm	16 cm	24 cm		

____

____

____

____

Name ____________________

Understanding Perimeter

The **perimeter** of a figure is the distance around it.

The perimeter is found by adding the lengths of the sides.

4 in. + 6 in. + 7 in. + 5 in. + 11 in. + 11 in. = 44 in.

The perimeter of the figure is 44 inches.

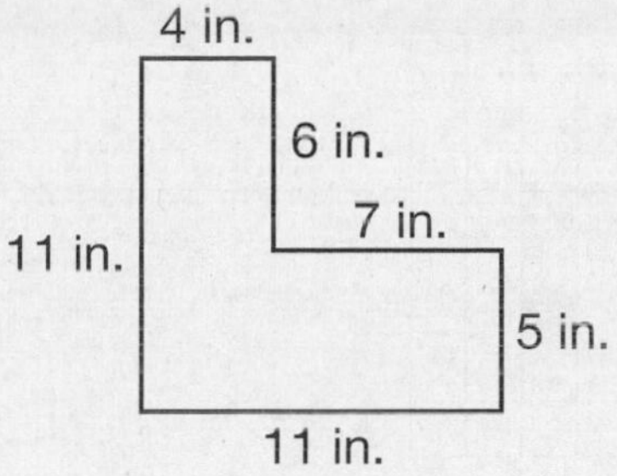

1. 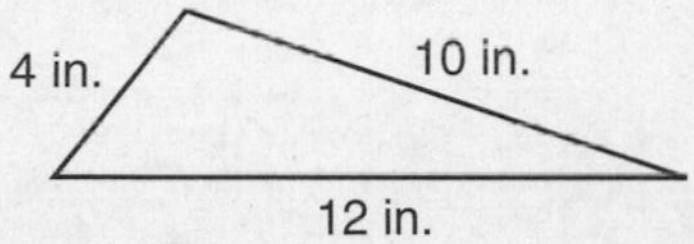

2. 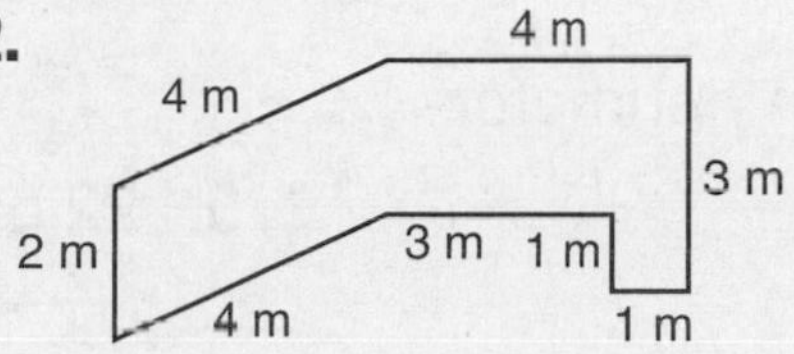

3. 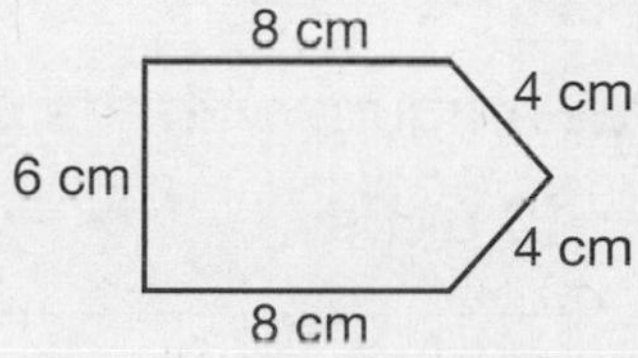

____________ ____________ ____________

Draw a figure with the given perimeter.

4. 6 units

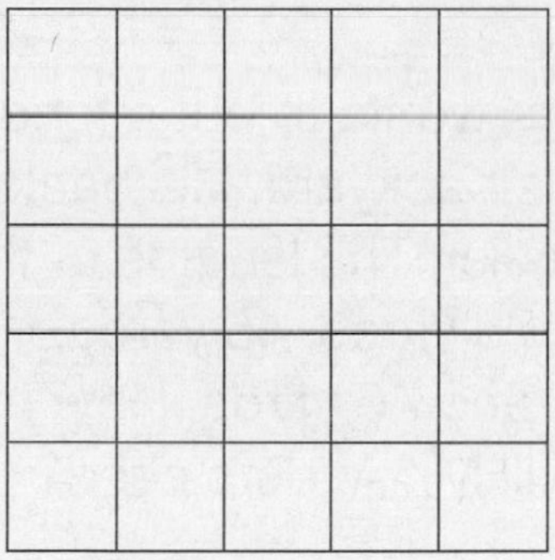

5. 10 units

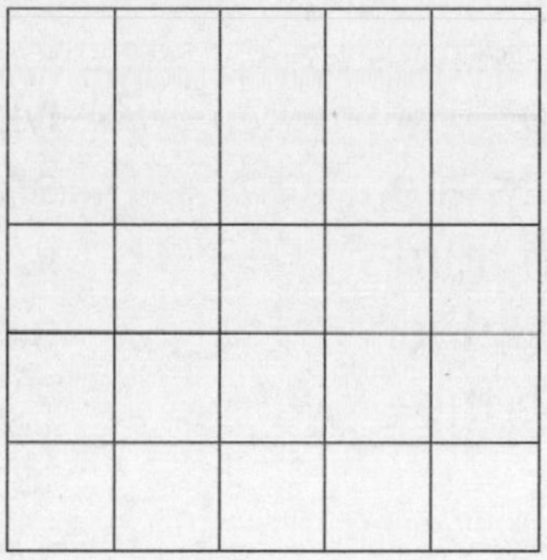

6. 10 units

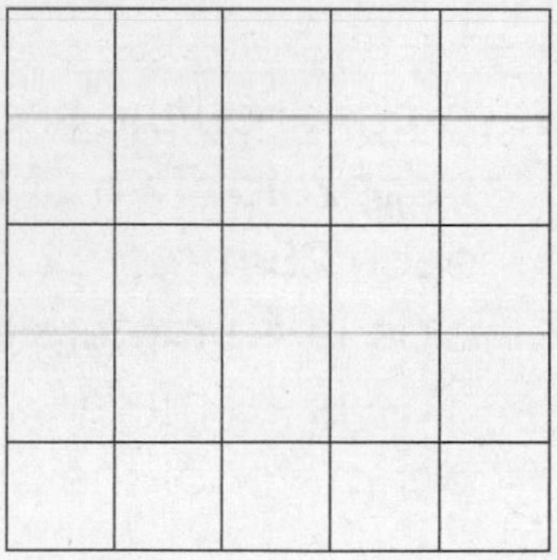

7. **Number Sense** A rectangle has a length of 5 yards and a width of 3 yards. What is its perimeter? Explain your answer.

____

____

Name ___________________________

Practice **18-1**

Understanding Perimeter

Find the perimeter of each polygon.

1. 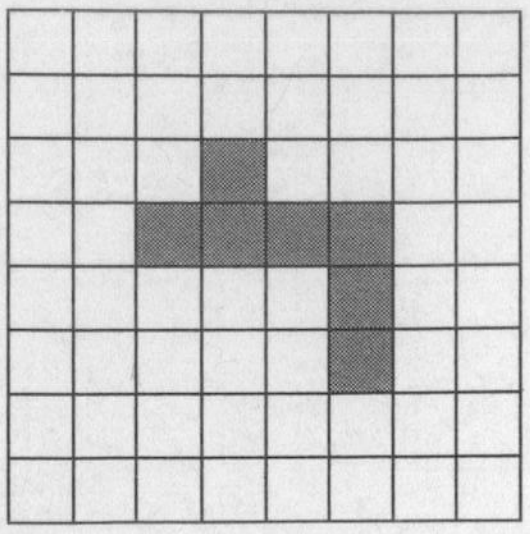

2. 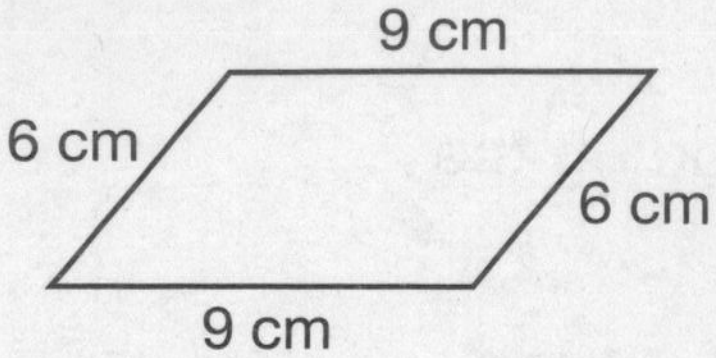

3. 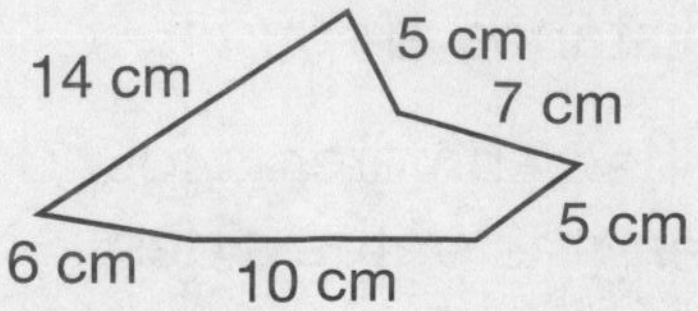

______________ ______________ ______________

Draw a figure with the given perimeter.

4. 10 units

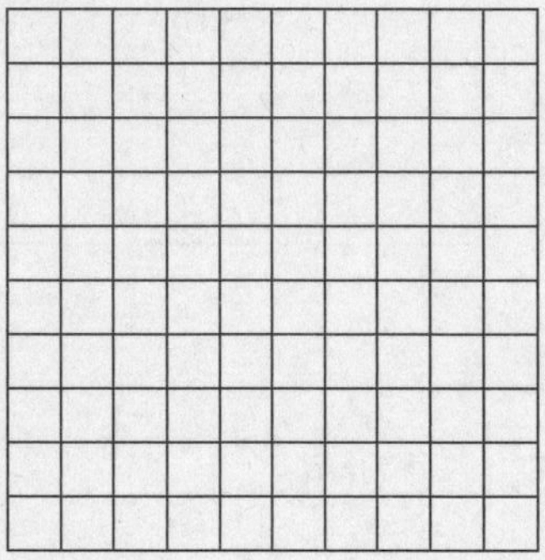

5. 22 units

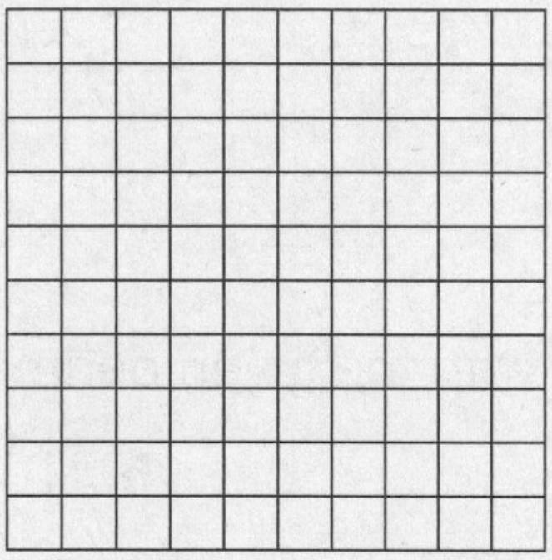

6. A park has the shape of a trapezoid. Two of the sides are each 25 meters long. The third side is 40 meters and the other side is 20 meters. What is the perimeter of the park?

____

7. Mr. Anders wants to put a fence around his backyard. His backyard is rectangular. The lengths of the sides are 75 yards, 45 yards, 75 yards, and 45 yards. How much fencing will Mr. Anders need?

____

8. **Writing to Explain** When finding the perimeter of a figure on a grid, why do you not count the spaces inside the grid?

____

____

9. Which rectangle has a perimeter of 16 units?

- ○ Length 5 units, width 3 units
- ○ Length 10 units, width 6 units
- ○ Length 8 units, width 1 unit
- ○ Length 6 units, width 3 units

Name ______________________________

Reteaching
18-2

Perimeter of Common Shapes

Use the properties of these common shapes to determine the missing side lengths. Then find the perimeter.

Rectangle

Two pairs of sides have the same length.

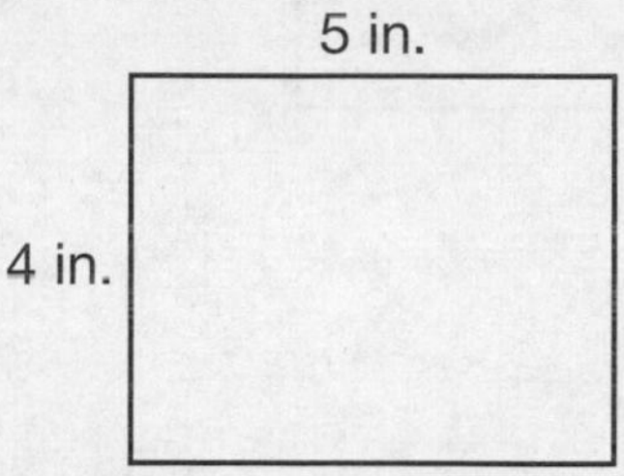

4 in. + 5 in. + 4 in. + 5 in. = 18 in.

Square

All 4 sides have the same length.

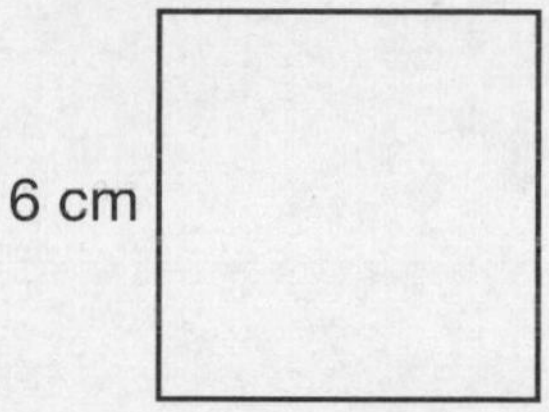

6 cm + 6 cm + 6 cm + 6 cm = 24 cm

Equilateral Triangle

All 3 sides have the same length.

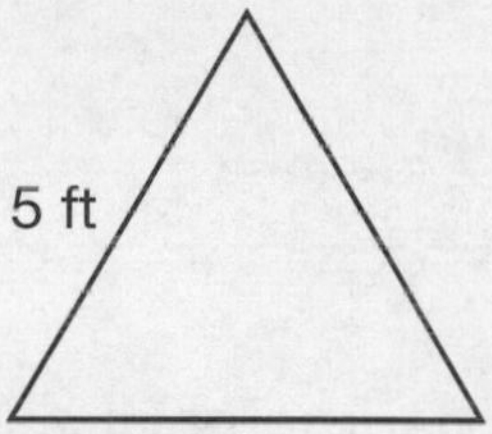

5 ft + 5 ft + 5 ft = 15 ft

Find the perimeter of each polygon.

1.

____

2.

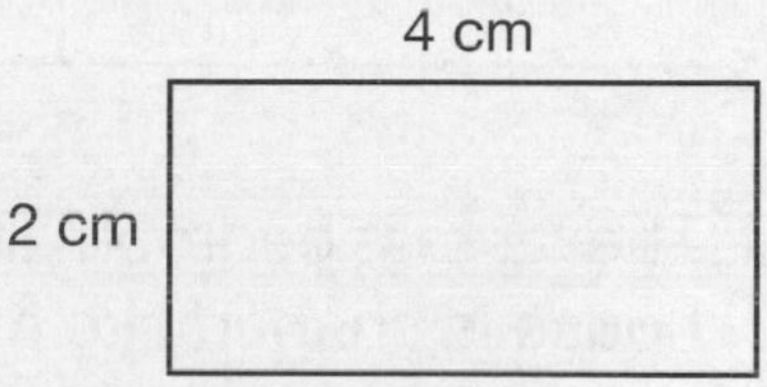

____

3.

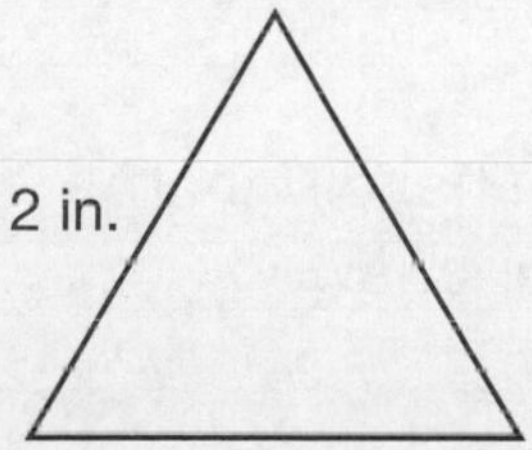

____

4.

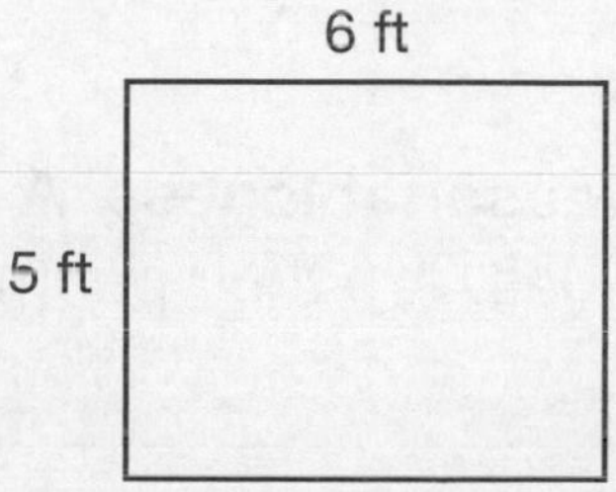

____

5. Reasonableness Can two different size squares have the same perimeter? Explain.

____

____

Name ______________________________

Perimeter of Common Shapes

Use a centimeter ruler to measure the length of the sides of the polygon. Find the perimeter.

1.

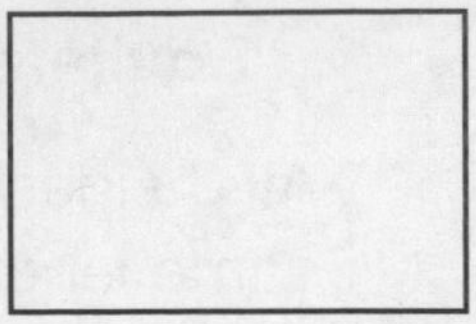

____

2.

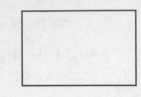

____

Find the perimeter of each figure.

3.

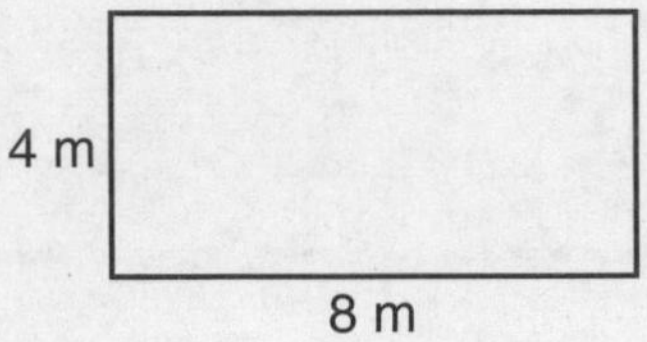

____

4.

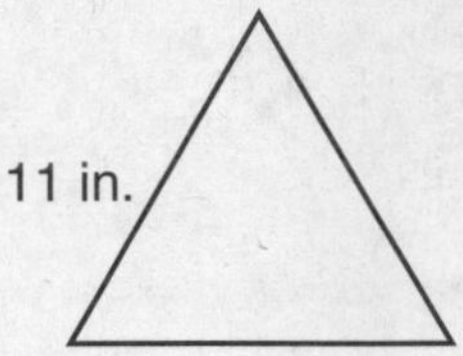

____

5. The largest bedroom in Lauren's house is shaped like a square with sides of 6 yards. What is the perimeter of that bedroom?

____

6. The basketball court at Johnson Elementary School is in the shape of a rectangle. It is 92 feet long and 46 feet wide. What is the perimeter of the basketball court?

____

7. Reasonableness A square and a pentagon each have 9-inch sides. Are their perimeters the same? Explain your answer.

____

____

8. What is the perimeter of a hexagon that has sides of 12 inches?

○ 60 inches ○ 66 inches ○ 72 inches ○ 84 inches

Name ____________________

Understanding Area

The **area** of a figure can be found in two ways.

A **square unit** is a square with sides that are each 1 unit long.

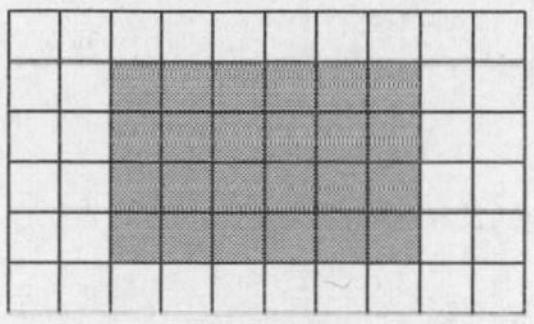

□ = 1 square inch

Count the square units in the shaded rectangle. There are 24 squares shaded. So, the area of the rectangle is 24 square inches.

You can think of the grid squares as an array.

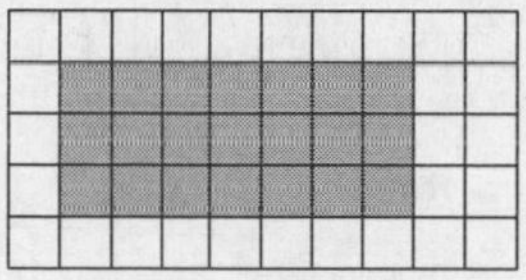

□ = 1 square centimeter

Each row has 7 squares. There are 3 rows, so multiply $3 \times 7 = 21$. The area of the rectangle is 21 square centimeters.

Find the area of each figure.

1.

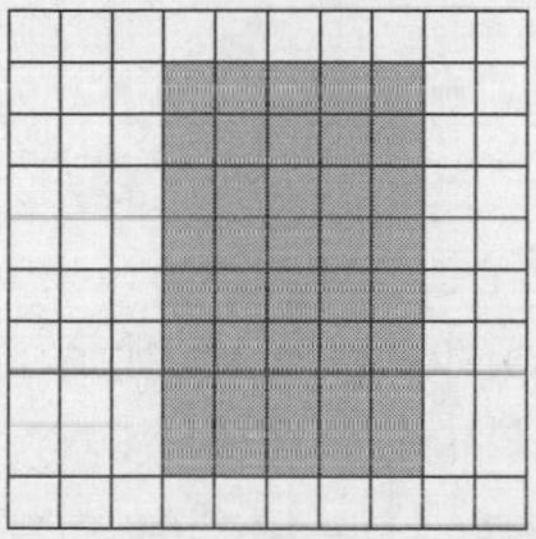

□ = 1 square inch

____

2.

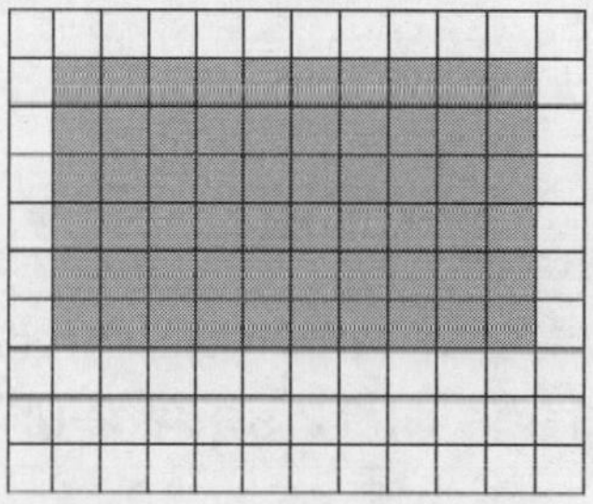

□ = 1 square meter

____

3.

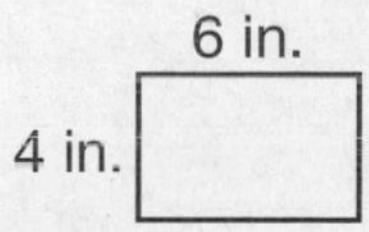

____

4.

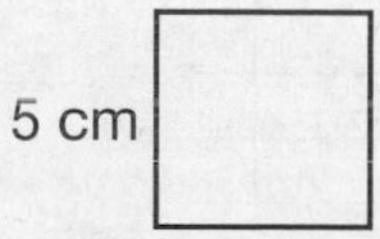

____

5. Reasonableness Can two different size rectangles have the same area? Explain.

____

____

Name ______________________

Practice **18-3**

Understanding Area

Find the area of each figure.

1.

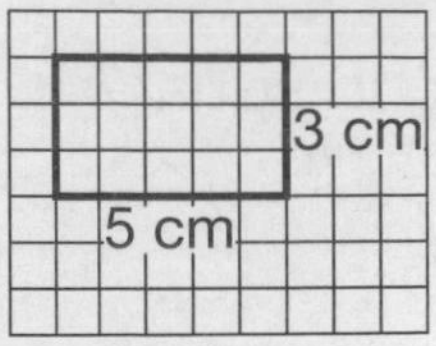

□ = 1 square cm

2.

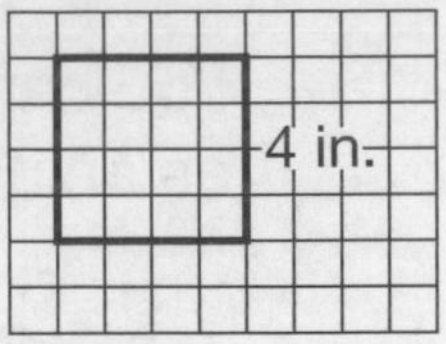

□ = 1 square in.

3.

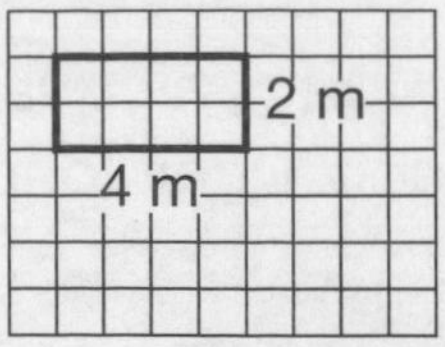

□ = 1 square m

4.

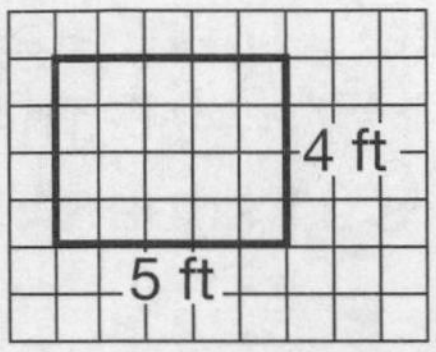

□ = 1 square ft

5.

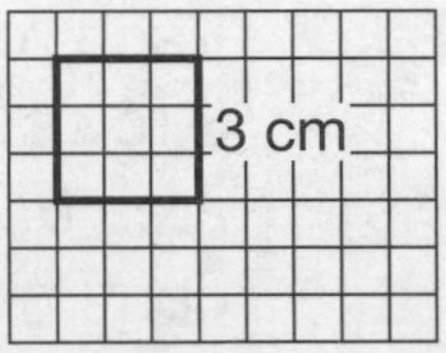

□ = 1 square cm

6.

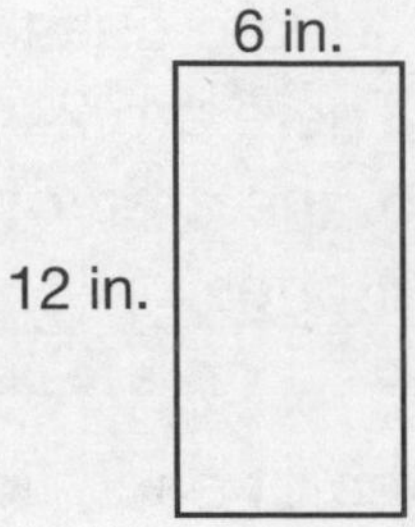

7. Draw a Picture On the grid, draw as many different rectangles as you can with areas of 12 square units.

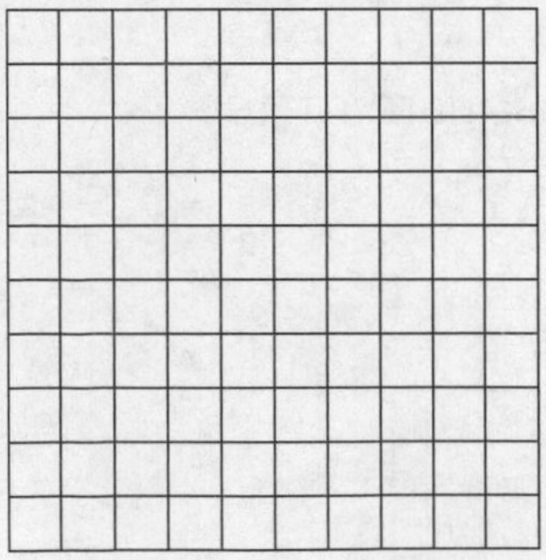

8. Reasoning Rectangular doghouses come in two sizes at the Super Z. The smaller size is 2 feet by 1 feet. The larger size is 4 feet by 2 feet. How many square feet greater is the larger doghouse?

9. What is the area of a square with sides of 5 inches?

○ 10 square inches
○ 20 square inches
○ 25 square inches
○ 50 square inches

Name ______________________________

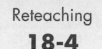

Estimating and Measuring Area

Two types of irregular figures can be placed on a grid.

If the shape completely fills the squares, count the squares.

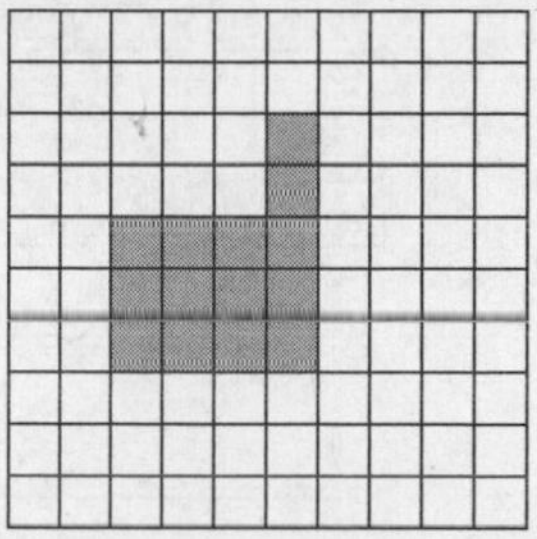

□ = 1 square inch

Count the squares by column or row. Let's try the columns from left to right.

3 + 3 + 3 + 5 = 14

The area is 14 square inches.

If the shape does not completely fill the squares, estimate the number of whole squares.

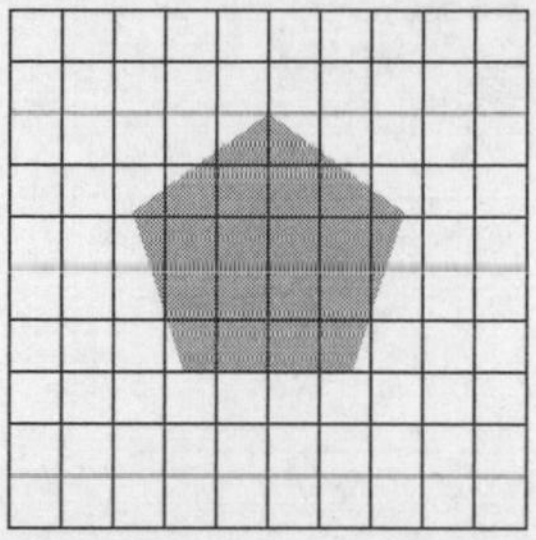

□ = 1 square inch

Count the number of whole squares. There are 12 whole squares.

Estimate the number of whole squares from the partial squares. About 5 whole squares could be made.

Add 12 + 5 = 17. The area is 17 square inches.

Find the area.

1.

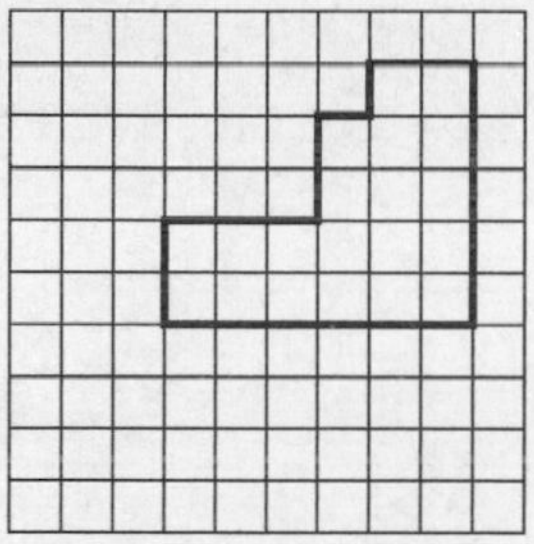

□ = 1 square foot

____

Estimate the area.

2.

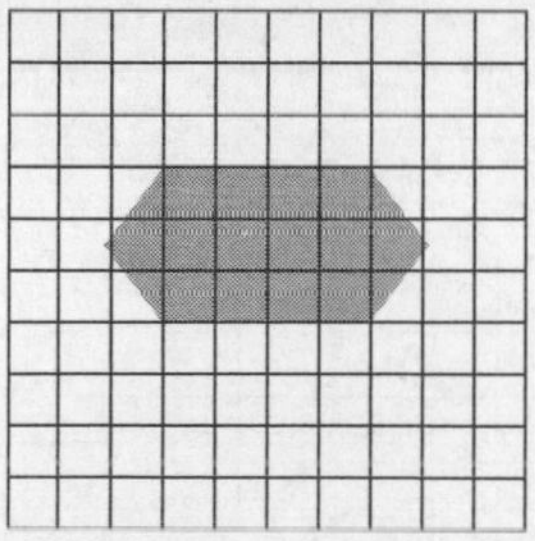

□ = 1 square centimeter

____

3. Writing to Explain A circle is on a grid. How can you estimate the area?

____

____

Name ____________________

Practice
18-4

Estimating and Measuring Area

Find the area of each figure in square units.

1.

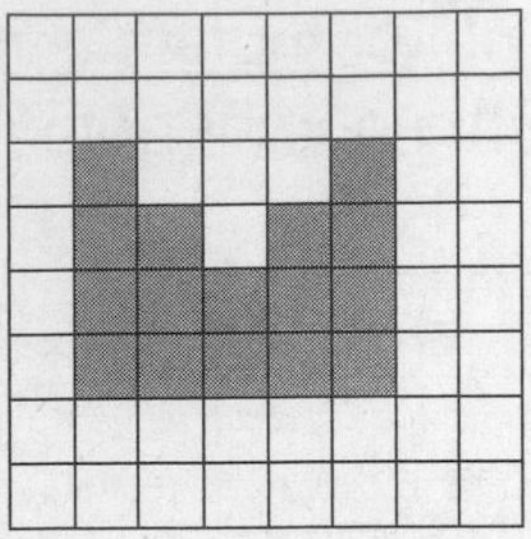

____

2.

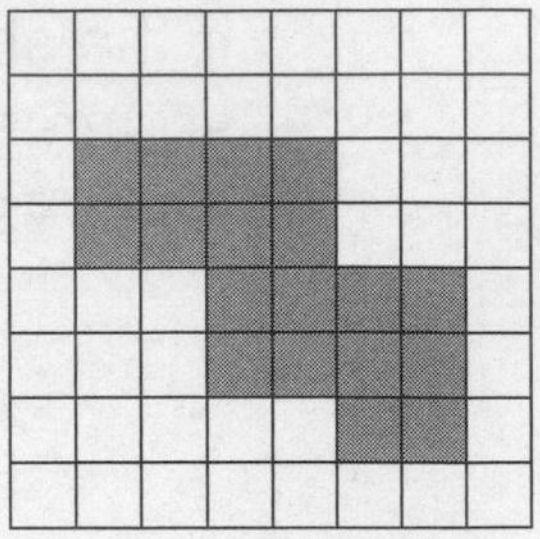

____

3.

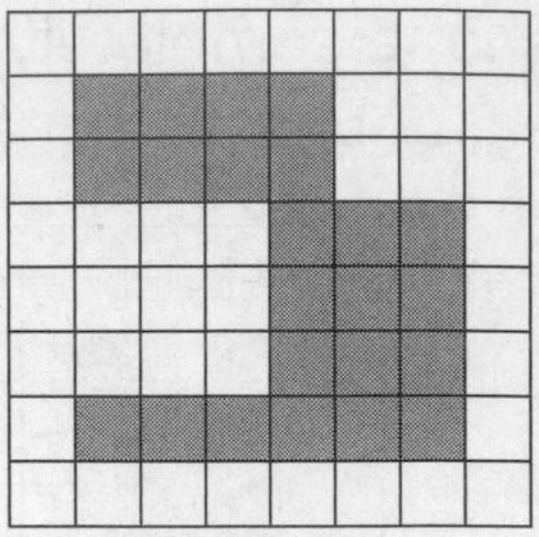

____

4.

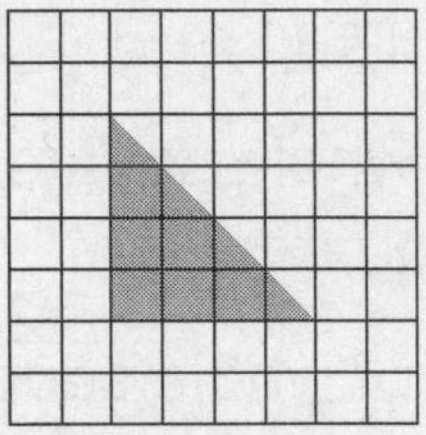

□ = 1 square cm

____

5.

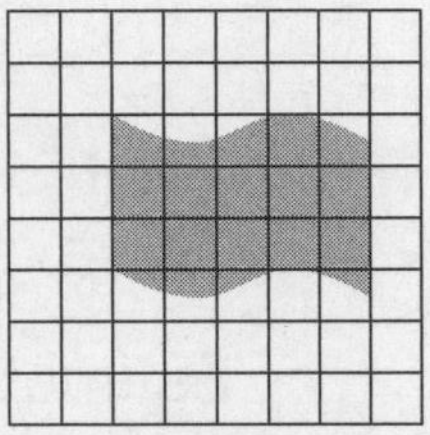

□ = 1 square foot

____

6.

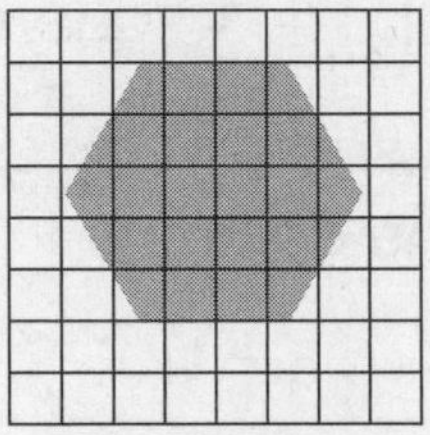

□ = 1 square inch

____

7. Reasoning Use the grid. Draw two different figures that each have a perimeter of 14 units. Then find the area of each.

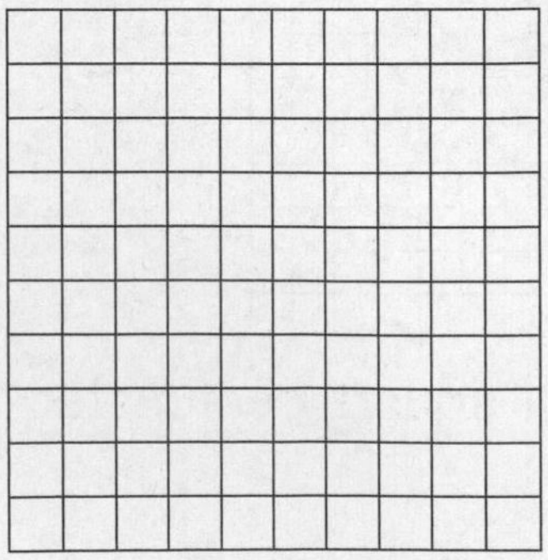

8. Journal What is the difference between the perimeter and the area of a polygon?

____

____

____

____

9. What is the area of the figure to the right?

- ○ 24 square units
- ○ 25 square units
- ○ 26 square units
- ○ 27 square units

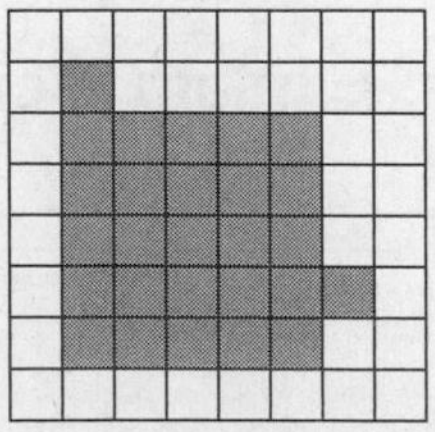

Name ______________________

Reteaching
18-5

Volume

Volume is the measure of the inside of a solid figure. Volume is measured in **cubic units**. A cubic unit is a cube with edges that are each 1 unit long.

To find the volume of a rectangular prism, follow these steps:

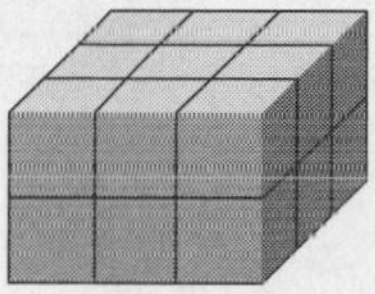

1. Count the number of cubes in each layer.

   There are 9 cubes in each layer.

2. Multiply the number of cubes in each layer by the number of layers.

   There are 2 layers.
   $2 \times 9 = 18$

The volume of the rectangular prism is 18 cubic units.

Find the volume of each figure in cubic units.

1. 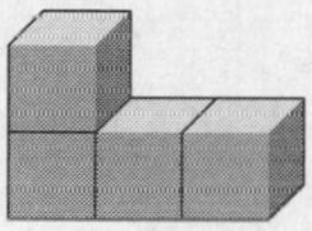

2. 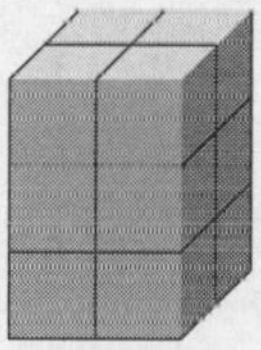

3. 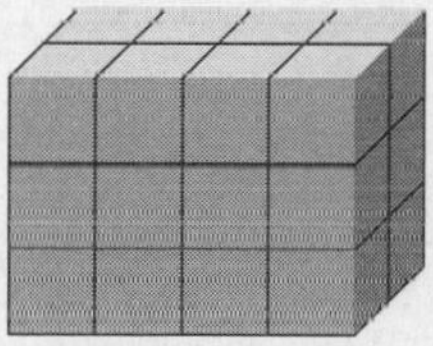

______

4. 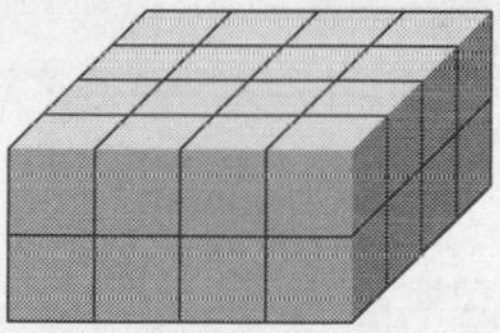

______

5. 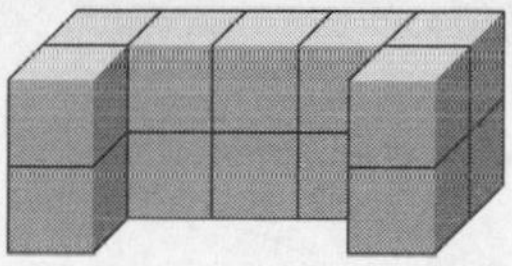

______

6. 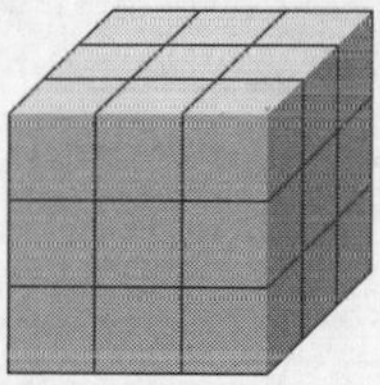

______

7. Writing to Explain How did you find the volume of the figure in Exercise 6?

______

______

______

Name ______________________________

Practice
18-5

Volume

Find the volume of each figure in cubic units.

1. 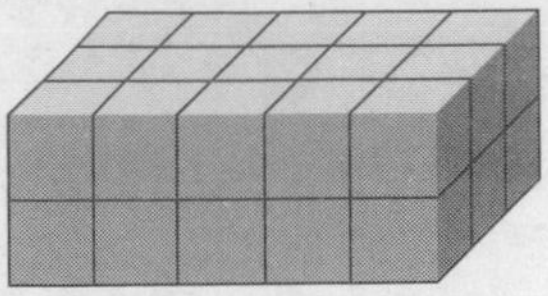

____

2. 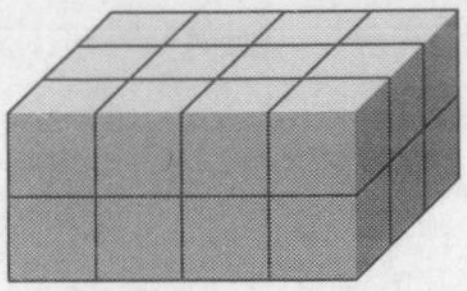

____

3. 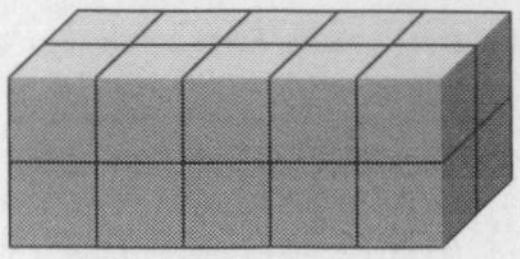

____

4. 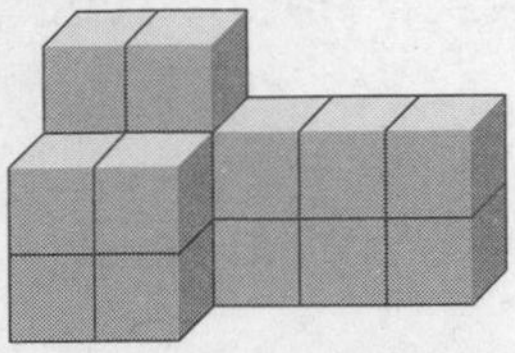

____

5. 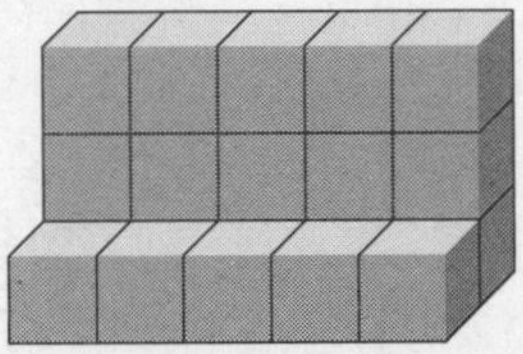

____

6. 

____

7. **Estimate** Use the cubes shown at the right to estimate the volume of the rectangular prism.

____

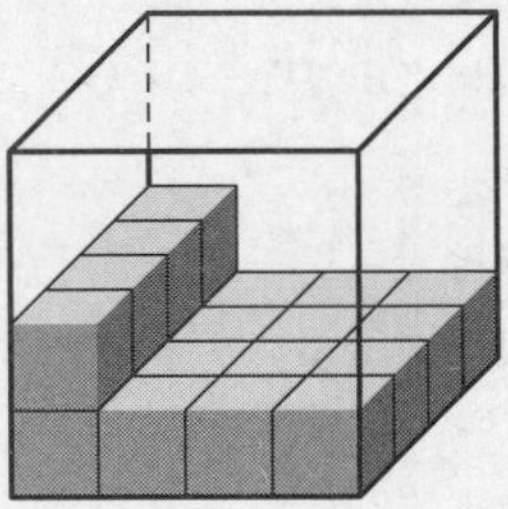

8. Kevin made a rectangular prism with 8 cubes in each layer. The prism had 4 layers. What is the volume of the rectangular prism?

____

9. **Journal** How is finding volume different from finding area?

____

____

____

10. What is the volume of the figure at the right?

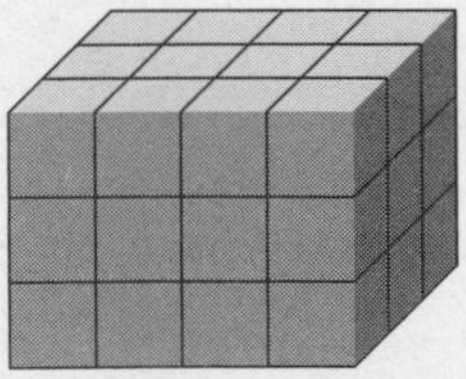

- ○ 12 cubic units
- ○ 24 cubic units
- ○ 27 cubic units
- ○ 36 cubic units

Name ______________________________

Problem Solving: Solve a Simpler Problem

How can you find the area of the shaded figure to the right?

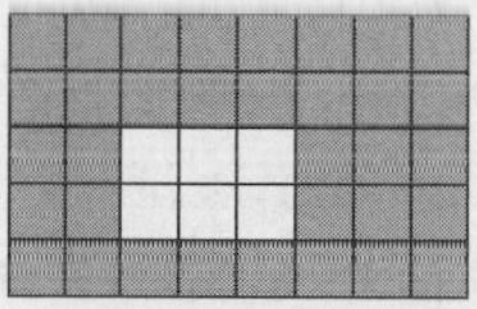

= 1 square inch

Think of it as 3 separate smaller figures.

Find the area of the 2 top rows.	2×8 sq in. $= 16$ sq in.
Find the area of the bottom row.	1×8 sq in. $= 8$ sq in.
Find the area of the two middle rows.	2×5 sq in. $= 10$ sq in.
Add the areas.	$16 + 8 + 10 = 34$

The area of the shaded figure is 34 square inches.

Solve. Use simpler problems.

1. Tyler High School has a T painted on the football field. The shaded part of the figure is the part that needs to be painted. What is the area of the painted part?

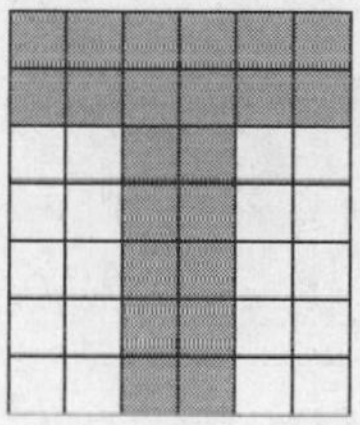

= 1 square meter

____

2. Maria is tiling one of the walls in her kitchen. The shaded part of the figure is the part that needs to be tiled. What is the area of the part that needs tiling?

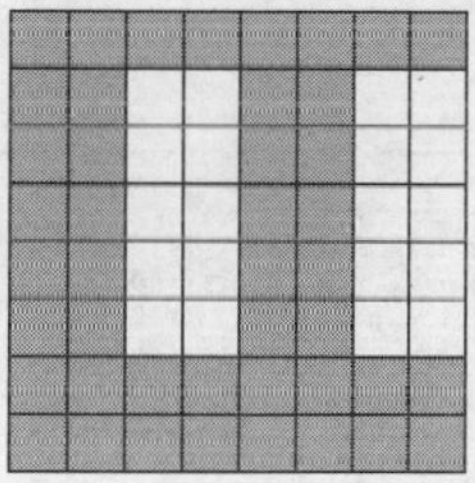

= 1 square yard

____

3. Writing to Explain Explain how you found your answer for Exercise 2.

____

____

____

Name ____________________

Practice
18-6

Problem Solving: Solve a Simpler Problem

Solve. Use simpler problems.

1. Ms. Finn is going to tile her kitchen floor. The shaded part of the figure is the part that needs to be tiled. What is the area of the shaded part?

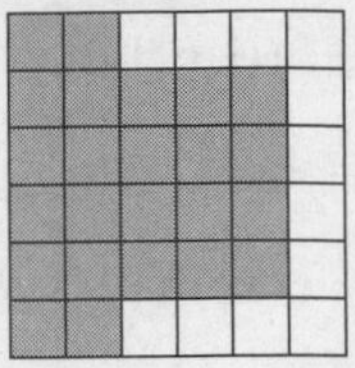

□ = 1 square yard

____

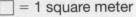

2. Alice is going to paint one of the walls in her bedroom. The shaded part of the figure is the part that needs to be painted. What is the area of the shaded part?

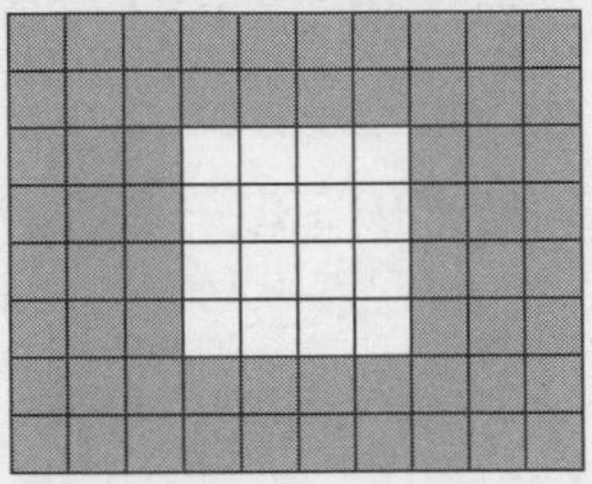

□ = 1 square foot

____

3. Harrison High School has an H painted on the football field. The shaded part of the figure is the part that needs to be painted. What is the area of the shaded part?

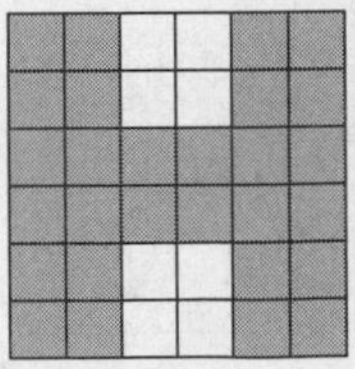

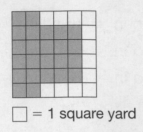

□ = 1 square meter

____

4. Mr. Rosen is going to repair the tiles in a shower. The shaded part of the figure is the part that needs to be tiled. What is the area of the shaded part?

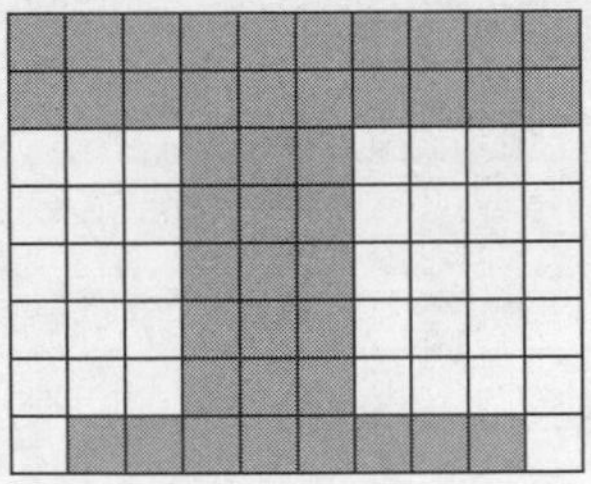

□ = 1 square foot

____

5. Luann is going to paint an L on her fence. The shaded part of the figure is the part that needs to be painted. What is the area of the shaded part?

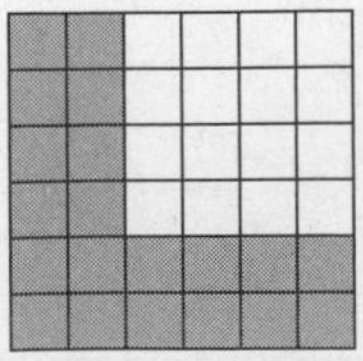

□ = 1 square inch

____

Name ____________________

Reteaching
19-1

Fractions and Decimals

Tenths show 10 equal parts of a whole. Hundredths show 100 equal parts of the whole. Fractions and decimals can be used to write tenths and hundredths.

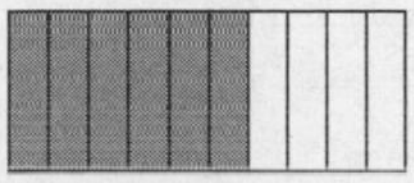

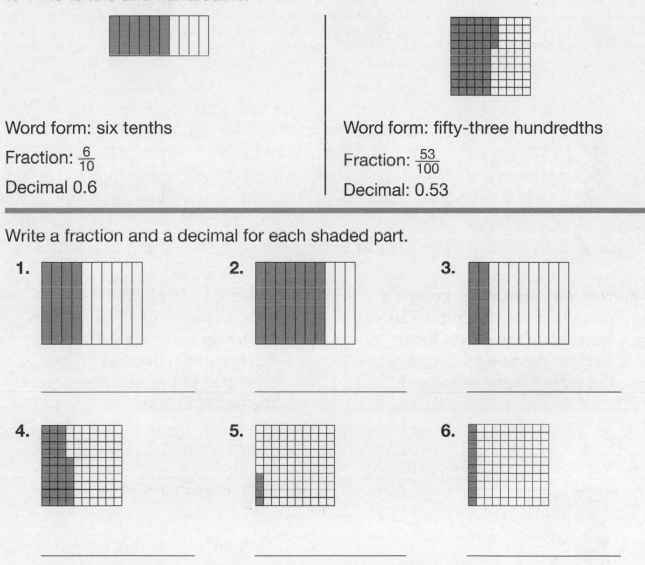

Word form: six tenths

Fraction: $\frac{6}{10}$

Decimal 0.6

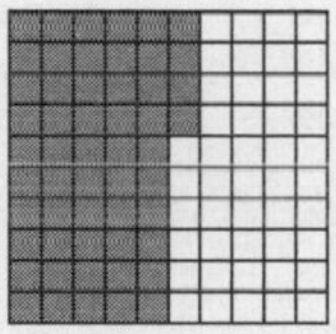

Word form: fifty-three hundredths

Fraction: $\frac{53}{100}$

Decimal: 0.53

Write a fraction and a decimal for each shaded part.

1. 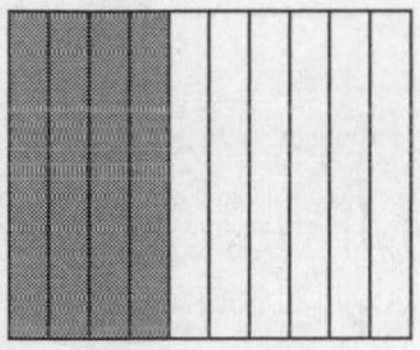
____

2. 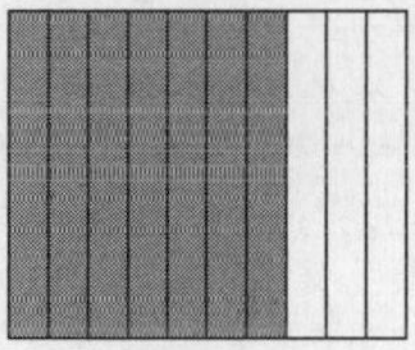
____

3. 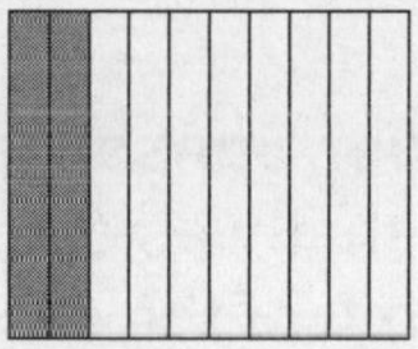
____

4. 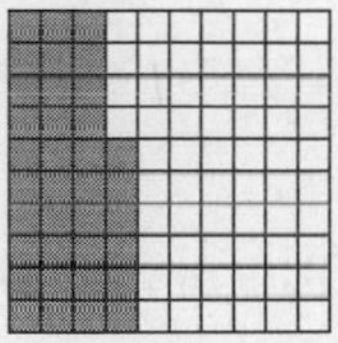
____

5. 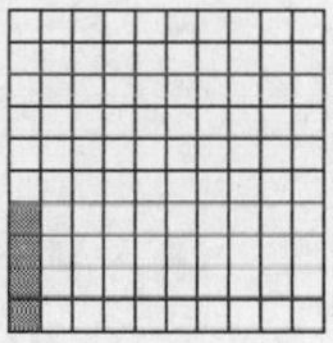
____

6. 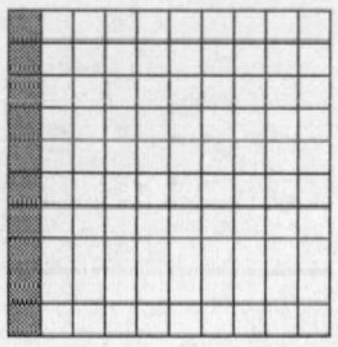
____

7. Number Sense How do you write $\frac{5}{10}$ as a decimal?

____

Name ______________________

Fractions and Decimals

Write a fraction and a decimal for each shaded part.

1.

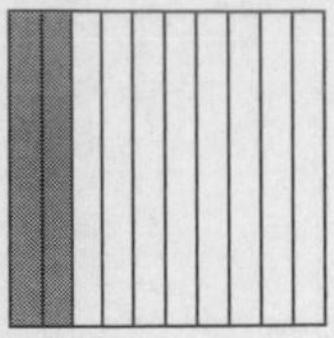

____

2.

____

3.

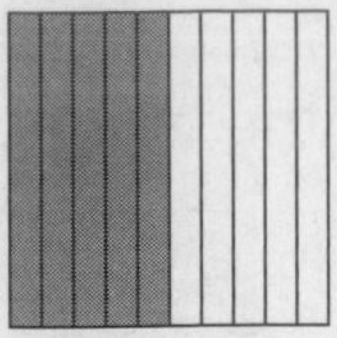

____

4.

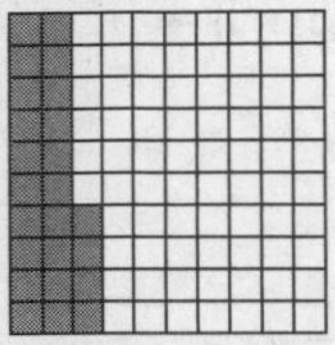

____

5.

____

6.

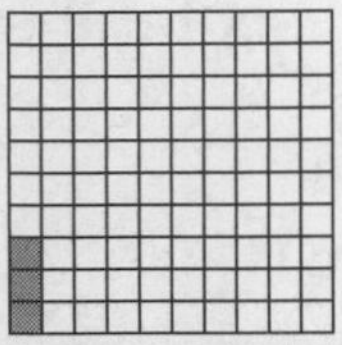

____

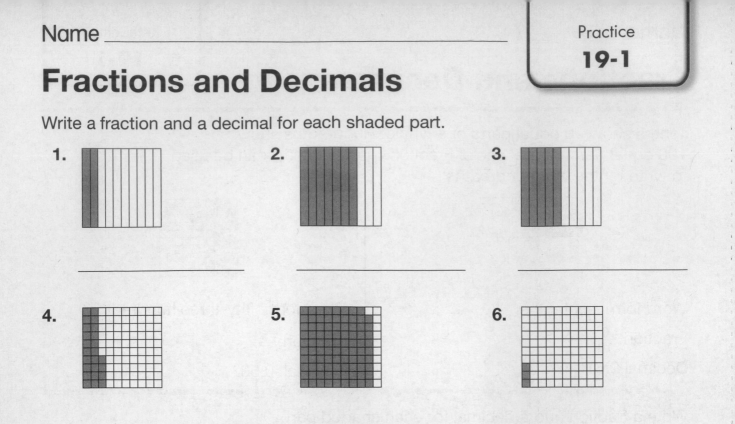

7. **Number Sense** Len bought a pizza that was cut into 10 slices. He ate 4 of the slices. What decimal represents the part of the pizza that remains?

____

8. There are 100 players in the soccer league. Of those players, 15 are on the Sharks. Write a fraction and a decimal to show what part of the league's players are on the Sharks.

____

9. What fraction is equal to 0.8?

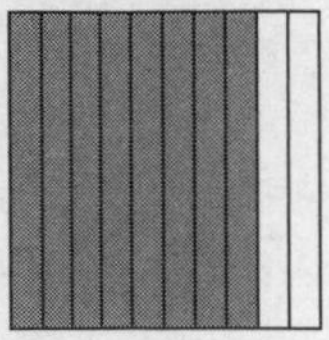

____

10. Which decimal is equivalent to $\frac{30}{100}$?

○ 30.0
○ 3.0
○ 0.3
○ 0.03

Name ____________________

Using Money to Understand Decimals

You can use money to help you to understand decimals. Coins are part of a dollar.

$0.01 $0.05 $0.10 $0.25 $0.50 $1.00

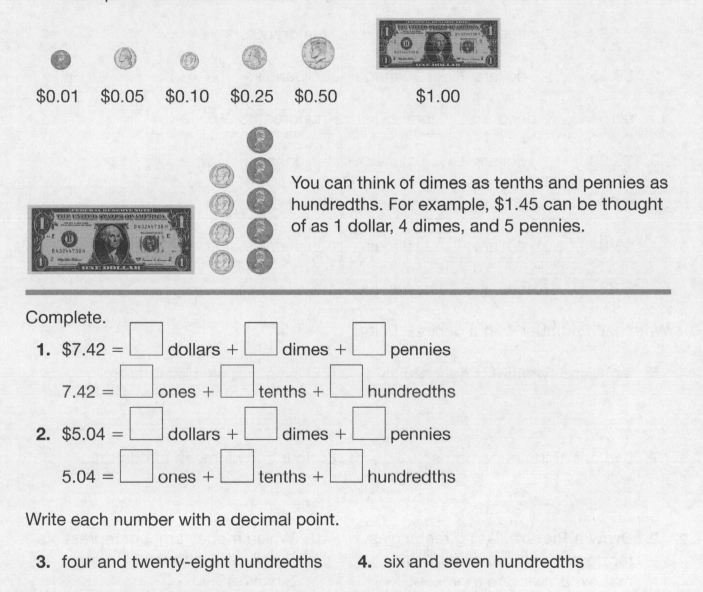

You can think of dimes as tenths and pennies as hundredths. For example, $1.45 can be thought of as 1 dollar, 4 dimes, and 5 pennies.

Complete.

1. $7.42 = ☐ dollars + ☐ dimes + ☐ pennies

7.42 = ☐ ones + ☐ tenths + ☐ hundredths

2. $5.04 = ☐ dollars + ☐ dimes + ☐ pennies

5.04 = ☐ ones + ☐ tenths + ☐ hundredths

Write each number with a decimal point.

3. four and twenty-eight hundredths ____________________

4. six and seven hundredths ____________________

5. **Reasoning** Rob has $2.30 with only dollar bills and dimes. Leslie also has $2.30, but she does not have any quarters, dimes, or nickels. What bills and coins could each have?

____

____

Name ____________________

Practice 19-2

Using Money to Understand Decimals

Complete.

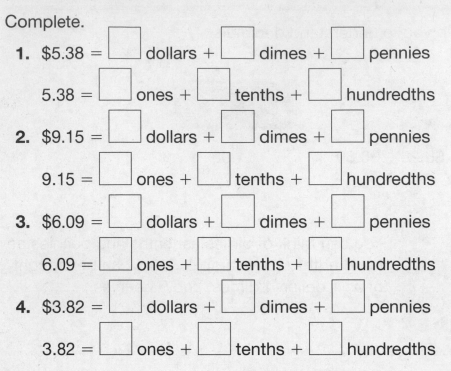

1. \$5.38 = ☐ dollars + ☐ dimes + ☐ pennies

   5.38 = ☐ ones + ☐ tenths + ☐ hundredths

2. \$9.15 = ☐ dollars + ☐ dimes + ☐ pennies

   9.15 = ☐ ones + ☐ tenths + ☐ hundredths

3. \$6.09 = ☐ dollars + ☐ dimes + ☐ pennies

   6.09 = ☐ ones + ☐ tenths + ☐ hundredths

4. \$3.82 = ☐ dollars + ☐ dimes + ☐ pennies

   3.82 = ☐ ones + ☐ tenths + ☐ hundredths

Write each number with a decimal point.

5. eight and twenty-six hundredths

   ____

6. seven and nine hundredths

   ____

7. two and thirty hundredths

   ____

8. four and nineteen hundredths

   ____

9. **Draw a Picture.** Using rectangles for dollars and circles for coins, make a drawing to represent \$2.65.

10. Which money amount represents 3 dollars, 4 quarters, 2 dimes, 3 nickels?

    ○ \$3.95
    ○ \$4.10
    ○ \$4.25
    ○ \$4.35

Name ______________________

Reteaching
19-3

Adding and Subtracting Money

You can add and subtract money as you would add and subtract whole numbers. The difference is that money has a dollar sign ($) and a decimal point. Place the decimal point in the sum or difference and then compute from right to left.

Add $12.50 + $9.25.

```
   0 12
  $1̶2̶.50
+   9.25
  $21.75
```

Subtract $15.85 − $8.79.

```
  0 15 7 15
  $1̶5̶.8̶5̶
−   8.79
   $7.06
```

1. $2.87 + 1.09

2. $15.21 − 2.27

3. $13.22 + 3.67

4. $10.07 − 0.88

5. $6.29 + 5.47

6. $20.00 − 9.52

7. $14.79 + 11.25

8. $17.21 − 12.33

9. $7.65 + $0.82 ________

10. $6.00 − $2.57 ________

11. $8.35 + $5.78 ________

12. $3.00 − $0.79 ________

13. $15.63 + $8.92 ________

14. $9.27 − $8.85 ________

15. Estimation George has a $10 bill. He buys a newspaper for $1.19 and a magazine for $3.67. Will George receive more or less than $5.00 in change? Explain.

____

____

Name ______________________

Practice
19-3

Adding and Subtracting Money

Find each sum or difference.

1. $7.29 − 1.03

2. $3.50 + 2.91

3. $6.00 − 2.59

4. $17.99 − 13.86

5. $20.00 − 18.42

6. $12.04 + 3.16

7. $4.21 + 3.99

8. $6.18 − 3.19

9. $7.83 + $0.62 ________

10. $16.02 − $5.19 ________

11. $18.21 + $14.36 ________

12. $27.36 − $15.29 ________

13. $1.25 + $0.59 + $3.57 ________

14. $30.00 − $21.78 ________

15. Cindy bought a T-shirt for $17.59 and a baseball cap for $12.85. How much money did Cindy spend all together?

____

16. Terrell bought a book for $15.97. He paid for the book with a $20 bill. How much change should Terrell receive back?

____

17. **Journal** How is adding and subtracting with money like adding and subtracting whole numbers?

____

____

____

____

____

18. Sam paid for a notebook that costs $2.76 with a $10 bill. What was his change?

○ $7.24 ○ $7.34
○ $8.24 ○ $12.76

Name ______________________________

Reteaching
19-4

Multiplying with Money

Multiplying with money is like multiplying with whole numbers. The difference is that there will be a dollar sign ($) and a decimal point.

Find $7.36 × 7.

Step 1

Multiply as you would with whole numbers.

```
 2 4
$7.36
×   7
$5152
```

Step 2

Place the dollar sign and the decimal point. The last two digits come after the decimal point.

```
  2 4
 $7.36
 ×   7
$51.52
```

Find each product.

1. $1.25 × 3

2. $6.98 × 2

3. $4.24 × 5

4. $3.42 × 8

5. $5.62 × 6

6. $0.09 × 5

7. $3.97 × 9

8. $9.37 × 7

9. 5 × $0.27 ________

10. 4 × $5.38 ________

11. 8 × $2.78 ________

12. **Estimation** A tuna sandwich costs $4.53. Kirk buys 3 sandwiches. Will it cost him more or less than $15.00? Explain your answer.

____

____

Name ______________________

Practice 19-4

Multiplying with Money

Find each product.

1. $1.32 × 6

2. $4.67 × 4

3. $6.04 × 9

4. $4.21 × 2

5. $7.49 × 3

6. $5.08 × 7

7. $8.29 × 3

8. $5.65 × 8

9. 6 × $0.82 ________

10. 7 × $6.49 ________

11. 5 × $3.22 ________

12. 4 × $7.90 ________

13. 5 × $0.78 ________

14. 9 × $1.78 ________

For **15–17**, use the table at the right.

15. What is the cost of 3 bagels?

____

Item	Cost
Sandwich	$2.99
Drink	$1.45
Donut	$0.72
Bagel	$0.87

16. Number Sense Mr. Dylan bought 2 sandwiches and 2 drinks. He paid with a $10 bill. How much change should Mr. Dylan receive?

____

17. How much money does 2 donuts and 2 bagels cost?

- ○ $1.59
- ○ $3.18
- ○ $3.38
- ○ $3.68

18. Write a Problem Write a problem that can be solved by buying more than one of the same item. Then solve your problem.

____

____

Name ______________________

Reteaching
19-5

Dividing with Money

Divide money the same way as you would divide whole numbers. The difference is you need to place the dollar sign and decimal point in the quotient. If the quotient is less than $1.00, write a 0 in the ones place.

Divide $5.80 ÷ 5.

Step 1

Divide the same way as with whole numbers.

```
     1 16
 5)$5.80
  − 5 00
      80
    − 50
      30
    − 30
       0
```

Step 2

Place the dollar sign and decimal point.

```
    $1.16
 5)$5.80
  − 5 00
      80
    − 50
      30
    − 30
       0
```

Complete. Find each quotient.

1.
```
    $1.
 3)$3.96
  − 3 00
  
  −____
  
  −____
       0
```

2.
```
    $0.8
 4)$3.56
  − 3 20
  
  −____
       0
```

3.
```
    $1.
 5)$8.85
  − 5 00
  
  −____
  
  −____
       0
```

4. **Number Sense** Nancy bought 6 notebooks for $8.46. Each notebook cost the same amount of money. How much money did each notebook cost?

____

Name ______________________

Practice
19-5

Dividing with Money

Complete. Find each quotient.

1.
```
      $1.
  4)$4.88
   - 4 00

    -____

    -____
        0
```

2.
```
      $0.7
  9)$6.57
   - 6 30

     -____
         0
```

3.
```
      $1.
  5)$6.35
   - 5 00

    -____

     -____
         0
```

Find each quotient.

4. $6.42 ÷ 6 ________

5. $9.72 ÷ 3 ________

6. $7.64 ÷ 4 ________

7. $8.05 ÷ 7 ________

8. Crystal bought 6 pens for $5.22. If each pen cost the same amount, what was the cost of one pen?

____

9. A box of cereal cost $3.68. The box is 8 ounces in weight. How much money does each ounce cost?

____

10. **Estimation** Mr. Franklin spent $15.33 to buy 7 gallons of gas. Is the cost of a gallon of gas greater than or less than $2.00 for each gallon? Explain.

____

____

____

____

____

11. Four friends go to lunch and order the same meal. The bill comes to $27.08. How much does each person owe?

○ $6.02 ○ $6.42
○ $6.77 ○ $7.02

Name ______________________________

Reteaching
19-6

Problem Solving: Missing or Extra Information

Henry is working to buy a new bicycle helmet. The helmet costs $22. Henry is earning $5 per hour helping his mother plant flowers. How much money has he made so far?

What do you know? The helmet costs $22. Henry earns $5 per hour.

What are you being asked to find? The amount of money Henry has earned.

What information do you need? The number of hours Henry has worked. It is not given.

You do not know how many hours Henry worked. Therefore, you cannot answer the question. This is missing information.

The cost of the helmet is extra information since it is not necessary to answer the question.

Decide if each problem has extra information or missing information. Solve if you have enough information.

1. Ralph has $55. He buys a sweatshirt for $17 and a pair of pants for $26. How much money did Ralph spend all together?

____

____

2. Lisa bought 4 magazines for a total of $16. She also bought 3 books that each cost the same amount of money. How much money did Lisa spend in all?

____

____

3. **Reasoning** The cast for the school play has 24 actors. There are 12 third-grade students in the cast. The rest are either second-grade students or fourth-grade students. Mr. Kemp wants to know how many more third-grade students are in the cast than fourth-grade students. Can Mr. Kemp answer the question? Explain.

____

____

Name ____________________

Practice
19-6

Problem Solving: Missing or Extra Information

For **1** and **2**, decide if the problem has extra or missing information. Solve if you have enough information.

1. Each time Kendra walks Mr. Karl's dog, he gives her $3. Kendra walks the dog for 30 minutes. If she walks the dog on Monday, Tuesday, and Thursday, how much money does Kendra make each week for walking Mr. Karl's dog?

____

____

____

____

2. Dylan trades baseball cards with his friends. He received all of his cards as a gift from his grandmother. If Dylan trades 58 baseball cards away and gets 62 back, how many cards does he have now?

____

____

____

____

3. Write a Problem Write a problem about Marie who has to do homework in math, reading, and social studies. Include extra information in your problem. Then solve it.

____

____

____

____

4. Tommy has 36 CDs and 24 DVDs. All of his CDs are either rock and roll or hip hop. He has 15 drama DVDs and 6 comedy DVDs. What information do you need to find how many hip hop CDs Tommy has?

○ the number of rock and roll CDs
○ the number of rap CDs
○ the number of music DVDs
○ the number of country CDs

Name ______________________________

Using Tally Charts

The list shows the letters that landed when Kevin spun a spinner.

A	B	C	A	B	B	A	D	C	D
A	A	B	D	C	B	D	A	C	A
B	A	A	A	C	D	C	D	D	A

A tally chart can be used to collect and organize data. Each | on a tally chart represents 1. Each 𝍸 represents 5. Make a tally chart.

Letters Spun

Letter	Tally	Number
A	𝍸 𝍸 |	11
B	𝍸 |	6
C	𝍸 |	6
D	𝍸 ||	7

There are blue, red, and green cards in a pile. Sheila is going to pick cards without looking. Use the data at the right for **1–3**.

1. Complete the tally chart to show the results.

Colors Picked

Color	Tally	Number

Colors Picked

Blue	Green	Red	Blue
Blue	Red	Green	Red
Red	Blue	Green	Blue
Red	Green	Blue	Red
Blue	Blue	Red	Green

2. How many more blue cards were picked than green cards? ______________

3. Explain It How does a tally chart help you to display data?

____

____

Name ______________________

Practice **20-1**

Using Tally Charts

For **1–5**, use the data at the right.

1. Complete the tally table.

Meal	Tally	Number

Favorite Meal

lunch	dinner	breakfast	lunch
breakfast	dinner	lunch	dinner
dinner	breakfast	dinner	breakfast
lunch	breakfast	breakfast	dinner
dinner	lunch	dinner	breakfast

2. How many people chose breakfast as their favorite meal?

____

3. How many people chose lunch as their favorite meal?

____

4. How many more people chose dinner than breakfast as their favorite meal?

____

5. How many people voted all together?

____

6. Phillip surveyed to find the age of each person in his class. He found that 6 students were 8 years old, 12 students were 9 years old, and 3 students were 10 years old. Which tally chart shows these results?

○

Age	Tally
8	卌 |
9	卌 卌 ||
10	|||

○

Age	Tally
8	卌 |||
9	卌 ||||
10	卌 卌

○

Age	Tally
8	卌 ||
9	卌 卌 ||
10	|||

○

Age	Tally
8	卌
9	卌 卌 |
10	|||

Name ______________________________

How Likely?

You can describe the chance of something happening by using the words **certain, likely, unlikely,** or **impossible.**

Look at this spinner.

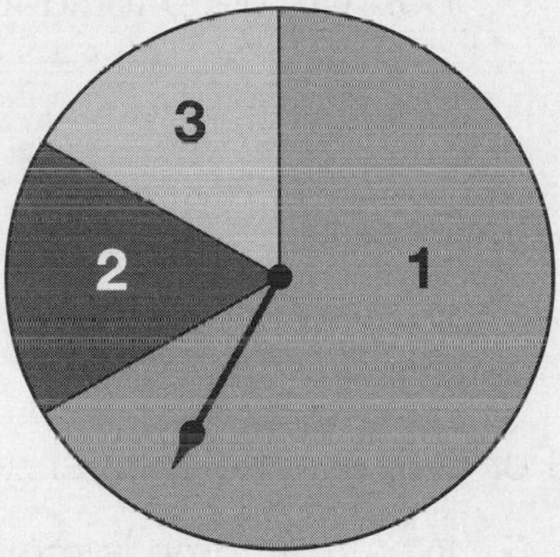

It is **certain** that the spinner will land on a number less than 4.

It is **impossible** that the spinner will land on 4.

It is **likely** that the spinner will land on 1.

It is **unlikely** that the spinner will land on 2.

You can use **more likely, less likely,** and **equally likely** to compare the chances of something happening.

It is **more likely** that the spinner will land on 1 than 2.

It is **less likely** that the spinner will land on 2 than 1

It is **equal likely** that the spinner will land on 2 or 3.

Describe each event as *likely, unlikely, impossible,* or *certain*.

1. Next week will have 7 days. ______________

2. Janet's dog has 4 legs. ______________

Suppose you pick a card from the hat without looking. Describe each pick as *likely, unlikely, impossible,* or *certain.*

3. Picking a shaded card

____

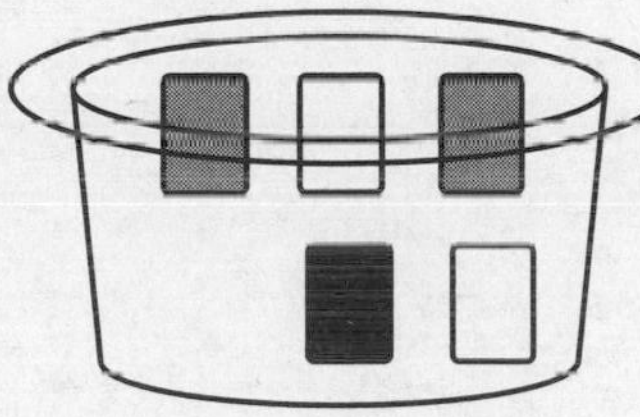

4. Picking a round card

____

5. Picking a black card

____

Name ______________________________

Practice
20-2

How Likely?

Gene is an adult with a dog named Bob. Describe each event as likely, unlikely, impossible, or certain.

1. Bob will sleep tonight.

____

2. Bob will weigh more than Gene.

____

3. Bob will eat.

____

4. Bob will read a book.

____

For **5–8,** use the spinner at the right.

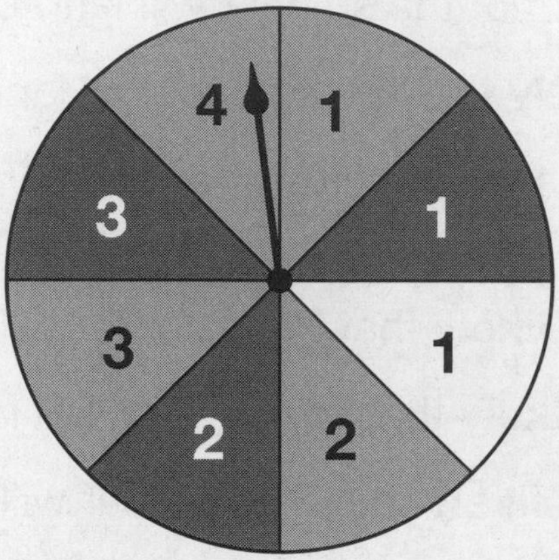

5. What outcome is more likely than 2?

____

6. What outcomes are equally likely?

____

7. Describe the chance of the spinner landing on 5.

____

8. What outcome is less likely than a 3?

____

9. **Writing to Explain** What is the difference between a likely event and an unlikely event?

____

____

____

____

10. Dana and Rose are playing a card game. Dana has cards with 3 circles, 4 squares, 2 triangles, and 1 rectangle. If Rose picks one card from Dana's hand without looking, which card will she most likely pick?

○ circle ○ square ○ triangle ○ rectangle

Name ____________________

Outcomes and Experiments

An experiment is used to try to test a theory. You can predict what will happen with an experiment. The prediction should be close to what will happen, although it may not.

Suppose you were going to spin the spinner to the right 30 times. How many times do you predict each number will occur?

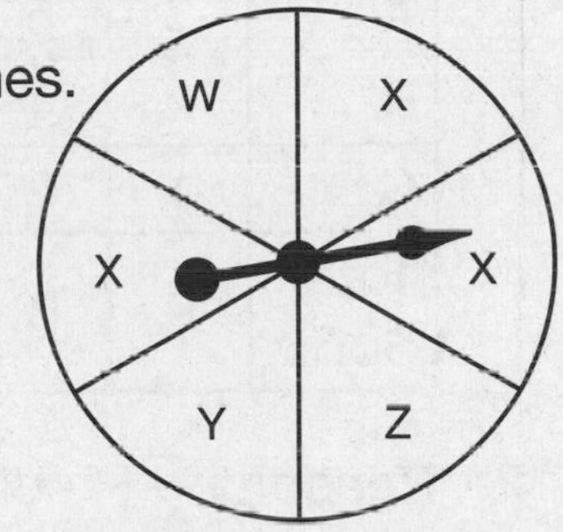

Step 1

Use what you know about the spinner. There are 6 sections in all.

W =1 section
X = 3 sections
Y = 1 section
Z = 1 section

Step 2

Make a table to predict what would happen with 60 spins.

W	1	2	3	4	5
X	3	6	9	12	15
Y	1	2	3	4	5
Z	1	2	3	4	5
Total Spins	6	12	18	24	30

So, the prediction is that W, Y, and Z would land 5 times and X would land 15 times.

In **1–3**, use the spinner and the table below.

1. Complete the table.

A	2	4		8	10	
B	1	2	3		5	10
C	1	2	3		5	10
Total Spins	4	8	12	16	20	

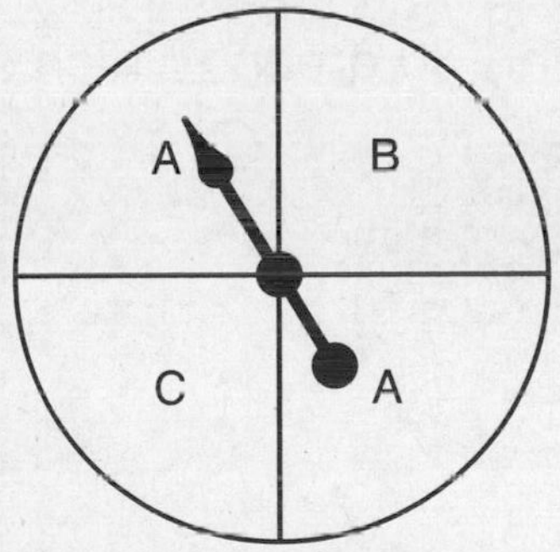

2. Reasoning If you spin the spinner 100 times will B land more times than A? Explain.

____

____

3. If you spin the spinner 100 times, how many times should it land on A? ________

Name ____________________

Outcomes and Experiments

For **1–3**, use the spinner to the right and the table below.

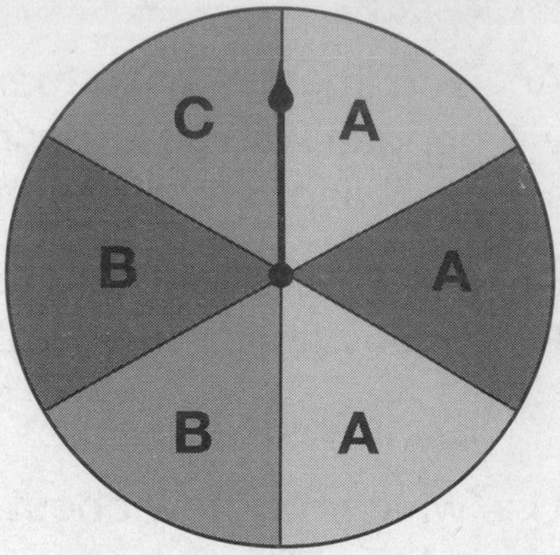

1. Complete the table.

A	3	6		12	15		45
B	2	4	6	8		20	30
C	1	2	3	4	5	10	
Total Spins	6	12	18		30	60	

2. Reasoning Predict what is likely to happen in 120 spins.

____

____

____

3. Do the experiment using a number cube. Let 1, 2, and 3 represent A, 4 and 5 represent B and 6 represent C. Toss the number cube 30 times. See if it matches your prediction above. What happened?

____

____

____

4. In a probability experiment, the spinner results were 10 blue, 10 red, and 30 green. Which spinner most likely gave these results?

○ 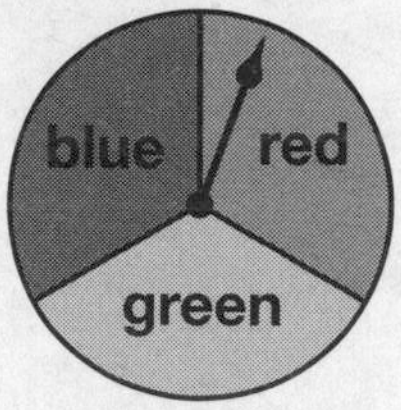

○ 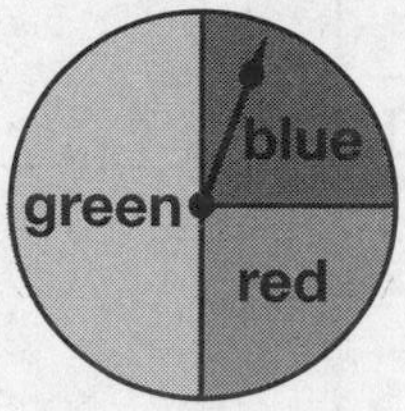

○ 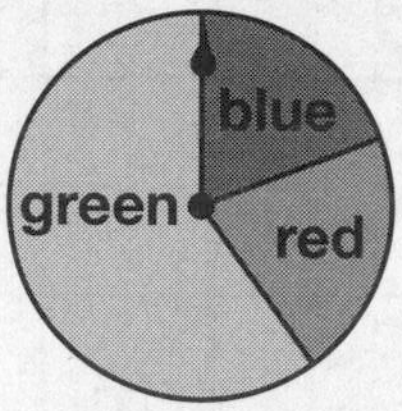

○ 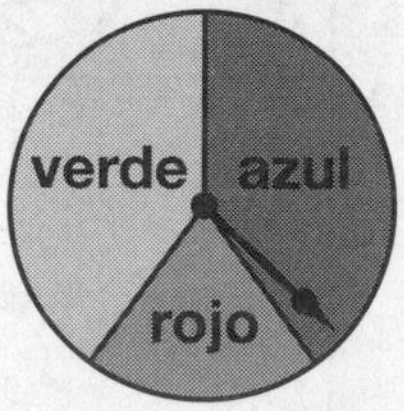

Name ______________________

Line Plots and Probability

A line plot is used in the same way as a tally chart. It is used to show numerical data. A line plot uses an X to represent 1.

The data shows the numbers that landed on Maria's spinner after 30 spins.

1	2	4	3	6	5	1	7	4	3
2	6	3	5	4	7	1	2	6	1
1	3	6	2	5	1	4	2	7	3

The line plot at the right can be used to show the data.

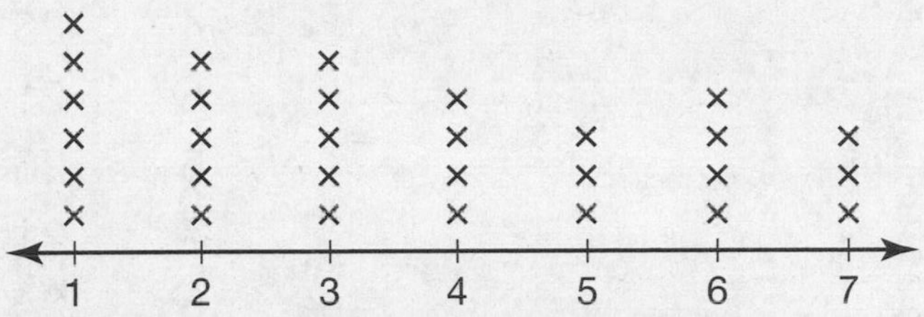

Mark played a game with two number cubes. He found the sum of the number cubes. The results are shown in the table.

1. Make a line plot to show the data.

Number Cube Tosses

Toss	Sum	Toss	Sum	Toss	Sum
1	7	11	6	21	7
2	4	12	9	22	10
3	6	13	9	23	9
4	8	14	10	24	7
5	5	15	10	25	5
6	5	16	5	26	12
7	6	17	8	27	7
8	2	18	5	28	9
9	10	19	3	29	8
10	8	20	8	30	12

2. How many Xs do you show for 8?

____

3. Which number from 2–12 did Mark not toss at all?

____

Name ____________________

Practice **20-4**

Line Plots and Probability

For **1–4**, use the data at the right.

1. Make a line plot to show the data.

Number of Points Katie Scored

Game	Pts	Game	Pts	Game	Pts
1	23	11	25	21	24
2	25	12	30	22	26
3	30	13	27	23	25
4	25	14	22	24	28
5	21	15	26	25	27
6	26	16	21	26	26
7	21	17	29	27	29
8	24	18	25	28	30
9	28	19	21	29	22
10	20	20	23	30	24

2. How many Xs do you show for 24?

____

3. Which number of points did Katie only score once?

____

4. Which number of points did Katie score the most?

____

5. Which two point totals did Katie score exactly four times each?

____

For **6–7**, use the line plot at right.

6. How many fewer students read 8 books than 6 books?

____

7. How many students read less than 7 books?

○ 11 ○ 14
○ 17 ○ 22

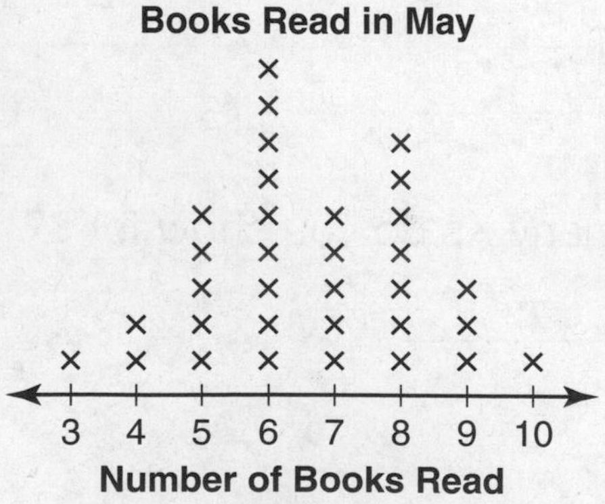

Name ______________________________

Making Bar Graphs to Show Outcomes

Victoria conducted an experiment by picking colored cards from a pile. The tally chart shows the results of her experiment. Victoria will make a bar graph.

Color	Tally	Number
Red	卌 卌	10
Green	卌 II	7
Blue	卌 卌 IIII	14
White	卌 IIII	9

To make a bar graph follow these steps.

Step 1

Write a title to explain what the bar graph shows.

This bar graph will be titled "Card Results."

Step 2

Choose the scale. Decide how many units each grid line will represent.

Each grid line will represent 2.

Write the scale and the labels.

Step 3

For each outcome, draw a bar for the number of picks.

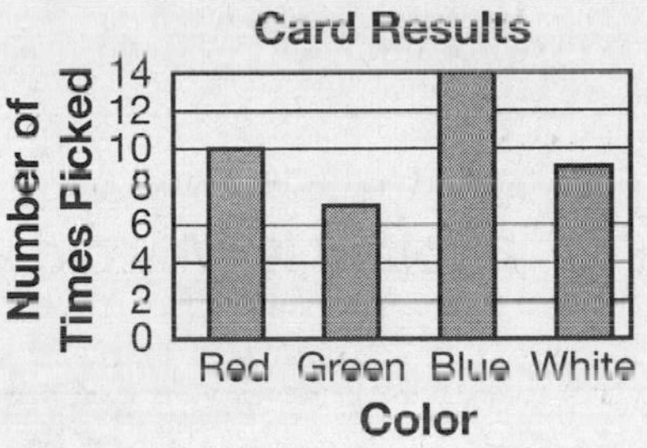

1. Use the table to make a bar graph.

Sports Played by 3rd Graders

Sport	Number of Students
Softball	7
Hockey	14
Baseball	6
Tennis	8

Name ____

Practice
20-5

Making Bar Graphs to Show Outcomes

Lorenzo made a tally chart to show the results of spinning a spinner 40 times. Use Lorenzo's chart in 1 and 2.

Letter	Tally	Number
A	~~IIII~~ ~~IIII~~ III	13
B	~~IIII~~ ~~IIII~~	10
C	~~IIII~~ IIII	9
D	~~IIII~~ III	8

1. Make a bar graph to show the data.

2. Explain It Why did you choose the scale that you chose?

____

____

____

3. Suppose you were going to make a bar graph from the data in the chart. Which would be the best scale to use?

○ 1 ○ 5

○ 20 ○ 50

Miles Driven by Day

Day	Miles
Monday	60
Tuesday	80
Wednesday	40
Thursday	50
Friday	80

Name ____________________

Problem Solving: Make and Use Graphs to Draw Conclusions

Students were asked to name their favorite type of dog. The pictograph shows the results of the survey.

Students' Favorite Dogs

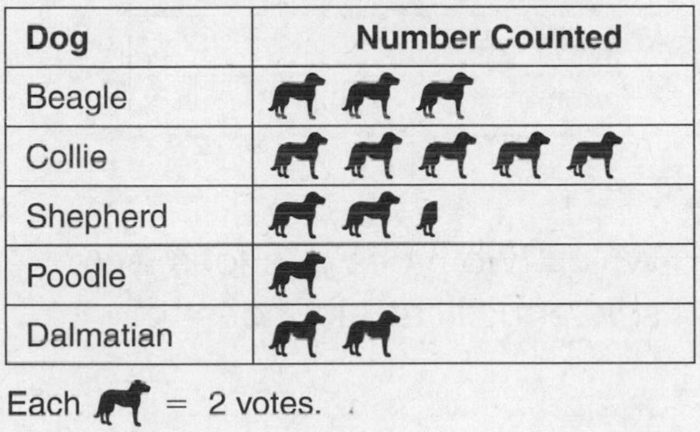

Which dog was chosen by *exactly* 5 students? Shepherd

Which dog was chosen by 2 more students than a Dalmatian? Beagle

For **1–3**, use the chart below.

Quarter	Points Scored
1st	7
2nd	3
3rd	10
4th	6

1. The chart shows how many points a football team scored. How many points were scored all together?

______

2. Write a Problem Write a word problem that is different from Exercise 1 that can be solved by reading the chart.

____

____

3. Make a graph to represent the data in the chart. Choose a bar graph or a pictograph.

Name ____________________

Practice
20-6

Problem Solving: Make and Use Graphs to Draw Conclusions

Use the pictographs for **1–4**.

Girls Shoes Sold at Just Shoes

Each [shoe] = 10 shoes.

Girls Shoes Sold at All Shoes

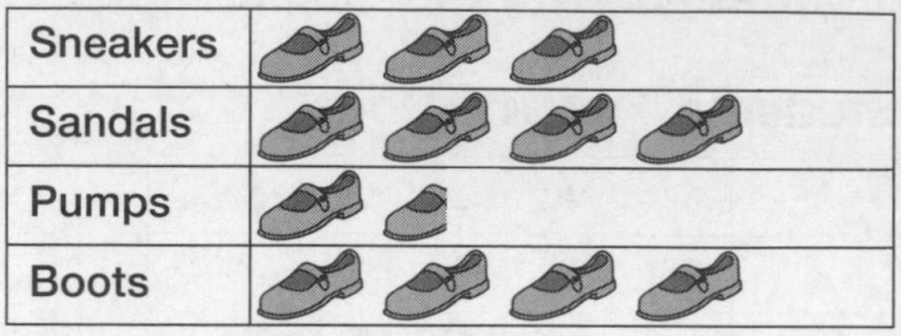

Each [shoe] = 5 shoes.

1. Which type of shoe was sold the most at Just Shoes?

____

2. Which two types of shoes were sold equally at All Shoes?

____

3. Which store sold the most pumps?

____

4. How many sneakers were sold in all?

____

For **5** and **6**, use the bar graph at the right.

Cars Washed by Grade

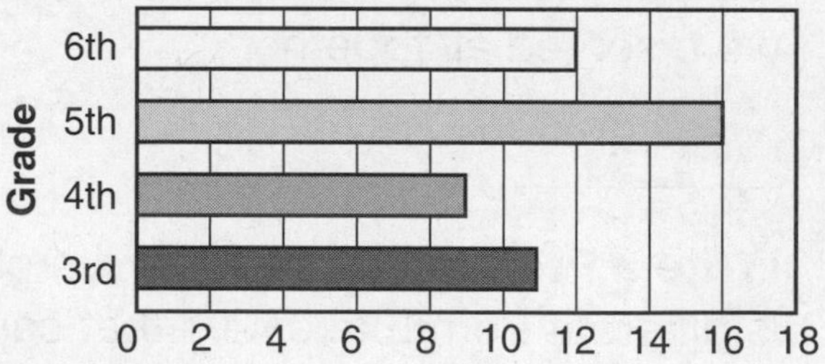

5. How many cars were washed all together?

____

6. **Write a Problem** Write a word problem different from Exercise 5 that can be solved by reading the graph.

____

____

Students Receiving an A or B

Test	Tally
1	卌 卌 ||
2	卌 卌 卌 |
3	卌 卌 卌
4	卌 |||

7. According to the tally chart, how many more students received an A or B in Test 2 than in Test 4?

____